PENGUIN BOOKS

THE PENGUIN DICTIONARY OF TELECOMMUNICATIONS

John Graham is a director of Kapiti, an international software company specializing in communications systems for banking and securities houses. He has worked for many years in communications and the computer industry developing software for a number of public service information systems. His books include the *Penguin Dictionary of Computers* and the *Macmillan Directory of Technology in Global Financial Markets.*

Sue J. Lowe is a freelance writer with an expertise in data communications. As an editor at *Data Communications* magazine she wrote about data transmission and switching equipment. She has also held editorial positions at *Business Week* magazine and the book publisher W.W. Norton & Company.

THE PENGUIN DICTIONARY OF TELECOMMUNICATIONS

JOHN GRAHAM

REVISED AND UPDATED BY SUE J. LOWE

PENGUIN BOOKS

PENGUIN BOOKS

Published by the Penguin Group
Penguin Books Ltd, 27 Wrights Lane, London W8 5TZ, England
Penguin Books USA Inc., 375 Hudson Street, New York, New York 10014, USA
Penguin Books Australia Ltd, Ringwood, Victoria, Australia
Penguin Books Canada Ltd, 10 Alcorn Avenue, Toronto, Ontario, Canada M4V 3B2
Penguin Books (NZ) Ltd, 182–190 Wairau Road, Auckland 10, New Zealand

Penguin Books Ltd, Registered Offices: Harmondsworth, Middlesex, England

First published by Facts On File, Inc. 1983
First published in Penguin Books and simultaneously by Allen Lane 1983
This revised edition first published by Facts On File, Inc. 1991
Published in Penguin Books 1991
1 3 5 7 9 10 8 6 4 2

Printed in England by Clays Ltd, St Ives plc

CONTENTS

Preface vii

Dictionary of Telecommunications 1

Appendixes:

1. International Alphabet No. 5 181
2. Notation Used for Abbreviation of Frequency Ranges 183
3. Wavelength 184
4. The Electromagnetic Spectrum 185
5. Visible Light Spectrum 186
6. Bandwidth and Information 187
7. Basis of Amplitude Modulation 188
8. Basis of Pulse Amplitude Modulation 189
9. Packet Switching Network 190
10. OSI Model Showing Layered Protocols for X.25 Transmission 191
11. Network Topologies 192

PREFACE

Our world has become an increasingly complex place in which, as individuals, we very dependent on other people and on organizations. An event in some distant part of the globe can rapidly and significantly affect the quality of life in our home country.

This increasing interdependence, on both a national and international scale, has led us to create systems that can respond immediately to dangers, enabling appropriate defensive or offensive actions to be taken. These systems are operating all around us in military, civil, commercial and industrial fields.

The electronic computer is at the heart of many such systems, but the role of telecommunications is no less important. As we proceed through the 1990s, there will be a further convergence between the technologies of computing and telecommunications. The changes will be dramatic: the database culture, the cashless society, the office at home, the gigabit-per-second data network.

We cannot doubt that the economic and social impact of these concepts will be very significant. Already, advanced systems of communication are affecting both the layman and the technician. Complex functions are being performed by people using advanced terminals which are intended to be as easy to use as the conventional telephone.

The aim of the book

Telecommunications principles are becoming increasingly important in education at undergraduate and graduate levels. All those engaged in the fast-growing systems industries are finding that a knowledge of telecommunications is essential for solving today's problems; this knowledge is also vital to those who are responsible for managing distributed organizations.

It is the aim of this book to help people understand the terminology of this subject and, at the same time, to provide a convenient reference for basic telecommunications and data communications principles.

In common with many other modern technologies, the subject of telecommunications has developed a language of its own. At first sight, the words appear to be intelligible English but, of course, with the inevitable sprinkling of acronyms such as FSK (FREQUENCY SHIFT KEYING). The close association with the computer industry gives rise to some major new fields of technical complexity, e.g., FAST PACKET SWITCHING.

This book sets out to define such terms and, as far as possible, to adhere to definitions in keeping with international practice. The scope of the publication is wide, dealing with fundamental concepts in telephone and telegraph communications, switched communications systems, broadcast systems and narrow and broad bandwidth systems.

The intention is to make the material intelligible to the layman as well as interesting and informative for the technician. It is hoped that it will assist readers in dealing with other technical documents they have to read and prove useful for browsing.

With these objectives in mind, I have aimed at a style that is informative rather than precise. There are also many cross-references to other definitions which complement, or contrast with, the definition of a particular term. In many definitions, it has been necessary to use other technical terms, which are themselves defined elsewhere in the book. Such terms have been printed in small capitals as they arise in the text.

Spellings and sequence

Certain words in this book have been spelled in accordance with the conventions adopted in the telecommunications and data communications industries, which owe so much to North American influences, e.g., computer program, analog computer, toll center, multiplexer.

The book has been arranged according to strict alphabetic sequence of each word and, where a term is composed of two or more words, the sequence is determined by the first word, and then by the second and so on, e.g.,

call accepted signal
call request signal
call setup
called line

In this way I have tried to spare the reader the task of interpreting the sequence in which a computer sorts strings of text and symbols. Hyphenated terms are treated as one word. Also, terms that begin with a numeral are given the exact significance of the corresponding word. Thus, the term 2-BIT ERROR appears immediately after TWO CONDITION CODE and immediately before TWO-STATE SIGNALING.

Many people and organizations have provided help in the preparation of the material, and I particularly wish to mention Jeremy Wood, who helped with the illustrations, and Tracey Mitchell, who typed some of the early drafts. Above all I must thank my wife, Dianne, who gave so much of her time, energy, patience and good humor to read, correct, index and sequence all the text for the first edition. She took care of all cross-references and made the preparation of the words such a straightforward operation. She also typed the final manuscript.

The North American version has been extensively revised and updated by Sue J. Lowe of Closter, New Jersey, USA; and I am immensely indebted to her for the revisions she made in 1990.

John Graham
Worplesdon, England

In compiling the new entries for this revised dictionary I debated the wisdom of including terms used by vendors to denote their proprietary offerings. Certainly many products and services available from large companies are so ubiquitous as to seem generic. I decided, however, that those definitions are more properly found in product literature available from the vendor and, perhaps, in trade publications.

I want to give special credit to the professional copy editor who worked on the final manuscript: Joan Atwood, of The Manuscript Doctors, Emmaus, Pennsylvania. Her rigorous attention to grammatical nuance was especially helpful.

Sue J. Lowe
Closter, New Jersey

A

abbreviated address calling A system in which a subset of ADDRESS characters is required to establish a CALL from a TERMINAL, and in which the NETWORK expands the abbreviated address to the full address. See also ABBREVIATED DIALING SERVICE.

abbreviated dialing service A service made available to USERS of a SWITCHED NETWORK, in which nonnumerical CODES are available to represent groups of DIGITS and specify code PREFIXES. This facility enables a caller to use an ADDRESS having fewer CHARACTERS than the full address of the CALLED SUBSCRIBER. See also SPEED DIALING.

abbreviated number An ADDRESS sent by a caller to indicate the number of a SUBSCRIBER to be called but which is preceded by a nonnumerical PREFIX indicating the use of an ABBREVIATED DIALING SERVICE.

abbreviated prefix dialing In the operation of a telephone service, the use of a nonnumerical code to indicate that the following DIGITS are an ABBREVIATED NUMBER.

AC See ALTERNATING CURRENT.

AC signal A SIGNAL in which the direction of the current is reversed in accordance with a frequency, e.g., a SPEECH SIGNAL varies within a range of AUDIO FREQUENCIES according to vibrations generated by a human voice.

accentuated contrast A technique used in FACSIMILE to transmit information relating to documents in which parts of a picture having a LUMINANCE less than a specified value are transmitted as black and parts having a greater luminance as white.

access code A PREFIX to an ADDRESS that enables a caller to obtain a connection to a specific service, e.g., to the international automatic TELEX network.

access path A path providing communication between two TERMINALS. In a TELEPHONE SYSTEM or a DATA NETWORK there may be a number of possible paths between two terminals, but for a particular CALL, a specific set of physical transmission resources must be allocated to provide a specific access path. Sometimes the path is established via one or more intermediate NODES in the NETWORK.

access path control In a communications system, there is usually more than one set of physical resources available to provide an ACCESS PATH from a CALLING LOCATION to a CALLED DESTINATION. There may also be a choice of intermediate nodes through which the CALL can be ROUTED. Access path control procedures are concerned with the selection of a particular TRANSMISSION PATH. The procedures usually reside in logic built into the EXCHANGES or nodes of the network, and the paths are selected automatically according to prevailing conditions.

access point A physical point of connection to a NETWORK that defines the limits of a LINE. For example, only one

LINE ACCESS POINT can exist at each end of an international line.

access-barred signal A SIGNAL sent back to a CALLING TERMINAL to indicate that the caller is not allowed to be connected to the CALLED LOCATION, i.e., not a member of a CLOSED USER GROUP having access to that location.

accounting rate A term that refers to communications TRAFFIC between zones controlled by different TELECOMMUNICATIONS authorities. It is used for the establishment of international accounts. The rate is expressed as a charge per TRAFFIC UNIT, e.g., per WORD, per minute, depending upon the type of service.

accounting rate quota That part of the accounting rate given to a TELECOMMUNICATIONS AUTHORITY for TRAFFIC between it and another such authority and relating to the facilities utilized in each country. This quota is fixed by predetermined agreement between the authorities concerned.

accounting revenue division procedure A procedure whereby revenue relating to a communications service is shared between the TELECOMMUNICATIONS authorities providing the service at each end.

ACK See ACKNOWLEDGE.

acknowledge (ACK) An international TRANSMISSION CONTROL CODE that is returned by a RECEIVING TERMINAL to a TRANSMITTING TERMINAL to acknowledge that a FRAME of information has been correctly received. Contrast with NEGATIVE ACKNOWLEDGE (NAK).

acknowledgment indicator A SIGNAL that is used to indicate whether or not an error has been detected in a FRAME, or some other unit of information. The signal is transferred back from the RECEIVING to the TRANSMITTING TERMINAL. See ACK and NAK.

acknowledgment signal unit A part of a BLOCK of signal information transmitted over a PUBLIC DATA NETWORK and containing information to indicate whether the other SIGNAL units in the block were correctly received.

acoustic coupler A TRANSDUCER for coupling a DATA TERMINAL (DTE) to a telephone NETWORK in which DATA SIGNALS from the TERMINAL are converted to SOUND WAVES and sounds received from the telephone LINE and intended for the terminal are converted to data signals. The DTE can thus communicate using a telephone HANDSET with a distant terminal or HOST PROCESSOR.

acoustically coupled modem A special MODEM that enables tones generated by a DATA TERMINAL to be transferred to a telephone HANDSET, thereby providing DATA COMMUNICATION over the PUBLIC SWITCHED TELEPHONE NETWORK (PSTN).

active lines In forming a TV picture, an ELECTRON BEAM traces a pattern of LINES known as a RASTER. Some lines do not contain LUMINANCE information, (e.g., FIELD FLYBACK). The lines that do contain luminance information are known as active lines.

actual final route The specific path followed by a CALL over an international SWITCHED telephone NETWORK, to be contrasted with the THEORETICAL FINAL ROUTE. The actual final route may or may not use all or part of the theoretical final route.

ACU Abbreviation of ACKNOWLEDGMENT SIGNAL UNIT.

adapter A device used to INTERFACE between DATA TERMINAL EQUIPMENT (DTE) and a CHANNEL and to carry out CODE and DATA RATE conversion to enable the DTE to be compatible with the communication standards required.

adaptive channel allocation A technique used by the INTELLIGENT TIME DIVISION MULTIPLEXER on PUBLIC DATA NETWORKS in which the information capacity of a CHANNEL is determined in response to demand rather than being predetermined.

adaptive differential pulse code modulation (ADPCM) A technique for compressing and digitizing analog speech signals. ADPCM uses 4-bit samples of the analog waveform. It can effectively double the number of VOICE CHANNELS carried on an INTEROFFICE T1 LINK. Some implementations of ADPCM compress the voice to 32 kbps; others to 40 kbps. See also PULSE CODE MODULATION, ANALOG and SPEECH SIGNALS.

adaptive equalizer A device that counteracts DELAY DISTORTION affecting ANALOG SIGNALS in transmission circuits. It is constructed to respond appropriately at different speeds and operating conditions. See EQUALIZATION.

ADCP See ADVANCED DATA COMMUNICATION PROTOCOL.

address The part of a SIGNAL that defines the destination for a CALL.

address digits Elements of signal information representing specified DIGITS, which together define the telephone number of a CALLED PARTY, or a CALLING PARTY.

address field A FIELD of information forming part of a FRAME that indicates a unique ADDRESS for a STATION connected to a NETWORK. See DESTINATION ADDRESS FIELD and SOURCE ADDRESS FIELD.

address information Part of the information contained in a MESSAGE or PACKET and intended to provide to the CONTROL system of the NETWORK the necessary information to identify the USER to whom the message or packet is to be sent and to allow a ROUTE to be selected.

address message A MESSAGE sent in a FORWARD DIRECTION over a PUBLIC DATA NETWORK and containing the information necessary to ROUTE and connect a CALL to a CALLED PARTY.

address signal A SIGNAL representing just one CHARACTER element of the complete ADDRESS (as, 9 or 5). For each address, a succession of ADDRESS SIGNALS will occur; also, depending upon the type of NETWORK, an END-OF-ADDRESS SIGNAL.

address-complete signal In a SWITCHED NETWORK, a SIGNAL sent in a BACKWARD CHANNEL, indicating that all DIGITS of an ADDRESS have been received and that the CALL should be charged on answer by the CALLED PARTY. Compare with ADDRESS-INCOMPLETE SIGNAL.

address-incomplete signal In a SWITCHED NETWORK, a SIGNAL sent by an EXCHANGE in a BACKWARD CHANNEL indicating that the number of ADDRESS DIGITS received is not sufficient to set up a CALL.

addressing Most communication systems apply the concept of several USERS sharing the same TRANSMISSION LINES (e.g., by CIRCUIT SWITCHING or by TIME SWITCHING in a TIME DIVISION MULTIPLEXING environment). Some method is required to make connections between specific users or to transmit PACKETS of information between specific users. To achieve connections, addressing information must be generated as part of the CALL ESTABLISHMENT process or be included in the DATA transmitted. Using this addressing information, a ROUTING operation takes place to connect the required TERMINALS, and the path remains available until the particular transmission has been completed. See also PACKET SWITCHING NETWORK.

addressing flexibility A quality desired in the construction of NETWORKS to allow FRAMES of information to be directed to a specific USER, a group of users or to all users on the network.

advanced data communication protocol (ADCP) A standard developed by the American National Standards Institute that specifies ERROR CONTROL protocols for DATA TRANSMISSION, to insure that information received at a TERMINAL is a replica of the BIT-PATTERN transmitted. See also HIGH LEVEL DATA LINK CONTROL (HDLC).

Advanced Research Projects Agency (ARPA) Part of the U.S. Department of Defense. See also ARPANET.

aerial A part of a radio system that either radiates SIGNALS into the atmosphere or receives RADIO SIGNALS from the atmosphere. See also ANTENNA.

AGC See AUTOMATIC GAIN CONTROL.

algorithm In computer science, a set of instructions that prescribe basic actions. Algorithms are sometimes synonymous with SOFTWARE. The processor executes the algorithms.

ALOHA Developed in the 1970s by Norman Abramson at the University of Hawaii, ALOHA is a method of data transmission that uses radio broadcasting techniques to determine how a single CHANNEL will be allocated among many USERS. See also PURE ALOHA.

alphabet Relating to a DATA COMMUNICATIONS CODE and defining an agreed set of CHARACTERS or symbols and the SIGNALS that represent them. See, for example, INTERNATIONAL ALPHABET NO. 5.

alphabetic telegraphy A conventional form of TELEGRAPHY using an alphabetic telegraph code (e.g., INTERNATIONAL TELEGRAPH ALPHABET NO. 2) transmitted between two TERMINALS. Such codes are used to represent letters, figures and punctuation marks, each as a unique pattern of pulses, and are known as DATA COMMUNICATION CODES. An example is shown in Appendix 1. The term "alphabetic telegraphy" is used to distinguish it from other forms of telegraphy (e.g., using FACSIMILE methods).

alphageometric coding A system of coding for storing, transmitting and displaying GRAPHICS INFORMATION (e.g., in a VIDEOTEX SYSTEM or COMPUTER AIDED DESIGN SYSTEM). Such a system can be defined to enable very complex color graphics images to be displayed.

alphamosaic coding A system of coding used in VIDEOTEX SYSTEMS to enable TEXT and GRAPHICS INFORMATION to be stored in a central COMPUTER and transmitted and displayed on a VIDEOTEX TERMINAL. The graphics displays produced by this technique are of relatively LOW RESOLUTION, but it provides an extremely cheap and effective way of conveying graphics in a public service system. The pictures are formed of individual GRAPHICS CHARACTERS, e.g., up to 63 different characters are defined from a character matrix of 2×3 elements. This is the most common method of coding graphics in PUBLIC VIDEOTEX SYSTEMS, which were introduced throughout Europe in the 1980s. Compare with ALPHAGEOMETRIC CODING and ALPHAPHOTOGRAPHIC DISPLAY SYSTEM.

alphamosaic graphics Graphics images composed of GRAPHICS CHARACTERS combined to form a picture in a VIDEOTEX SYSTEM. See ALPHAMOSAIC CODING.

alphanumeric Any set of symbols consisting of alphabetic CHARACTERS and special symbols as well as NUMBERS.

alphaphotographic display system A graphics display system providing HIGH RESOLUTION images comparable in quality to a color television picture. An example is described under the entry PICTURE PRESTEL. See also ALPHAMOSAIC CODING and ALPHAGEOMETRIC CODING.

alternate digit inversion A technique used to prevent loss of SYNCHRONIZATION in REPEATERS used for regenerating DIGITAL SIGNALS. In order to identify incoming pulses, some repeaters have internal CLOCKS that are synchronized to the incoming stream of BITS. During periods of low activity, the incoming stream will be all zeros, and there is a tendency under these conditions for the clock to lose synchronization. Deliberate inversion of the TIME SLOTS relating to alternate bits is used to prevent the occurrence of continuous zeros and thus maintain synchronization.

alternate mark inversion (AMI) A system for line transmission in which the MARK condition of a coded SIGNAL is represented alternately by a positive and negative voltage of equal AMPLITUDE and in which SPACE is represented by zero amplitude.

alternate mark inversion violation An error condition in which two consecutive MARK signals have the same polarity.

alternate path routing In a NETWORK, a ROUTING involving the selection of an ACCESS PATH other than the basic or normal theoretical access path. Usually selected because of failure in the normal access path or because an intervening NODE or TRANSMISSION LINK is heavily overloaded.

alternating code A CODE in which BITS or CHARACTERS may be represented under a given set of rules by two different conditions, e.g., "1" digit alternately represented as a positive or negative pulse. This technique assists maintenance of timing in a long sequence of digits. An example is given under ALTERNATE MARK INVERSION. Also known as PAIRED-DISPARITY CODE.

alternating current (AC) An electric circuit in which the direction of the current is reversed. For example in Britain the electrical power supply varies at a frequency of 50 cycles per second, in the United States at 60 cycles per second. ELECTRICAL SIGNALS that represent sounds such as speech and music are AC SIGNALS, but they have complex forms consisting of many harmonic frequencies and varying AMPLITUDES.

alternative coding See ALTERNATING CODE.

alternative routing A ROUTING other than the BASIC ROUTING for a call is known as an alternative routing. See EXCHANGE HIERARCHY.

alternative routing indicator Information sent in the FORWARD DIRECTION of a CALL over a PUBLIC DATA NETWORK indicating that an ALTERNATIVE ROUTING has been used.

AM See AMPLITUDE MODULATION.

American National Standards Institute (ANSI) A nonprofit organization that serves as the U.S. representative to the INTERNATIONAL ORGANIZATION FOR STANDARDIZATION, ANSI is supported by trade groups, professional societies and companies—not by the government.

American Standard Code for Information Interchange (ASCII) A CODE used in DATA TRANSFER, ASCII (pronounced "askey") represents the alphabet, numerals and computer CONTROL CHARACTERS. It is a variation of the 7-bit code known as the International Alphabet No. 5. See also EBCDIC.

American Telephone and Telegraph Company (AT&T) The largest COMMON CARRIER in the United States, AT&T was even larger before DIVESTITURE of the 22 BELL OPERATING COMPANIES. Its main competitors are MCI and US Sprint.

Ameritech See REGIONAL BELL HOLDING COMPANY.

AMI See ALTERNATIVE MARK INVERSION.

amount of traffic carried In a SWITCHED SYSTEM, the amount of TRAFFIC carried is the sum of the HOLDING TIME of all the CALLS made in any given period over a given TRUNK or through a given EXCHANGE. Usually measured in hours.

amplification The process involved in increasing the power of a SIGNAL. This is often done to overcome loss of power that arises due to the electrical resistance in the materials used to construct a TRANSMISSION CHANNEL.

amplifier A device used to increase the power of an ELECTRICAL SIGNAL to overcome cable losses and to deliver a signal of the appropriate MINIMUM SIGNAL LEVEL to a device at the MESSAGE destination.

amplifier bandwidth The effective FREQUENCY BAND over which an AMPLIFIER operates, e.g., in a telephone CIRCUIT, amplifiers are required to amplify MESSAGE SIGNALS derived from VOICE SIGNALS spoken into a MICROPHONE. For this purpose, a BANDWIDTH of from 0.3 to 3.4 kHz is suitable. Very often amplifier bandwidth is selected to filter out NOISE occurring outside the critical band occupied by the message signal.

amplifier gain The factor by which an AMPLIFIER increases the power of a SIGNAL—a ratio of the input to output power. See also GAIN.

amplitude A measure of the strength or loudness of a SIGNAL. Two ELECTRICAL SIGNALS may have the same frequency, but if one is of greater amplitude than the other, it will be represented by higher voltage peaks than the other. Amplitude is the peak value (in a positive or negative direction) of an ALTERNATING CURRENT signal.

amplitude modulation (AM) A form of modulation in which the AMPLITUDE of a CARRIER WAVE is made to vary in sympathy with the frequency of a SIGNAL that is to be transmitted. Any form of modulation in which different conditions are indicated by currents of different amplitude. See MODULATION and Appendix 7.

analog A direct representation of a phenomenon in another form: e.g., the representation of voice-sounds as electrical AUDIO SIGNALS. See ANALOG ELECTRICAL SIGNAL.

analog data channel A CHANNEL designed to carry ANALOG ELECTRICAL SIGNALS as distinct from DIGITAL SIGNALS. There is an increasing tendency to carry DATA TRAFFIC on high speed digital circuits. A MODEM is used to convert digital signals to and from the analog format expected on the LINE.

analog electrical signal An ELECTRICAL SIGNAL that directly represents another form of energy or activity. The most obvious example is the representation of SOUND WAVES in electrical form as an AUDIO SIGNAL that directly corresponds in frequency to the sound waves it represents.

analog line terminating system A unit that converts ANALOG ELECTRICAL SIGNALS representing speech and other forms into digital form and vice versa. See PULSE CODE MODULATION.

analog repeater An AMPLIFIER designed to regenerate ANALOG SIGNALS and used at regular intervals along a TRANSMISSION PATH to overcome the problem of ATTENUATION. Compare with DIGITAL REPEATER.

analog signal See ANALOG ELECTRICAL SIGNAL.

analog techniques The use of one medium to directly represent a phenomenon or activity occurring in another medium, e.g., the use of ELECTROMAGNETIC WAVES to represent SOUND WAVES.

ancillary device A device (e.g., a HARD COPY PRINTER) that is attached to, and under the control of, another device such as a TERMINAL or NODE.

AND gate A CIRCUIT with two (or more) inputs and a single output in which an output signal is provided if all inputs are present.

ANI See AUTOMATIC NUMBER IDENTIFICATION.

anisochronous system A communication system in which a common TIME INTERVAL is not established between TRANSMITTING STATIONS and RECEIVING STATIONS. The timing is established by START and STOP BITS that FRAME each transmitted unit of DATA, e.g., CHARACTER. Strictly speaking, a system in which there is an integral number of time units within a given unit of data (e.g., character) but not necessarily between successive units in the same MESSAGE. More commonly referred to as an ASYNCHRONOUS SYSTEM. Contrast with ISOCHRONOUS SYSTEM.

annual charge ratio A ratio used to express the quality of service and charges in the operation of a TELEPHONE SYSTEM. The ratio is determined by taking the annual charge of one additional CIRCUIT on the ALTERNATIVE ROUTE and dividing this sum by the annual charge of one additional circuit on the HIGH-USAGE ROUTE.

ANSI See AMERICAN NATIONAL STANDARDS INSTITUTE.

answer back simulator A device, or a program routine, that is not part of a TELEPRINTER but that behaves in the same way as an ANSWER BACK UNIT in response to a specific WHO ARE YOU signal.

answer back unit A device in a TELEPRINTER that automatically sends an identification signal to a CALLING TERMINAL in response to a specific WHO ARE YOU signal.

answer signal A SIGNAL sent in the BACKWARD DIRECTION when a CALL is answered. The signal usually initiates the next stage in the progress of the call. In public service systems, this signal also triggers the metering process that is used to calculate the charge for the call.

answer signal, charge A SIGNAL sent in the BACKWARD DIRECTION when a CALL is answered. It is used to start metering the call to calculate the charge to be made to the CALLING PARTY.

answer signal, no charge A SIGNAL sent in the BACKWARD DIRECTION when a CALL is answered. It is used to indicate this call is not subject to any charge, e.g., a call made to public emergency services.

answering, automatic See AUTOMATIC ANSWERING.

answering, manual See MANUAL ANSWERING.

answering time The time interval between the completion of the transmission of a CALLING SIGNAL and the answer by an operator or by an AUTOMATIC ANSWERING system at the distant location.

antenna A device constructed to transmit or receive RADIO WAVES. The physical characteristics of the antenna determine its suitability to send or receive radio waves in a particular FREQUENCY BAND; may be DIRECTIONAL or NONDIRECTIONAL.

A directional antenna used for transmission radiates a greater degree of energy in a particular direction and is usually arranged to beam radio waves in the direction of a particular RECEIVING TERMINAL. Thus, it is used in point-to-point communication.

application The task to which a system is applied and the procedures that relate to the execution of it. For example, a COMPUTER system and a TELECOMMUNICATIONS system may be used to handle the application of making an airline ticket reservation.

application code The programs that perform a particular task for USERS, as distinct from the OPERATING SYSTEM or other general-purpose SOFTWARE forming part of the COMPUTER environment.

application layer Relating to the ARCHITECTURE of a communications system and defining the levels of HARDWARE or SOFTWARE that relate to the APPLICATION to be performed rather than the levels that are concerned with managing and controlling DATA TRANSMISSION. See, for example, ISO REFERENCE MODEL FOR OPEN SYSTEMS ARCHITECTURE.

application program In any computer system, a program (or set of programs) that performs a specific task for end users, but not a program concerned with controlling the COMPUTER or parts of its OPERATING SYSTEM. Similarly, in DATA COMMUNICATIONS it works on TEXT transmitted by the system and has no responsibility for system functions such as ERROR CHECKING, DIALOGUE MANAGEMENT, ADDRESSING, ROUTING and LINK CONTROL.

architecture The architecture of a system relates to its design and the way in which the component parts interrelate. The term can be applied to the design of any machine, such as a MINICOMPUTER, or to an overall communications network. The architecture refers to the logical structure of a system rather than the specific details of the individual components used to construct the system. See OPEN SYSTEMS ARCHITECTURE.

Arcnet A type of LAN named after the first commercially marketed version, which was called Attached Resource Computer, or ARC (from Datapoint Corp. in San Antonio, Tex.). It uses the TOKEN PASSING access method and a BASEBAND transmission technique at speeds up to 20 Mbps. Broadband Arcnet is available.

area code A three-digit number identifying geographical areas of the United States and its territories and Canada, the area code is part of the 10-digit numbering plan used for placing telephone calls.

ARPA See ADVANCED RESEARCH PROJECTS AGENCY.

ARPANET A PACKET SWITCHING NETWORK developed by ARPA in 1969, ARPANET is used to link computers at many U.S. universities, research laboratories and government sites.

ARQ See AUTOMATIC REPEAT REQUEST.

articulation test A test made for the quality of line transmission in a TELEPHONE network. These tests are usually conducted to show the variation of sound articulation against ATTENUATION, comparing an object system with a standard reference system.

artificial ear A device used to permit the calibration of earphones in telephone transmission systems, and having an acoustic impedance the same as the average human ear.

ASCII See AMERICAN STANDARD CODE FOR INFORMATION INTERCHANGE.

aspect ratio The physical proportions of a viewing screen in a TELEVISION RECEIVER or other VISUAL DISPLAY device, expressed as the ratio of width to height. The usual standard is 4:3.

ASR See AUTOMATIC SEND AND RECEIVE.

assembler A HARDWARE or SOFTWARE device that translates statements from one form to another, e.g., operates upon statements written in a programming language to produce a machine language program that can run on a particular processor.

associated channel signaling See CHANNEL ASSOCIATED SIGNALING.

asymmetrical duplex transmission A system in which transmission takes place simultaneously in both directions over a CIRCUIT but not at the same rate in each direction.

asynchronous operation A method of DATA TRANSMISSION in which each CHARACTER is framed by BITS or pulses (e.g., START AND STOP SIGNALS). The START BIT triggers a timing mechanism in the RECEIVING TERMINAL that counts off succeeding bits of the character as a series of fixed time intervals. The STOP BIT resets the receiver ready for the next character. This technique is usually associated with slow-speed devices like TELEPRINTERS. Contrast with SYNCHRONOUS OPERATION.

asynchronous system A communications system in which units of DATA (e.g., CHARACTERS, WORDS or BLOCKS) are preceded and followed by START-STOP SIGNALS that provide timing at the RECEIVING TERMINAL.

asynchronous terminal A transmitting/receiving device that operates using ASYNCHRONOUS SIGNALS, i.e., in which units of DATA are bounded by START OR STOP SIGNALS.

asynchronous transfer mode (ATM) A technique for PACKET transfer that is expected to be used on networks built with FIBER OPTIC CABLE. The units of DATA that travel through the SWITCH FABRIC have a fixed length and are called CELLS. The process is sometimes called CELL RELAY. Compare with FRAME RELAY. See also FAST PACKET SWITCHING.

ATM See ASYNCHRONOUS TRANSFER MODE.

ATM See AUTOMATED TELLER MACHINE.

AT&T See AMERICAN TELEPHONE AND TELEGRAPH COMPANY.

attenuation An undesirable condition in which the MESSAGE SIGNALS transmitted along a CHANNEL are corrupted due to the waveform of the SIGNAL being chopped off. Attenuation is related to the frequency of the message signal and the TRANSMISSION MEDIUM used in the link.

The attenuation attributed to any part of a system is usually measured in DECIBELS. For example, in a pair of wires, attenuation is measured in dB per unit length and is related to the resistance (R), the inductance (L) and the capacitance (C) between the pair per unit length.

To overcome the effects of attenuation, it is normal practice to use REPEATERS, which regenerate the signal to maintain a high SIGNAL-TO-NOISE RATIO. Repeaters also overcome other signal impairments.

In planning communication networks, it is necessary to consider the NOMINAL TOTAL ATTENUATION resulting from different ROUTING situations.

audio amplifier A device used to increase the magnitude of a SIGNAL that is in the range of frequencies audible to the human ear.

audio circuit A CIRCUIT designed to carry a SOUND PROGRAM suitable for a radio broadcast or the sound component of a television broadcast. The BANDWIDTH of the circuit would therefore allow a range of frequencies suitable for the representation of speech and music (i.e., in the range from 20 Hz to 20 kHz). A circuit designed for telephone TRAFFIC would be referred to as a SPEECH CIRCUIT or VOICE CIRCUIT.

audio frequency See AUDIO FREQUENCY BAND.

audio frequency band The spectrum of frequencies associated with the range of SOUND WAVES that humans can perceive; i.e., within the band from 20 Hz to 20 kHz. In communication systems it is necessary to distinguish between TRANSMISSION PATHS able to cover the full range of such sounds, and more limited media used to carry only speech, as in TELEPHONY.

Speech circuits in telephony only require a BANDWIDTH from 300 to 3,300 Hz, whereas AUDIO CIRCUITS able to carry music and speech to the level of quality expected in radio and television broadcasts may cover the full audio frequency band.

audio frequency waveband The band of electromagnetic frequencies that equate to SOUND as perceived by humans. Same as AUDIO FREQUENCY BAND.

audio signal An ELECTRICAL SIGNAL corresponding to SOUND WAVES. The electrical signal represents the sound pressure fluctuations. A direct means of conversion from sound to audio can be achieved by a MICROPHONE and conversely from audio to sound by a LOUDSPEAKER. The audio signal is an electrical ANALOG of sound.

automated teller machine (ATM) Typically connected to remote MAINFRAMES, ATMs provide bank customers with access to computer DATABASES for multiple TRANSACTIONS, such as deposit and withdrawal of money, without the assistance of a human being.

automatic alternative routing A facility that enables a CALL that is blocked by busy LINES on a PRIMARY ROUTE to be automatically diverted to a different one. See also ALTERNATIVE ROUTING.

automatic announcements A facility provided in modern telephone NETWORKS in which digitally recorded segments of speech are delivered to USERS in specific situations, e.g., early morning calls and speaking clocks.

automatic answering A facility in which a TERMINAL automatically responds to a CALLING SIGNAL; the CALL may be established even though the CALLED TERMINAL is unattended.

automatic calling A facility that enables a device to automatically CALL another TERMINAL over a PUBLIC DATA NETWORK by generating an ADDRESS in the CALLING TERMINAL.

automatic dialer A device that, in response to a given input SIGNAL, will automatically call a distant TERMINAL over a NETWORK.

automatic equalizer See EQUALIZATION.

automatic gain control A unit designed to compensate for variations in the strength of a SIGNAL received by radio propagation or along a TRANSMISSION PATH. It includes features to generate a control voltage that will increase the GAIN of an AMPLIFIER to maintain a more or less constant output despite fluctuations in the power of the received signal.

automatic number identification (ANI) A feature of some TELECOMMUNICATIONS equipment at the CENTRAL OFFICE that recognizes the telephone number of the CALLING PARTY, so it can be used for billing purposes and/or to let the CALLED PARTY know who is calling before answering the phone.

automatic recall A facility whereby a TERMINAL can automatically attempt to call back a terminal that is busy so that the desired CALL is established when the CALLED TERMINAL is free.

automatic repeat attempt In a TELEPHONE or DATA NETWORK, a facility provided to automatically repeat an attempt to establish a CALL when difficulty has been experienced in establishing the call. The repeat attempt may use the same CIRCUIT or select another circuit.

automatic repeat request (ARQ) A method of ERROR CORRECTION in DATA TRANSMISSION in which any BLOCKS of DATA found to contain errors at the RECEIVING TERMINAL are automatically requested for repeat transmission from the TRANSMITTING TERMINAL. See also HALF DUPLEX ERROR PROTOCOL and FULL DUPLEX ERROR PROTOCOL.

automatic send and receive (ASR) Pertaining to a TERMINAL that has TRANSMITTING and RECEIVING STATIONS and logical facilities that enable incoming or outgoing MESSAGES to be stored (e.g., on PAPER TAPE, MAGNETIC TAPE or in COMPUTER memory).

automatic sequential connection A facility provided in PRIVATE and PUBLIC DATA NETWORKS in which a particular TERMINAL can call other terminals at specified ADDRESSES in a predetermined sequence. For example, a COMPUTER dialing REMOTE BATCH TERMINALS to collect batches of input data from distant locations.

automatic service Any service such as the public TELEPHONE SYSTEM in which a caller can make a necessary connection without the intervention of an operator at an EXCHANGE.

automatic switching equipment That part of an EXCHANGE in a SWITCHED SYSTEM that routes calls automatically to make the connections requested by CALLING PARTIES.

automatic transfer A special procedure used to transfer an incoming CALL from one EXCHANGE to another or from one subscriber TERMINAL to another.

availability of service The design of any communication system includes an attempt to minimize the use of resources (i.e., reduce system costs) while maintaining a high level of USER satisfaction. One criterion by which the quality of service is measured is the availability of the system, e.g., whether a user TERMINAL can gain access to the network without unreasonable delay. The performance of the system in this respect is expressed as a target probability of a CALL being blocked. For example, the target PROBABILITY OF CALL BLOCKING on a LOCAL EXCHANGE might be 0.02. See also QUALITY OF SERVICE and RELIABILITY OF SERVICE.

average call duration A statistic used in TRAFFIC THEORY and obtained by dividing the total number of minutes of conversation by all CALLS, by the number of EFFECTIVE CALLS in a given period.

average operating time A statistic used in expressing the quality of service of a TELEPHONE SYSTEM, in which the total operating time in minutes for the period under review is divided by the number of EFFECTIVE CALLS recorded in the period.

average traffic The mean volume of TRAFFIC (E) handled in a given period of time by a particular part of a TELECOMMUNICATIONS system and expressed as:

$$E = \frac{nh}{T}$$

where n = number of calls; h = the mean holding time per call; and T is the duration of the period. See also TRAFFIC THEORY and MEAN HOLDING TIME.

awaiting digits state A state that exists when a LINE is activated but awaiting SIGNALS from a TERMINAL about to make a CALL over a telephone NETWORK.

B

B channel One of the communications CHANNELS carried on the DIGITAL TRANSMISSION LINE between the CENTRAL OFFICE and the ISDN SUBSCRIBER. The B channel carries 64 kbps of USER DATA (as opposed to SIGNALING information), PCM-encoded digital voice or a combination of slower-speed subchannels for both types of traffic.

back space (BS) A function represented as a special FORMAT EFFECTOR in a DATA COMMUNICATIONS CODE and serving as an instruction to move a PRINT MECHANISM or a CURSOR of a VISUAL DISPLAY UNIT backwards for one position.

backbone routing A ROUTING that uses only the MAIN TRUNK routes in an EXCHANGE HIERARCHY.

backing store That part of a COMPUTER store that contains programs and DATA not immediately needed for processing. Usually, backing store is on magnetic disk or MAGNETIC TAPE, and access can be obtained to segments of DATA that are available in amounts of several thousand BYTES. Access time may take several milliseconds whereas, once in MAIN MEMORY, data can be accessed as discrete operands for processing in access time measured in nanoseconds.

back-off A procedure whereby the load is systematically reduced from an overloaded CHANNEL to prevent COLLISION or to RESTART in a PEAK LOAD situation. This technique is used in LOCAL AREA NETWORKS.

backward channel A CHANNEL in which transmission takes place in the reverse direction to the intended DATA FLOW; the backward channel is normally used for supervisory or ERROR CONTROL signals concerned with the main data flow over the FORWARD CHANNEL. DATA COMMUNICATION systems can transfer information in both directions; it is, therefore, necessary to relate this term to the DATA SOURCE at any instant.

backward direction Relating to the transmission of supervisory and ERROR CONTROL signals in a DATA NETWORK that takes place on a BACKWARD CHANNEL, i.e., in the reverse direction to that in which information is being transferred.

badge reader A DATA TERMINAL used for DATA COLLECTION in which the USER inserts a badge (or plastic card) to initiate a transaction. The badge contains information to identify the user and may have authorization codes that delimit the nature of the transaction that can be performed.

balanced double-current interchange circuit An INTERFACE circuit between DATA TERMINAL EQUIPMENT (DTE) and a MODEM, having certain electrical characteristics as defined in the CCITT recommendation V.11 concerned with DATA TRANSMISSION over telephone CIRCUITS.

band pass filter A FILTER that allows a band of frequencies to pass along a CIRCUIT while blocking all frequencies above and below the band. Contrast with HIGH PASS FILTER and LOW PASS FILTER.

bandwidth The bandwidth of a COMMUNICATION CHANNEL defines the range of frequencies that can effectively be conveyed in the channel. If an attempt is made to transmit signals outside the nominated bandwidth, the signals may be distorted such that information carried is lost or corrupted. For example, in a simple INTERCOM system, the objective is to communicate VOICE SIGNALS between two USERS, and for this purpose a bandwidth of 20 Hz to 3 kHz is sufficient. This will cover the DYNAMIC RANGE of sounds made in normal conversation and enable recognition of familiar voices. It will not provide a high fidelity reproduction of sounds occurring at each STATION.

In a TELEPHONE SYSTEM, the restriction of the allowed bandwidth can reduce the effect of NOISE at frequencies where there is little information transmitted, and a planned limitation of the bandwidth reduces the cost necessary for AMPLIFIERS and transmission links in the system while retaining a SIGNAL acceptable to the users.

For public telephone systems, the CCITT recommendation for the VOICE BAND is 0.3 to 3.4 kHz. This can be compared with the bandwidth of 15 Hz to 20 kHz, which is necessary for high quality music transmission systems.

See also RADIO FREQUENCY CARRIER WAVE, MODULATION, VIDEO SIGNAL.

A circuit that is capable of carrying only LOW FREQUENCY signals, e.g., AUDIO FREQUENCY signals, is said to be of NARROW BANDWIDTH. A circuit that is capable of carrying HIGH FREQUENCY signals, e.g., a RADIO FREQUENCY SIGNAL, is said to be of BROAD BANDWIDTH. Very often a BROADBAND CHANNEL is used to carry several narrow band channels at the same time by modulating the narrow band channels onto a high frequency CARRIER.

The electrical properties of the TRANSMISSION MEDIUM have a great effect on the bandwidth of a particular TRANSMISSION CHANNEL. Serious ATTENUATION or CROSSTALK affecting the MESSAGE SIGNAL will arise if the frequency characteristics of the signal are not matched to the properties of the medium. These problems can be overcome with equipment known as REPEATERS spaced at intervals along the transmission channel. However, this is expensive, and research to find improvements in transmission media is important for the growth of the industry and the economics of communications.

See also FIBER OPTIC CABLE, OPTICAL FIBERS.

The table shown below gives an indication of the bandwidth potential of different transmission media. It assumes that appropriate repeaters are installed.

Medium	Practical Frequency Band
twisted wire pairs	up to 500 kHz
co-axial cable	60 kHz to 60 MHz
waveguides	2 GHz to 11 GHz

DIGITAL SIGNALS can be transmitted over a variety of transmission channels of different bandwidths. The digital signals exist usually at two discrete levels (e.g., corresponding to the BINARY NOTATION 0 and 1). In the example shown in Appendix 6, two BITS of information are represented by a signal inversion corresponding to a single cycle of an AC signal. The higher the channel bandwidth, therefore, the greater possible inversion rate and therefore the greater possible speed of information transfer.

The terminal equipment in a digital system is built to send and receive message signals consisting of pulses of a defined duration. The duration of the pulses determines the amount of information that can be received by the terminal in a second, and devices are rated in terms of pulses per second, known as the BAUD RATE. Some rates of data transmission recommended by the CCITT are 200, 600 and 1,200 bauds. Compare with BIT RATE.

Computer-to-computer links often require several thousand bits (kilobits) to be transferred per second and, in some cases, millions of bits (megabits) or even billions of bits (gigabits) per second. For this purpose, a broadband channel allowing high frequency transmission is needed. It is common in data transmission to use the term BIT RATE as though it were synonymous with channel bandwidth.

baseband coaxial system A communications system, suitable for a LOCAL AREA NETWORK, in which information is directly encoded onto a TRANSMISSION MEDIUM consisting of a COAXIAL CABLE.

baseband modem A modem that has a more limited technical specification than is required for connecting DATA TERMINAL EQUIPMENT (DTE) to a PUBLIC SWITCHED TELEPHONE NETWORK. A baseband modem can be used on PRIVATE LINES and for limited distance communication. Also known as a DATA SERVICE UNIT.

BASIC A PROGRAMMING LANGUAGE classed as a HIGH LEVEL LANGUAGE and used for developing programs to run on a particular computer HARDWARE. The name is derived from: Beginners' All-purpose Symbolic Instruction Code.

basic access See BASIC RATE INTERFACE.

Basic Rate Interface (BRI) A configuration of CHANNELS used to transfer DATA and SIGNALING information when accessing an INTEGRATED SERVICES DIGITAL NETWORK. The Basic Rate Interface consists of two 64-kbps bearer channels (which carry USER information and are called B CHANNELS) and one 16-kbps D CHANNEL (which carries signaling information). The BRI is commonly referred to as 2B+D. See also PRIMARY RATE INTERFACE.

basic routing The ROUTING involving the least number of TRUNK LINKS.

batch processing A form of DATA PROCESSING in which transactions are collected in batches to be processed at a convenient time. A batch processing system may provide a useful information system (e.g., for accountancy purposes). It would not, however, be used to monitor and control fast-moving events in a real-time application, because the delays in collecting, preparing and processing batches may result in FILES being hours, or days, behind in recording the status of real events. Compare with REAL-TIME SYSTEM.

batch systems Any DATA PROCESSING SYSTEM that uses BATCH PROCESSING techniques.

baud A term used to express the rating of equipment or a TRANSMISSION CHANNEL in a communications system. The number of pulses that can be transmitted in a second is the BAUD RATE. Baud translates as pulses per second, just as HERTZ equals cycles per second. The definition is named after Emile Baudot, an early contributor in the development of TELECOMMUNICATIONS. See also MODULATION RATE, and compare with DATA SIGNALING RATE.

baud rate The speed of operation of a device or CHANNEL in pulses per second. Also known as MODULATION RATE and should be compared with DATA SIGNALING RATE.

Baudot See EMILE BAUDOT.

B8ZS (Bipolar with eight zeros substitution) A coding scheme used with the 1.544-Mbps version of the PRIMARY RATE INTERFACE, B8ZS facilitates SYNCHRONIZATION between the sender and receiver. See also HDB3.

bel A unit of measure for the overall LOSS or GAIN in power attributable to a CIRCUIT or device. The loss or gain is given by the formula:

$$N = \log_{10} \frac{P_2}{P_1} \text{ bels}$$

where N = the number of bells; P_1 = power sent; and P_2 = power received. In practice, it is more convenient to use the measure DECIBEL, which is one-tenth of a bel.

BEL A SIGNAL forming part of a DATA COMMUNICATION CODE and used to activate an audible alarm at a RECEIVING TERMINAL. An abbreviation of bell and used to attract an operator's attention.

Bell Atlantic See REGIONAL BELL HOLDING COMPANY.

Bell Communications Research (Bellcore) As a result of DIVESTITURE the organization called Bellcore was established to represent the RBOCS, which fund it.

Bell operating company (BOC) Previously subsidiaries of AT&T, the 22 Bell operating companies were consolidated into seven REGIONAL BELL HOLDING COMPANIES after DIVESTITURE. They provide local service. See also LATA.

Bellcore See BELL COMMUNICATIONS RESEARCH.

BellSouth See REGIONAL BELL HOLDING COMPANY.

BER See BIT ERROR RATE.

BERT See BIT ERROR RATE TEST.

bid In any SWITCHED SYSTEM an attempt, successful or otherwise, to secure a CIRCUIT in a CIRCUIT GROUP.

bidirectional communication A form of communication in which two USERS are able to send and receive information over a NETWORK. This can be achieved by a FULL DUPLEX operation in which both parties can send and receive simultaneously or by a rapid exchange of information in which the parties alternately send and receive information.

bids per circuit per hour (BCH) A ratio intended to indicate to operators of a switched network the TRAFFIC PRESSURE for a group of CIRCUITS. The ratio is given as the number of BIDS per hour divided by the number of working circuits.

bilateral control Relating to the synchronization of NODES at different locations in which the CLOCK at each node can control the clock at the other, i.e., one node is not a slave to the other.

billing The process concerned with preparing invoices that are intended to charge USERS for their utilization of a communications system. This includes the procedures concerned with measuring their use of the NETWORK.

binary coded information Information that has been represented as BINARY NUMBERS, or patterns of BINARY DIGITS, in order that the information may be transmitted or processed.

binary digit A DIGIT in BINARY NOTATION, i.e., 0 or 1. A group of binary digits may represent a number (e.g., 011011 in binary represents 27 in decimal form), or they may be used in groups to form binary codes that represent alphabetic CHARACTERS, numerals or special symbols. As an example, it is common in COMPUTERS and other electronic systems to use 6-bit groups to form up to 64 unique patterns which represent 64 separate characters. See also Appendix 1.

binary digital signal A SIGNAL in which information is represented as BINARY NUMBERS, e.g., by two voltage levels in a CIRCUIT.

binary notation A system for representing numbers in which each digit position may contain either an integer 1 or 0 (i.e., in a radix of two). In the addition of integers, the following rules apply:

$$\begin{array}{r}0\\+0\\\hline 0\end{array}\qquad\begin{array}{r}0\\+1\\\hline 1\end{array}\qquad\begin{array}{r}1\\+1\\\hline 10\end{array}$$

Numbers in binary notation thus appear as rows of 1's or 0's, and the range of values that can be represented increases with the number of positions. For example, four digit positions give 16 unique patterns of BITS including:

0000 = 0 in decimal notation
0001 = 1 in decimal notation
0010 = 2 in decimal notation
1110 = 14 in decimal notation
1111 = 15 in decimal notation

Inside a DIGITAL COMPUTER, or any other digital machine, binary information is easily handled since each integer can be represented by a high or low voltage.

binary number A number in which the radix for each DIGIT position is two, and the numbers are represented by the digits 0 and 1.

binary string A succession of contiguous electrical pulses representing BINARY CODED INFORMATION and treated as a unit of DATA for processing or transmission purposes but not necessarily a complete DATA ELEMENT or set of data elements intended for an end USER.

binary synchronous communications (BSC) A DATA COMMUNICATIONS PROTOCOL for HALF-DUPLEX TRANSMISSION that uses CONTROL CHARACTERS and procedures for managing DATA TRANSFER and network connections. Compare with SYNCHRONOUS DATA LINK CONTROL.

binary tariff system A system of charge made up of two elements. For example, in the operation of a TELEGRAPH NETWORK, a fixed charge is made for the acceptance and delivery of a telegram, and a further variable charge is made, depending upon the length of the telegram in words.

bipolar transmission A technique used in the transmission of DIGITAL SIGNALS to reduce the apparent effect of a DIRECT CURRENT (DC) component in the BINARY SIGNAL. This effect arises because the number of 0's and 1's is not equal, and, on average, this creates the effect of a DC element in the signal. In bipolar transmission, a 1 is represented by either a positive or negative voltage, and a zero by 0 volts. The positive and negative values are used alternately, and therefore the average value of the signal is always zero.

BISDN See BROADBAND ISDN.

bit See BINARY DIGIT.

bit error In digital systems, DATA is transmitted as a series of discrete electric pulses at levels representing the 1 or 0 DIGITS of a BINARY NUMBER. It is possible for intermittent errors to arise that cause BITS (binary digits) to be received incorrectly. These are known as bit errors. Various ERROR CHECKING procedures are used to detect and correct bit errors, including the automatic retransmission of FRAMES known to contain errors. See also ERROR CHECKING and ERROR RATE.

bit error rate A measure of the quality of a CIRCUIT used for DATA TRANSMISSION, expressed as a ratio of the number of BITS incorrectly received to the total number of bits transmitted (e.g., 1 in 10^7 bits).

bit error rate test (BERT) A comparison of bit patterns, the bit error rate test matches the transmission of a known path with the received version of the same pattern. The number of bits received in error are counted.

bit parallel transmission See PARALLEL TRANSMISSION.

bit pattern A specific pattern of BINARY DIGITS used in a system to represent a particular instruction or meaning.

bit rates Pertaining to the speed of operation of digital equipment. For example, a 9.6 KILOBIT channel can handle DIGITAL SIGNALS at speeds of 9,600 BINARY DIGITS per second. See also MODULATION RATE and DATA SIGNALING RATE.

bit serial transmission See SERIAL TRANSMISSION.

bit stuffing In TIME DIVISION MULTIPLEXING it is necessary to synchronize TIME SLOTS in SWITCHING operations. To ensure that one CHANNEL coincides with the CLOCK of another, the technique of bit stuffing is sometimes used. This entails the insertion of redundant BITS into an incoming BIT-STREAM to increase the rate; the presence of the stuffed bits is signaled to the receiver so that they can be removed to restore the original DATA. See also TIME SHIFTING.

bit synchronization Whenever digital devices communicate over a NETWORK, the individual pulses that represent BITS have to be synchronized by an electronic CLOCK, which maintains the timing sequence required between two communicating devices to ensure that bits are not lost. Such clocks in SYNCHRONOUS DIGITAL SYSTEMS are in the DATA TERMINAL or the MODEM of the TRANSMITTING STATION. The signals sent create transitions on the LINE, and the clock at the RECEIVING STATION adjusts its clock rate to these transitions. Where long high-speed DIGITAL TRANSMISSIONS take place, special synchronizing characters (SYN) are inserted into the data at the beginning of transmission to establish SYNCHRONIZATION. See also CHARACTER SYNCHRONIZATION and MESSAGE SYNCHRONIZATION.

bit-clocking The process of maintaining SYNCHRONIZATION, say between a TERMINAL and a NETWORK, by the transmission of BITS (binary digits), which provide coordinating timing pulses for various CONTROL and transmission activities.

bit-order of transmission Describes the arrangement for the transmission of any unit of DATA in a system where SERIAL TRANSMISSION is used. For example, the most significant DIGIT of a number or FIELD may be sent first, or the least significant digit first.

bit-stream BIT is an abbreviation of BINARY DIGIT and is used to represent 0 or 1 in a BINARY NUMBER. In modern TELECOMMUNICATIONS, many of the techniques associated with DIGITAL COMPUTERS have been applied; thus, both TEXT (i.e., user information) and CONTROL INFORMATION are transmitted as streams of binary digits or bit streams.

blackbox An expression referring to any item of equipment that carries out a specific set of functions. Usually used to simplify a discussion between technician and layman, in which the significant objective is to convey the idea of the function of and inputs and outputs required by the blackbox.

BLERT See BLOCK ERROR RATE TEST.

block A group of BITS, CHARACTERS or WORDS transmitted as a unit of DATA over which any DATA LINK CONTROL procedures may be applied to effect ERROR DETECTION and/or ERROR CORRECTION.

block check A check performed in a DATA NETWORK to facilitate ERROR CONTROL and usually concerned with predetermined rules for the formation of blocks.

block error rate In a DATA NETWORK, a measure of the quality of a CIRCUIT used for transmission, expressed as a ratio of the number of BLOCKS incorrectly received to the number of blocks sent.

block error rate test (BLERT) A comparison of patterns in which a known blocked bit pattern is transmitted and matched against the received version of the same pattern. The number of blocks having ERROR BITS is counted.

block separator A CHARACTER that defines the format of information structured in BLOCKS and used to indicate that the next character in a sequence belongs to a new block of information.

block-acknowledged counter A facility provided in a TERMINAL that is transmitting BLOCKS of DATA to record the number of blocks that have been acknowledged as received by a distant RECEIVING TERMINAL. Compare with BLOCK-COMPLETED COUNTER.

block-completed counter A facility provided in a TERMINAL that is transmitting BLOCKS of DATA to record the number of blocks that have been transmitted. Compare with BLOCK-ACKNOWLEDGED COUNTER.

blocked call A CALL is said to be blocked when ACCESS PATHS from the CALLED TERMINAL to the CALLING TERMINAL are fully engaged with existing TRAFFIC.

blocking signal 1. A SIGNAL sent to an EXCHANGE (or NODE) to indicate that the exchange should not use a particular CIRCUIT for any OUTGOING CALL. The exchange is, however, able to receive an INCOMING CALL on that circuit. This signal is used in maintenance procedures.

2. Any signal sent on an idle circuit to prevent the circuit being seized by another exchange or user TERMINAL.

blocking signal acknowledgment A SIGNAL sent by an EXCHANGE to acknowledge that a particular CIRCUIT has been blocked in response to a BLOCKING SIGNAL.

bounded medium See BOUNDED TRANSMISSION MEDIUM.

bounded transmission medium A physical set of materials used to carry SIGNALS is known as a TRANSMISSION MEDIUM. A COAXIAL CABLE is an example of a bounded transmission medium; i.e., the signal is propagated along a physical path determined by the properties of the medium. By contrast, the atmosphere through which RADIO SIGNALS are propagated is known as an UNBOUNDED MEDIUM.

bps Abbreviation of BITS per second; a measure of the rate of operation of a CIRCUIT or device.

bridge LANS are connected at the Media Access Control portion of the PHYSICAL LINK LAYER of the OSI model by means of bridges. The PROTOCOLS or LAN OPERATING SYSTEMS being used are irrelevant to the operation of a bridge. Compare with ROUTER.

British Telecom A public corporation (at press time, the British government owned almost half the ordinary shares but was expected to reduce that stake soon) responsible for the operation of public TELECOMMUNICATION services throughout the United Kingdom of Great Britain and Northern Ireland, including TELEPHONE, TELEX, VIDEOTEX and PUBLIC DATA NETWORKS. The corporation was given a separate identity during 1981, prior to which it had operated as the Telecommunications Division of the British Post Office.

broad bandwidth See BANDWIDTH.

broadband channel A TRANSMISSION PATH having a wide BANDWIDTH. For example, a TELEVISION CHANNEL uses a specified bandwidth of approximately 5.5 MHz, but a telephone SPEECH CHANNEL uses a specified bandwidth of only 3 kHz. A broadband channel would be constructed of materials that do not offer significant resistance, ATTENUATION or DISTORTION of high frequency ELECTROMAGNETIC WAVES. See also BANDWIDTH, HDTV.

broadband ISDN (BISDN) An emerging standard specifying data rates higher than the U.S. T1 rate of 1.544 Mbps or the European CEPT rate of 2.048 Mbps, BISDN uses SONET at the NETWORK-to-network INTERFACE. It is based in part on the switching technique called ASYNCHRONOUS TRANSFER MODE. Broadband ISDN is expected to support switched VOICE, DATA and VIDEO SIGNAL transmissions at up to 145 Mbps. Research is under way to develop commercial offerings at 600 Mbps. Experimental networks at gigabit speeds are also emerging for use by scientists and scholars. And a special 2.5-Gbps network has been established for the 1992 Olympic games in Spain.

broadband multiplexing channels A CHANNEL that has a sufficiently high BANDWIDTH to enable a number of MESSAGE SIGNALS to be combined and transmitted over the same channel using MULTIPLEXING techniques. For example, a 2,000 MHz channel can accommodate 500,000 TELEPHONE CHANNELS where each telephone channel is allowed 4 kHz. See also MULTIPLEXING.

broadband transmission channel See BROADBAND CHANNEL.

broadcast Any form of transmission in which all SUBSCRIBERS connected to a particular service are addressed at the same instant with the same MESSAGE SIGNAL. The CHANNEL for communication could be a BOUNDED MEDIUM, such as a CABLE NETWORK, or an UNBOUNDED MEDIUM, such as a television signal broadcast as RADIO WAVES in the atmosphere.

broadcasting organization Any organization that is concerned with SOUND and/or vision broadcasting, e.g., providing radio, television or TELETEXT facilities.

brouter Used on LANS, brouters perform some of the tasks of a BRIDGE with a portion of ROUTER functionality.

BS See BACKSPACE.

BSC See BINARY SYNCHRONOUS COMMUNICATIONS.

buffer A storage unit used to retain a unit of DATA until it can be processed by another device, e.g., to balance the capacity of a high-speed DIGITAL COMPUTER with the relatively slower speed of a TRANSMISSION CHANNEL.

buffered terminal Any TERMINAL that has a magnetic memory device that can be used to store incoming or outgoing MESSAGES. For example, any terminal that is activated remotely by the POLLING action of a COMPUTER must have the ability to store information until its turn in the polling sequence arises.

buffering A technique used in DATA TRANSMISSION SYSTEMS to balance the TRAFFIC to the capacity of some part of the system. For example, incoming MESSAGES are held in a BUFFER until they can be serviced and outgoing messages until they can be transferred along the TRANSMISSION LINE.

bulletin board service (BBS) A BBS consists of a FILE (such as an ELECTRONIC MAIL SYSTEM, a computer-based messaging system or a TELECONFERENCING system) residing in a commonly accessible location—usually a HOST PROCESSOR. Users LOG-ON to the BBS to place or to retrieve information.

burst errors Errors occurring in a CIRCUIT used for DATA TRANSMISSION, in which the frequency of the errors is such that less than a specified number of CORRECT BITS occurs between ERROR BITS. See also TRANSMISSION ERRORS.

burst isochronous transmission The transmission of SYNCHRONOUS DATA in bursts over a PUBLIC DATA NETWORK to produce a mean DATA SIGNALING RATE on an INFORMATION BEARER CHANNEL, compatible with the INPUT DATA SIGNALING RATE of a receiving device.

bursty traffic Refers to TRAFFIC that arises in bursts and, in particular, to DATA NETWORKS in which the traffic level may change in a short time period from very low to very high, approaching the PEAK VOLUME planned for the NETWORK.

bus A physical transmission path or CHANNEL; or, in LAN technology, a TOPOLOGY whereby all NODES are aware of all transmissions but choose to receive only those having certain ADDRESSES.

business terminal A DATA TERMINAL used in a business environment or a telephone TERMINAL used in a business rather than a residential environment.

busy hour A period of uninterrupted time (nominally 1 hour), for which the TRAFFIC in a TELECOMMUNICATIONS system is at its maximum level.

busy hour average traffic The mean TRAFFIC VOLUME arising in the period of peak utilization of a TELECOMMUNICATIONS system.

busy hour traffic In planning the capacity required in a communications system, it is necessary to assess the TRAFFIC VOLUME expected during the busiest period. For example, in a PUBLIC SWITCHED TELEPHONE NETWORK, the traffic tends to reach a peak during the morning of a normal working weekday. An hour is the period chosen because a shorter period would make demarcation of the period difficult, whereas a longer duration would tend to average out peaks to be considered.

busy tone The SIGNAL heard by the USER of a TELEPHONE when the SUBSCRIBER being called has already lifted the HANDSET to speak to another party.

bypass Some users choose to bypass local telephone company installation and service charges by using another medium of TRANSMISSION, such as private LEASED LINES or MICROWAVE equipment. Bypass may provide the user with more transmission capacity and higher speeds.

byte A unit of DATA. It usually consisting of two CHARACTERS or 8 INFORMATION BITS.

byte-order of transmission Pertaining to the sequence in which the successive BYTES that make up a unit of DATA are transmitted. For example, the most significant byte may be transmitted first or the least significant byte first.

byte-serial transmission A method of transmission in which successive bytes are transferred serially in the appropriate sequence of the DATA. It should be noted that the individual BITS (BINARY DIGITS) that make up each BYTE may not necessarily be transmitted serially.

C

C band Used mainly for SATELLITE and MICROWAVE transmission, the C band portion of the electromagnetic spectrum covers about 4 GHz to 6 GHz.

cable loop A cable used for transmission in a LOCAL NETWORK, arranged in a loop to which all devices are connected for communication. Thus, all devices share the same CHANNEL and CONTENTION may arise.

cable network A NETWORK for DATA COMMUNICATION or for the transmission of television or radio broadcast signals. Usually refers to a network of COAXIAL TUBES and in the case of broadcast transmission, to a closed-circuit one-way path for the delivery of VIDEO and SOUND SIGNALS.

cable pressurization A technique used to protect cables in underground cable ducts by pumping dry compressed air into the cable itself. This tends to reduce damage caused by the ingress of water and thus reduces faults on cables; it serves also to identify cable damage by a loss of pressure.

CAD See COMPUTER AIDED DESIGN.

call A term used to describe the process of communication between USERS and more particularly to refer to the process that takes place in communication over the PUBLIC SWITCHED TELEPHONE NETWORK or PUBLIC DATA NETWORKS. This process can be considered in three phases, CALL ESTABLISHMENT (making the initial connection between TERMINALS), CONVERSION or DATA TRANSFER (transferring MESSAGES between user terminals) and CALL CLEARING (the orderly disengagement of terminals at the completion of a CALL).

call accepted packet A response given to the NETWORK by a TERMINAL in a PACKET SWITCHING SYSTEM when it is ready to accept a CALL REQUEST from another terminal. This action allows the network to establish a VIRTUAL CIRCUIT between the CALLING TERMINAL and CALLED TERMINAL so that DATA TRANSFER can take place.

call accepted signal A control SIGNAL sent by a TERMINAL to indicate that it has accepted an INCOMING CALL on a DATA NETWORK.

call accounting system A subsystem in an EXCHANGE that collects and processes charging information in respect of CALLS made by SUBSCRIBERS.

call answered signal A SIGNAL that arises when a CALLED TERMINAL responds to a CALL, e.g., when a CALLED SUBSCRIBER lifts the HANDSET of a TELEPHONE to respond to a call. This signal establishes a SPEECH PATH between the two terminals and usually starts a BILLING PROCEDURE.

call blocking If all the CHANNELS in a particular TRUNK ROUTE are in use, then any new CALL arising will be BLOCKED, i.e., the requested connection will not be accepted and an engaged tone may be sent.

TELECOMMUNICATION systems are usually planned to present a low probability of call blocking. The probability is expressed as:

$$B = \frac{C_B}{C_O}$$

where C_O = calls offered and C_B = calls blocked.

In practice, the probability of blocking in the BUSY HOUR is targeted to be around 0.01. It should be seen that the AVERAGE TRAFFIC must be less than the number of channels available to provide such a performance.

The probability of call blocking is an important measure of the performance of a CIRCUIT SWITCHED system. In MESSAGE SWITCHING, the equivalent performance is measured in terms of the MESSAGES taking more than a specified time to reach their destination. See also TRAFFIC THEORY.

call clear-down time The time taken to clear a CALL, from the moment the action is initiated by a TERMINAL to the moment a free condition is signaled on the DATA TERMINAL originating the call. Same as CALL RELEASE TIME.

call clearing The activity associated with making a CALL on a SWITCHED CIRCUIT is usually considered in three phases. These are: CALL ESTABLISHMENT, MESSAGE TRANSFER and CALL CLEARING. Call clearing covers the procedures and the activity associated with the correct and orderly disengagement of the two TERMINALS at the completion of the message transfer.

The concept applies to switched circuits for both DIGITAL TRANSMISSION and VOICE TELEPHONY, but the detailed procedures are different.

call connected packet A control PACKET transmitted in a PACKET SWITCHING network to signify the establishment of a VIRTUAL CIRCUIT.

call connected signal A control SIGNAL in CIRCUIT SWITCHING that signifies to a CALLING TERMINAL that a connection has been completed in response to its CALL REQUEST.

call control procedure The set of actions and SIGNALS that are required to establish, maintain and release a CALL in a NETWORK.

call control signals The complete set of SIGNALS that are required to establish, maintain and release a CALL in a NETWORK.

call disestablishment The procedures concerned with the orderly termination of a CALL at the completion of the phase in which information has been transferred and concerned with the release of CIRCUITS and resources that have been allocated to the call.

call duration For a given CALL, the period of time that elapses from the moment when the CALL ACCEPTED SIGNAL is received by the control system for the NETWORK until the CLEAR FORWARD SIGNAL (or CLEAR BACKWARD SIGNAL) is received as a result of a TERMINAL clearing the connection. See also AVERAGE CALL DURATION.

call establishment The activity associated with making a CALL on a SWITCHED CIRCUIT is usually considered in three phases. These are: call establishment, MESSAGE TRANSFER and CALL CLEARING. Call establishment covers the procedures and the activity concerned with the CALLING TERMINAL making a connection with the CALLED TERMINAL.

The concept applies to switched circuits for both DIGITAL TRANSMISSION and VOICE TELEPHONY, but the detailed procedures are different.

call failure signal A SIGNAL transmitted on a BACKWARD CHANNEL to notify a CALLING TERMINAL that its CALL REQUEST cannot be completed, e.g., because an event in the CALL CONTROL PROCEDURE has not been completed in the specified time.

call not accepted signal A SIGNAL sent by a DATA TERMINAL to indicate that it will not accept an INCOMING CALL.

call processing system A subsystem in a DIGITAL EXCHANGE that controls the progress of each CALL on the basis of instructions received from USERS.

call progress signal A SIGNAL between DATA CIRCUIT TERMINATING EQUIPMENT (DCE) and DATA TERMINAL EQUIPMENT (DTE) to notify the DTE of the progress in making a CALL that has been requested. The call progress signal may indicate positive or negative progress.

call release time See CALL CLEARDOWN TIME.

call request See CALL REQUEST SIGNAL.

call request packet In PACKET SWITCHING, the CALLING TERMINAL delivers a CALL REQUEST PACKET to the NETWORK when it attempts to establish a VIRTUAL CIRCUIT to another terminal.

If a CIRCUIT is available and if the called terminal is able to accept the CALL, a CALL ACCEPTED PACKET is delivered by the network to the calling terminal and the DATA TRANSFER PHASE is started. When this phase is completed, the calling terminal instructs the network to deactivate the link by a CLEAR REQUEST.

call request signal A control SIGNAL requesting service from a NETWORK sent by a CALLING TERMINAL to the network in which the ADDRESS of the terminal to be called is indicated. In the case of a TELEPHONE, the CALL REQUEST is indicated by lifting the HANDSET and dialing the required address.

In DATA COMMUNICATION SYSTEMS, the call request may include other information sent as a pattern of BITS to the LINE.

call setup The process of establishing a link between two TERMINALS, including the identification of the ADDRESS required by the CALLING TERMINAL, the selection of a path through the NETWORK and the acceptance of the connection by the CALLED TERMINAL.

call setup time The overall length of time required to establish a CALL between two TERMINALS, starting from the time for the initiation of the CALLING SIGNALS until a CALL CONNECTED SIGNAL is delivered to the terminal originating the call.

call-back This facility can be invoked by a CALLING TERMINAL when it has received a busy SIGNAL from a terminal to which a CALL has been requested. The facility will act as an instruction to the CONTROL system to establish the desired call when the busy terminal becomes free.

called line identification A system in which the NETWORK confirms to the CALLING TERMINAL the identity of the terminal with which a connection is about to be made, thus allowing the connection to be cancelled. See also CALLING LINE IDENTIFICATION.

called location The TERMINAL addressed as the destination for a particular CALL or MESSAGE SIGNAL.

called party The person who is to receive a particular CALL or MESSAGE SIGNAL at a CALLED LOCATION.

called subscriber The USER to whom a MESSAGE is sent or the user who is addressed by a CALL REQUEST originated by a CALLING SUBSCRIBER. Also known as CALLED PARTY.

called terminal A TERMINAL that has been identified by a CALL REQUEST issued by another terminal wishing to transmit a MESSAGE or conduct a CONVERSATION. Contrast with CALLING TERMINAL.

called terminal alerted state A STATE that exists when a SUBSCRIBER in a TELEPHONE SYSTEM has completed dialing another TERMINAL that is available to receive a CALL and the call bell is being rung.

called terminal answered signal A SIGNAL sent in the BACKWARD DIRECTION indicating that a CALLED TERMINAL has answered and CALL ESTABLISHMENT is in progress.

called terminal engaged signal A SIGNAL sent back to a CALLING LOCATION to indicate that the CALLED TERMINAL is engaged in another CALL.

called terminal free signal A SIGNAL (e.g., ringing signal) that indicates to the CALLING TERMINAL that the CALLED TERMINAL is available but has not yet answered.

calling The action involved in making connections between SUBSCRIBERS to a switched network. See also ABBREVIATED ADDRESS CALLING, AUTOMATIC CALLING, MANUAL CALLING and MULTI-ADDRESS CALLING.

calling indicator signal On a SWITCHED DATA CIRCUIT, this is an INTERCHANGE SIGNAL between a MODEM (or DCE) and DATA TERMINAL EQUIPMENT (DTE). The calling indicator signal is switched on when the DCE receives the ringing signal from a CALLING TERMINAL. If the DTE is switched on and in operable condition, it responds to the DCE with a DATA TERMINAL ready signal, which, in turn, causes the DCE to respond to the calling terminal with a DATA SET READY signal.

calling line identification A process whereby CALLED SUBSCRIBERS are advised of the caller before MESSAGE TRANSFER can take place, thus allowing the CALLED TERMINAL to accept or reject the connection. Sometimes used in DATA COMMUNICATION to regulate priorities. See also CALLED LINE IDENTIFICATION.

calling location The TERMINAL that originates a CALL or MESSAGE SIGNAL.

calling party See CALLING SUBSCRIBER.

calling party clear A method of CALL CLEARING in which the CALL is not cleared until the CALLING PARTY puts down the HANDSET. If the CALLED PARTY alone puts down the handset, it can be lifted to continue the call. Contrast with FIRST-PARTY CLEARING.

calling party's category indicator A special item of information attached to a MESSAGE to notify the CALLED PARTY about the nature of the CALL. For example, indicating priority.

calling rate The measure of the use made by USERS of a specific TERMINAL connected to a TELECOMMUNICATIONS system, i.e., a calling rate of 3 CALLS an hour of average duration of 4 minutes per call give 12 minutes' utilization of the system per hour. Thus, the terminal originates 0.2 ERLANGS of TRAFFIC in one hour.

calling signals Coded information that instructs a NETWORK to establish a ROUTE to a particular subscriber TERMINAL in a TELEPHONE, TELEX or DATA NETWORK. Also known as ADDRESS DIGITS or SELECTION DIGITS.

calling subscriber In a NETWORK conversation, the USER who initiates a CALL is known as the calling subscriber (or CALLING PARTY). The user who receives the call is known as the CALLED SUBSCRIBER (or CALLED PARTY).

calling terminal A TERMINAL that has issued a CALL REQUEST to a NETWORK to identify that it wishes to send a MESSAGE or conduct a CONVERSATION with another terminal. Contrast with CALLED TERMINAL.

calls barred A facility that prevents a TERMINAL from making OUTGOING CALLS or receiving INCOMING CALLS. For example, to reserve a CIRCUIT for a planned event.

CAN See CANCEL.

cancel (CAN) A special CODE appearing in a MESSAGE recorded in BINARY CODE form and giving a specific instruction to the RECEIVING STATION to disregard the preceding DATA in the MESSAGE or BLOCK.

capacitance The property of CONDUCTORS to store an electrical charge. The capacitance is defined as the ratio of the electrical charge between two conductors and their potential difference (Q/V). This property can create limitations in the transmission of SIGNALS over CIRCUITS.

carriage return (CR) A function represented as a special FORMAT EFFECTER in a DATA COMMUNICATIONS CODE and serving as an instruction to return a PRINT MECHANISM or a CURSOR of a VISUAL DISPLAY unit backward to the beginning of the same LINE.

carried traffic The volume of TRAFFIC accepted by a system as distinct from the demand offered to it by the USERS. Contrast with OFFERED TRAFFIC.

carrier 1. Same as CARRIER WAVE or CARRIER SIGNAL.
2. Sometimes used to describe a communications authority providing CIRCUITS to carry the private TRAFFIC of individuals or corporations. See also COMMON CARRIER.

carrier detector signal An INTERCHANGE SIGNAL between a MODEM and its associated DATA TERMINAL EQUIPMENT (DTE) indicating that the modem has responded to a distant modem and is about to accept DATA. The DTE will not accept data unless the carrier detector is on, and this is designed to prevent the DTE responding to line noise that might be acted upon as data. When the carrier detector is switched off, the CALL is terminated. See also REQUEST-TO-SEND and READY-TO-SEND.

carrier sense multiple access/collision detection (CSMA/CD) A NETWORKING PROTOCOL, CSMA/CD permits any STATION to transmit data at any time. The inevitable collisions are detected and stations must wait for an opportunity to transmit. This potential delay lasts for a period of time that is variable and unpredictable.

carrier sense signal In some implementations of LOCAL AREA NETWORKS, a number of STATIONS may be connected to the same physical TRANSMISSION CHANNEL. Due to the high speed of the CHANNEL, it is possible for stations to interchange FRAMES of information along the channel by simply sharing the channel availability on a random basis. A carrier sense signal is automatically applied to the channel when at least one station is attempting transmission. This normally acts to instruct other stations to defer to the transmitting channel and to be ready to examine the frames being transmitted.

carrier signal A SIGNAL generated for the purpose of carrying another MESSAGE SIGNAL at a particular point in a FREQUENCY SPECTRUM and used in the process of MODULATION. Sometimes called carrier wave.

Carterphone Decision A 1968 FCC regulation named after a ruling that permitted the Carter Electronics Corp. to link radio equipment to the BELL SYSTEM, the Carterphone Decision legalized the attachment of devices that are not supplied by the CARRIER to the carrier's telephone network. Sometimes spelled Carterfone.

cathode ray tube (CRT) A device used to display information in which the information to be displayed is input in electrical form and is converted to light on a luminescent screen. Used in TELEVISION RECEIVERS, DATA TERMINALS and RADAR equipment.

CATV See COMMUNITY ACCESS TELEVISION.

CCIR Abbreviation of *Comité Consultatif International de Radiocommunication.* An international committee established to promote standards for the development of radio communication. This committee is set up under the ITU—INTERNATIONAL TELECOMMUNICATIONS UNION.

CCIS See COMMON-CHANNEL INTEROFFICE SIGNALING.

CCITT Abbreviation of International Telegraph and Telephone Consultative Committee (from the French, *Comité Consultatif International Télégraphique et Téléphonique.)* An international committee established to promote standards for the development of TELEPHONE, TELEGRAPH SYSTEMS and DATA NETWORKS and to create the environment for interworking between the NETWORKS of the different countries of the world. This committee is set up under the ITU—INTERNATIONAL TELECOMMUNICATIONS UNION. See also INTERNATIONAL TELEGRAPH AND TELEPHONE CONSULTATIVE COMMITTEE.

cell In CELLULAR RADIO, a geographic area wherein subscribers are served by a low-power transmitter. In ASYNCHRONOUS TRANSFER MODE, the fixed-length unit of DATA traveling through the SWITCH FABRIC.

cell relay See ASYNCHRONOUS TRANSFER MODE.

cellular radio A communications service, cellular radio uses mobile phones that are often, but not necessarily, in automobiles. Radio waves are the TRANSMISSION medium. The service provider's COMPUTER equipment switches the RADIO frequencies as the caller moves from one geographical district (or CELL) to another.

center A term used to define a SWITCHING facility as an INTERNATIONAL SWITCHING CENTER.

central office TELEPHONE lines terminate at the CENTRAL OFFICE where the COMMON CARRIER'S SWITCHING EQUIPMENT interconnects them. Also called a switching center.

centralized control signaling A process whereby CALL CONTROL SIGNALS relating to a group of DATA TRANSMISSION circuits are transmitted over a dedicated CIRCUIT. The same as COMMON CHANNEL SIGNALING. Contrast with CHANNEL ASSOCIATED SIGNALING.

Centrex A TELEPHONE service, Centrex assigns an individual number to each of the SUBSCRIBER's phones so that they can be dialed directly on the public NETWORK. The SWITCHING EQUIPMENT may be on the CUSTOMER'S PREMISES, as it is with PBX equipment, but it is more commonly located at the CENTRAL OFFICE. Compare with PBX.

CEPT See CONFERENCE OF EUROPEAN POSTAL AND TELECOMMUNICATIONS ADMINISTRATIONS.

chain A series of CIRCUITS connected together by devices for a particular purpose. For example, an international chain is made up of 4-wire INTERNATIONAL CIRCUITS connected to other national or international 4-WIRE CIRCUITS.

changeback The process of transferring TRAFFIC back to a regular CIRCUIT after it has been temporarily transferred to a RESERVE LINK for maintenance operations.

changed-number signal A SIGNAL sent automatically in the BACKWARD DIRECTION to indicate to a CALLING TERMINAL that the number of the CALLED PARTY has been changed recently.

changeover The process of transferring TRAFFIC to a new CIRCUIT because the existing circuit is faulty or needs to be used for another purpose.

channel A CHANNEL is a link between two TERMINALS over which the USERS at each end can communicate with one another.

The simplest form of channel might consist of a pair of wires connecting two TELEPHONES, but a channel can consist of a complex set of physical resources linked to make a particular CALL feasible. In DATA COMMUNICATIONS, a channel may be a one-way communication path providing a GO or RETURN PATH for a CIRCUIT.

Some channels may be referred to as BROADBAND CHANNELS, i.e., they allow hundreds or thousands of calls to be passed simultaneously along a physical path using the technique known as MULTIPLEXING.

A MULTIPLEXED CHANNEL is a single channel that occupies a particular FREQUENCY BAND or TIME SLOT in a MULTIPLEXING system and is used for the duration of a particular call.

In some cases (e.g., a LOCAL LOOP network), all terminals may share the same channel without any attempt to separate different MESSAGES by frequency.

channel associated signaling A method of SIGNALING in which the SIGNALS needed to control TRAFFIC on a particular CHANNEL are carried on the channel itself or in a channel permanently associated with the traffic channel.

Contrast with CENTRALIZED CONTROL SIGNALING and COMMON CHANNEL SIGNALING.

channel bank CENTRAL OFFICE equipment that MULTIPLEXES lower speed digital CHANNELS into a higher speed combined channel. The equipment also perceives SIGNALING information for each channel and transmits it as well as FRAMING BITS.

channel identification 1. In DATA NETWORKS, information is often transmitted in TIME SLOTS that are designated to carry particular MESSAGES in the form of DIGITAL SIGNALS. The concept arises when several LOGICAL CHANNELS occur over a single PHYSICAL CHANNEL. Each logical channel has to be identified, and a channel identifier is used for each designated channel.

2. In modern SIGNALING systems, a specific channel is designated to carry signals that control the progress of CALLS on a large number of TRANSMISSION PATHS. Each signal has to include information to identify the channel to which the signal relates. This information is termed channel identification.

channel service unit (CSU) DIGITAL CIRCUITS terminate at the CPE in a device called the channel service unit. The CSU does some LINE CONDITIONING and checks the BIT STREAM for standard networking parameters.

character 1. A letter, numeral or special symbol (e.g., A, 1 or $) forming part of a DATA COMMUNICATIONS CODE.

2. A group of BITS representing a letter, numeral or a special symbol in BINARY CODED form.

3. See also CHECK CHARACTER.

character check A part of an ERROR CHECKING procedure designed to ensure that CHARACTER CODES conform to a valid BIT PATTERN for the formation of a CHARACTER.

character code A unique pattern of bits representing a numeric, alphabetic character or a punctuation mark or special symbol. A method for representation of such CHARACTERS in a DATA COMMUNICATIONS CODE.

character error rate In a DATA NETWORK, a measure of the quality of a CIRCUIT, expressed as a ratio of the number of CHARACTERS incorrectly received to the total number of characters sent.

character framing Relating to a method of DATA TRANSMISSION in which SYNCHRONIZATION is observed between the TRANSMITTING and RECEIVING STATIONS for the duration of a single CHARACTER only and not between characters. Each character is "framed" by a START

CODE and a STOP CODE. See also CHARACTER SYNCHRONIZATION.

character generator A device that creates CHARACTERS for display on a screen of a VISUAL DISPLAY terminal. For example, in a VIDEOTEX TERMINAL, the characters to be displayed are received as CODES from the telephone LINE and held in a PAGE STORE. The character generator processes information in the page store to create a character in the form of a dot matrix to be displayed in appropriate position on the screen.

character set A group of CHARACTERS (i.e., letters, number, punctuation marks or special symbols) and the code formats by means of which they are represented in electronic systems. See example in Appendix 1.

character signal A set of SIGNAL elements that represent a character in the particular form required for transmission. For example, in PULSE CODE MODULATION the quantized value of a sample.

character synchronization Character synchronization is relevant to both ASYNCHRONOUS SYSTEMS (also known as start-stop systems) and SYNCHRONOUS SYSTEMS.

With asynchronous systems, synchronization is maintained for the duration of a single CHARACTER only; each character starts with a START CODE and the subsequent BITS (say, 8 per character) are counted off and then terminated by a STOP CODE. The stop condition is maintained on the LINE until another character is to be transmitted, whereupon a further start code followed by an 8-bit character sequence occurs, and so on.

With high-speed synchronous DATA TRANSMISSION, the start-stop method is considered inefficient, and instead, bits are transmitted as a continuous stream with an electronic CLOCK at the TRANSMITTING STATION serving to maintain the rate of inversion on the line. The RECEIVING TERMINAL adjusts to this timing and counts off characters as groups of bits. Special synchronization characters (SYN) are transmitted at the beginning of a transmission to allow the RECEIVING STATION to adjust to this timing. See also BIT SYNCHRONIZATION and MESSAGE SYNCHRONIZATION.

character-mode terminal An ASYNCHRONOUS TERMINAL operating in start-stop mode (e.g., to the X.28 operating standards of the CCITT) and covering a range of slow-speed DATA TERMINALS operating in the range, say, of 100 to 2,000 BITS per second. The method of operation is characterized by a method of transmission in which each CHARACTER transmitted is framed by a START BIT and STOP BIT.

character-order of transmission Pertaining to the sequence in which the successive CHARACTERS that make up a unit of DATA are transmitted. For example, the most significant character may be transmitted first or the least significant first.

character-serial transmission A method of transmission in which successive CHARACTERS of information are transferred serially. It should be noted that the individual BITS (BINARY DIGITS) that make up each character may not necessarily be transmitted serially but perhaps as a PARALLEL TRANSMISSION.

chargeable duration The time interval upon which the charge for a CALL in a PUBLIC NETWORK is based. In TELEPHONE SYSTEMS, there is often a minimum chargeable duration (e.g., a 3-minute charge), but beyond this minimum duration the CALLING SUBSCRIBER pays per minute. In TELEX systems or PUBLIC DATA NETWORKS based upon SWITCHED SYSTEMS, the chargeable duration begins at the moment the CALL is established and ends when either party terminates the call; the TARIFF may be based upon small fractions of a minute.

check bit A BIT associated with a CHARACTER or BLOCK of DATA and used for checking the presence of an error in the character or block. See also PARITY BIT.

check character A CHARACTER generated by an arithmetic process that is performed upon a unit of DATA; the character itself is added to the data to provide the basis for a REDUNDANCY CHECKING operation.

check digits A pattern of BINARY DIGITS derived from a unit of DATA (generated by an arithmetic process) and to be appended to the data for performing a REDUNDANCY CHECKING operation.

check loop A device that is connected across the GO and RETURN PATHS of a CIRCUIT to enable a LOOP TEST to be made upon the circuit.

checksum The sum of a group of data items. It is used for ERROR CORRECTION.

chrominance components The elements of a color television picture that carry information related to the color of the picture. The chromaticity of a color source is measured independently of the LUMINANCE.

circuit A set of physical transmission resources (e.g., LINES and EXCHANGES) that provide for two-way transfer of MESSAGE SIGNALS from source to destination in a TELECOMMUNICATIONS system. The term "circuit" usually implies that there are two CHANNELS, one for the GO PATH and one for the RETURN PATH. Where DATA TERMINAL EQUIPMENT (DTE) is transmitting to a LINE via a MODEM (DCE), channel 1 usually modulates (i.e., transmits), and channel 2 demodulates (i.e., receives). However, since DATA can be exchanged by two terminals, the modem has to be able to receive on channel 1 when required.

This concept occurs in various forms of communication, and it is common to describe a circuit as having a FORWARD CHANNEL over which data is transferred and a BACKWARD CHANNEL over which control SIGNALS and supervisory information are transferred. The forward and backward designations are relative to the direction of transmission at any instant in time.

circuit access points Points in a CIRCUIT that are accessible to engineers to enable transmission measurements to be made.

circuit group A group of CIRCUITS established for some particular purpose, e.g., to provide international communication between two communication authorities. See also GROUPING.

circuit group congestion signal A signal sent in the BACKWARD DIRECTION to indicate that a particular CALL is unable to secure a connection due to congestion of a CIRCUIT GROUP that must carry the call.

circuit switched connection A CIRCUIT that is established by a switching center in an EXCHANGE upon request from a TERMINAL wishing to communicate with another.

The two terminals have exclusive use of the TRANSMISSION PATH until the connection is released. Contrast with MESSAGE SWITCHED SYSTEM.

circuit switched exchange An exchange in which TRANSMISSION PATHS are created by making connections between INCOMING LINES and OUTGOING LINES. Once a CALL is established between two USERS, the connection remains available and dedicated to the call until it is terminated. See also SWITCHED TELECOMMUNICATIONS SYSTEM and SWITCHING EQUIPMENT.

circuit switching See SWITCHED TELECOMMUNICATION SYSTEM.

circuit-switched data network A DATA NETWORK in which TRANSMISSION PATHS are established by a SWITCHING operation to make connections between TERMINALS for the duration of a CALL.

DATA TRANSMISSION can take place only when connections are made from end to end. Contrast with MESSAGE SWITCHED SYSTEM.

classes of exchange See OFFICE CLASS.

clear A process or a SIGNAL associated with a CALLING PARTY or a CALLED PARTY taking action to terminate a CALL.

In a TELEPHONE NETWORK, if the called party replaces the HANDSET before the calling party, then a CLEAR-BACK SIGNAL (also known as a HANG-UP SIGNAL) is initiated.

In contrast, if the calling party clears first, a CLEAR-FORWARD SIGNAL is initiated.

These signals occur similarly in PUBLIC DATA NETWORKS as a result of instructions originating in DATA TERMINAL EQUIPMENT (DTE) that pass to the associated DATA CIRCUIT TERMINATING EQUIPMENT (DCE). The DCE in turn instructs an EXCHANGE to terminate the call.

Although the clearing procedures vary for different types of networks, the principal actions remain the same: the circuits utilized for the call are released, the measurement of CALL DURATION is stopped, and charging is stopped.

clear channel DIGITAL CIRCUITS that provide the full BANDWIDTH for USER DATA rather than reserving part of the transmission path for the CARRIER'S CONTROL bits or FRAMING information.

clear confirmation A CALL CONTROL SIGNAL between a TERMINAL and a MODEM acknowledging a request to clear a CALL.

clear request A control SIGNAL sent to a NETWORK by a TERMINAL to terminate a CIRCUIT or VIRTUAL CIRCUIT connection.

clear request packet An instruction given to the NETWORK in a PACKET SWITCHING SYSTEM by a CALLING TERMINAL when it wishes to deactivate a VIRTUAL CIRCUIT between it and another TERMINAL. See also CALL REQUEST PACKET and CALL ACCEPTED PACKET.

clear-back signal A control SIGNAL sent in the BACKWARD DIRECTION to signify that the CALLED PARTY has terminated a CALL. Also called clear-backward signal.

clear-forward signal A SIGNAL sent when a CALLING PARTY has decided to terminate an established CALL or an attempted call.

clearing The sequence of events associated with the disconnection of a CALL and enabling the two TERMINALS concerned to return to the READY STATE.

clearing phase The action of releasing a connection in a CIRCUIT SWITCHED call, at the completion of the CALL, in response to a CLEAR REQUEST issued by a TERMINAL. Same as CALL CLEARING.

clear-to-send A CONTROL SIGNAL that indicates a DATA TRANSMISSION LINE is available. See also READY-TO-SEND.

client layer In specifying a DATA NETWORK, it is usual to provide for different levels of control as a hierarchy of procedures. An ISO standard, in fact, defines seven levels of control. See OPEN SYSTEMS INTERCONNECTION.

Not all levels are provided by the NETWORK, but it is usual to provide at least the two lowest ISO levels: PHYSICAL LINK LAYER and DATA LINK LAYER. Other levels may be provided by the NETWORK OPERATOR or be left to USERS of the network. The levels left to be provided by the users are referred to as the client layer.

clock A device that emits pulses to synchronize the operation of system elements in a digital system.

In a SYNCHRONOUS DIGITAL SYSTEM, pulses are transferred at a series of discrete intervals, and devices within the system can obtain access to others by observing an exact timing sequence defined by the clock.

closed user group (CUG) A system in which USERS of a service in a PUBLIC

NETWORK can only make CALLS to, or receive calls from, predesignated SUBSCRIBERS forming the same group. Note it is possible for a user to belong to more than one CUG.

closed user group indicator Information included in a DATA TRANSMISSION sequence to indicate whether the CALLING PARTY belongs to a CLOSED USER GROUP.

closed user group with outgoing access Same as CLOSED USER GROUP, except that a SUBSCRIBER in the group can call other subscribers outside the group but may not receive CALLS from outside.

cluster A concentration of devices at a point in a NETWORK, e.g., two or more units of DATA TERMINAL EQUIPMENT (DTE) connected to a CONCENTRATOR, which controls their INTERFACE to other terminal devices over a COMMUNICATIONS CHANNEL.

cluster controller Equipment at a remote location that concentrates a number of TERMINALS at that location and handles the communication functions between those terminals and a DATA NETWORK or HOST PROCESSOR. It may also include certain APPLICATION PROGRAMS and sections of a PARTITIONED DATABASE. The more complex cluster controllers may be programmable.

CØ A standard subset of CODES defined for VIDEOTEX SYSTEMS to provide for various CONTROL functions, including CURSOR CONTROL, FORMAT EFFECTORS and TRANSMISSION CONTROL character.

CO See CENTRAL OFFICE.

coaxial cable Sometimes used to refer to a single conducting CHANNEL, which more correctly should be known as a COAXIAL TUBE. Coaxial tubes are often grouped into cables, i.e., a number of tubes are housed in the same cable duct.

coaxial cable interface specification A specification that defines the method for connection of NODES or STATIONS to a COAXIAL CABLE LOOP as in a LOCAL AREA NETWORK. This specification governs the PHYSICAL INTERFACE and the correct behavior of a station and includes electrical, mechanical and logical aspects.

coaxial cable loop A TRANSMISSION PATH in a LOCAL AREA NETWORK utilizing a COAXIAL TUBE as a CABLE LOOP.

coaxial tube A TRANSMISSION LINK constructed of a pair of CONDUCTORS held in position by insulating material such that the physical distance between the conductors is maintained. The conductors are arranged so that one is a core within an outer sheath, or tube, formed by the other. The outer conductor operates as a shield to reduce the electrical interference and CROSSTALK.

For TELEPHONE communication, coaxial tubes are often bunched together to form a cable, and the shield then becomes ineffective at frequencies below 60 kHz. Coaxial tubes have been used up to a BANDWIDTH around 60 MHz, which is the equivalent of 10,800 TELEPHONE CHANNELS in a MULTIPLEXED system.

code Any CHARACTER or group of characters forming a specific meaning. Any system of rules to which information must conform in order to be transmitted, received and/or processed.

code compression A technique used in the storing and transmission of information to save storage space of transmission time across a NETWORK. For example, GRAPHICS INFORMATION can be reduced for transmission by converting lines or curves into coordinates known as PICTURE DESCRIPTION INSTRUCTIONS, which can be used to recreate an original picture in a RECEIVING TERMINAL.

code conversion A process whereby DATA constructed in accordance with the rules of a particular CODE is transformed into a format and structure required in another code.

code dependent system In DATA COMMUNICATIONS, a system that is dependent upon the use of a particular DATA COMMUNICATIONS CODE used by the TERMINALS connected to the system. The system will not function correctly if other CODES are used. Contrast with CODE INDEPENDENT SYSTEM.

code independent system A DATA COMMUNICATIONS system that can operate correctly, irrespective of the DATA COMMUNICATIONS CODES used by TERMINALS connected to the system. Contrast with CODE DEPENDENT SYSTEM.

code insensitive system Same as CODE INDEPENDENT SYSTEM.

code sensitive system Same as CODE DEPENDENT SYSTEM.

codec A device that incorporates encoding and decoding logic in the same assembly. See also ENCODER and DECODER.

code-string A sequence of BITS (BINARY DIGITS) transmitted to or from a TERMINAL, or some other element in a TRANSMISSION SYSTEM, to convey status or CONTROL INFORMATION. This practice has arisen with the development of high-speed digital techniques and enables a single connection to be used for a number of different control SIGNALS that otherwise would have to be conveyed by discrete CIRCUITS.

coherent detection One method of DETECTION used in DEMODULATION in which the original CARRIER SIGNAL is only partially suppressed for transmission along with a SIDEBAND signal. The method allows most of the energy to be concentrated in the MESSAGE SIGNAL, but sufficient energy is used to transmit the CARRIER for creation of a REFERENCE WAVE.

collision A form of CONTENTION that arises in a LOCAL LOOP when two or more STATIONS try to transmit at the same time. Due to the high DATA RATES possible in such systems, collisions are usually avoided by allowing one station to defer to another without noticeable delay to USERS. Collisions can arise because at the beginning of transmission, before a SIGNAL has been propagated to all parts of the loop, there is a period in which no station has officially acquired the loop. This is known as the COLLISION WINDOW. The resolution of collisions usually entails terminating transmission and scheduling retransmission for some randomly selected time. Fragments of FRAMES that may have been received incomplete are rejected by RECEIVING STATIONS. The retransmission is repeated until successful.

collision resolution A procedure that is followed to recover from a situation in which two or more STATIONS start transmitting simultaneously in a LOCAL LOOP. See COLLISION.

collision window A period of time during transmission on a LOCAL LOOP in which there can be undetected CONTENTION for the PHYSICAL CHANNEL. See COLLISION.

color television receiver A TELEVISION RECEIVER in which there are three GUNS corresponding to red, green and blue outputs from a color television signal. The beams from the three guns are designed to scan separately over red, green and blue phosphor dots on the screen of a CATHODE RAY TUBE. The dots are placed close together in sets of three known as TRIADS. Combinations of colors are thus generated to represent the range of colors captured by the television camera. There are about 500,000 triads on a single screen.

command Any instruction issued to a NETWORK by a human operator or by a logical process within an automated system to indicate to the network that a particular CONTROL PROCEDURE is to be invoked.

common carrier A private or public corporation responsible for the provision of TELECOMMUNICATION services in a given territory. It provides access to these facilities at appropriate hire charges to enable private or business USERS to communicate with one another via government-regulated public communications services (TELEPHONE, TELEGRAPHY, TELEX, DATA COMMUNICATIONS).

A common carrier is normally not concerned with the content of the messages carried by its services but is concerned that connections to its services are made using authorized equipment and protocols.

common carrier bureau An FCC entity that makes recommendations regarding TELECOMMUNICATIONS regulations.

common carrier costs This refers to the true operational costs of TELEPHONE or DATA NETWORKS as experienced by the public authorities operating such facilities. The expression distinguishes the cost factors from the charges rendered by the carrier authority as TARIFFS. An economic analysis based upon costs of a service might produce a different conclusion from an analysis based upon the actual tariff.

common channel signaling A method of providing control in a TELECOMMUNICATIONS NETWORK in which several hundred traffic CIRCUITS may be controlled by a single pair of signaling CHANNELS along a particular route. The route may contain several EXCHANGES, each of which must be equipped with centralized control to respond to the SIGNALING functions. Common channel signaling reduces the cost required for separate signaling units in each exchange and permits greater flexibility for the future development of the service. Also known as CENTRALIZED CONTROL SIGNALING, and contrasted with CHANNEL ASSOCIATED SIGNALING.

common control The CONTROL function in a SWITCHED TELEPHONE EXCHANGE is responsible for recognizing CALL REQUESTS from USERS and for managing the correct setup, maintenance and clearing of CALLS. In early forms of switched systems, these controls were associated with signaling units that were permanently associated with each individual LINE. With the advent of DIGITAL EXCHANGES, the signals concerned with control functions are handled in high-speed DIGITAL COMPUTERS, which have fast electronic systems that can work for a few milliseconds, first on one call and then on another. Thus, all the lines in an exchange may be controlled by a single common system. This can serve to greatly reduce the cost of the overall signaling system and lead to flexible and more economic maintenance procedures. This method also allows control signals passing between EXCHANGES in a NETWORK to be handled along CHANNELS that are dedicated to provide CONTROL INFORMATION; therefore, control information is not transported within the same channel as MESSAGE INFORMATION. See also COMMON CHANNEL SIGNALING.

commonality Pertaining to the way in which two devices or systems can work in harmony, or to the ease with which one can replace another. See also COMPATIBILITY.

common-channel exchange An exchange that uses a COMMON-CHANNEL SIGNALING system.

common-channel interoffice signaling (CCIS) A version of the CCITT specification for COMMON CHANNEL SIGNALING whereby one independent channel carries the CONTROL SIGNALS for the traffic of many CHANNELS; CCIS assumes that the switching OFFICES are computerized.

communication channel A link between two TERMINALS to provide a GO or RETURN PATH. See CHANNEL.

communication interface A specification that defines the necessary conditions for connecting two parts of a system or two separate systems that have different functions. This requires a definition of:

The LOGICAL INTERFACE (e.g., what various SIGNALS mean and how they represent functions).

The MECHANICAL INTERFACE (how physical components connect, such as the significance of pin positions on a plug connector).

The ELECTRICAL INTERFACE (the strength, frequency and duration of signals across the interface).

The PERSON/MACHINE INTERFACE (the way in which a human USER interacts with a system, e.g., the rules governing the operation of the KEYBOARD of a TELETYPEWRITER).

The SOFTWARE INTERFACE (a high-level specification that defines information flows and application procedures).

A considerable amount of work has been done by the *CCITT* and other regulatory and standards bodies to standardize interfaces so that systems developed in different countries and by different manufacturers can communicate. This work includes the publication of specifications for INTERCHANGE CIRCUITS and INTERCHANGE SPECIFICATIONS.

In most forms of TELECOMMUNICATIONS over DATA NETWORKS, the DATA TERMINAL EQUIPMENT (DTE) is interfaced to the LINE by DATA CIRCUIT TERMINATING EQUIPMENT (DCE), and it is necessary to consider the interface between DCEs at each end of the CHANNEL, and between each DCE and its DTE. An example of such a specification is given by the CCITT V.24 recommendation, which is a HARDWARE interface for establishing a CALL and ensuring appropriate ERROR DETECTION and CORRECTION takes place. This is sometimes known as the PHYSICAL LEVEL INTERFACE.

Efforts are continually being made to improve standardization of these different levels of interface, and an example of this work is described under the heading ISO REFERENCE MODEL FOR OPEN SYSTEMS ARCHITECTURE.

communication interface standard A standard PROTOCOL designed to ensure that TERMINALS using the same logical, mechanical and electrical connections can communicate with one another and with PUBLIC DATA NETWORKS (PDN). Examples given in this book include V SERIES interface and X SERIES interface.

communications control Relating to the coordination and management of any communications NETWORK and the SIGNALING SYSTEMS used to set up, maintain and clear CALLS, as well as the FLOW CONTROL of MESSAGES in networks that handle DATA or TEXT.

communications controller A device used in a DATA NETWORK to manage all DATA LINK CONTROL activities between a MAINFRAME (or HOST PROCESSOR) and a large distributed TERMINAL population. Usually it would be sited adjacent to a host processor to which it would be connected by a high-speed link. Some communications controllers take responsibility for ROUTING, DIALOGUE MANAGEMENT and PROTOCOL CONVERSION also and remove as much of the communications load as possible from the host processor.

Communications controllers are really programmable COMPUTERS, having a great deal of power and flexibility to be applied in a number of different networking environments. See also COMMUNICATIONS PROCESSOR or FRONT-END PROCESSOR.

communications processor In a DATA PROCESSING SYSTEM, a COMPUTER that INTERFACES the main HOST PROCESSOR to a communications NETWORK to handle all the TRAFFIC to and from the host processor and to communicate with TERMINALS or other processors in the network. A communications processor will not normally process DATA (i.e., look at the APPLICATION content of MESSAGES) but is reserved specifically to managing the TELECOMMUNICATION functions related to its host. See also COMMUNICATIONS CONTROLLER.

communications satellite A STATION placed in orbit around the Earth to provide TRANSMISSION CHANNELS for TRAFFIC to be transmitted over great distances, e.g., intercontinental traffic. The SATELLITE STATION is equipped with ANTENNAE, which are able to receive radio beams from an EARTH STATION transmitter and to retransmit the SIGNALS to another earth station. The orbit of the satellite is chosen so that signals can be propagated between specific locations.

A worldwide system of satellites has been created, and it is possible to transmit signals around the globe by bouncing them from one satellite to an earth station and thence to another satellite.

Originally designed to carry VOICE TRAFFIC, they are able to carry hundreds or thousands of separate simultaneous CALLS. The RADIO SIGNALS used to carry the calls contain great numbers of channels by MULTIPLEXING techniques.

These systems are being increasingly adopted to provide for business communications, including the transmission of traffic for VOICE, FACSIMILE, DATA and VISION.

So far, satellite signals have been distributed through the normal EARTH NETWORKS when received at the RECEIVING EARTH STATION.

In the United States, business organizations are hiring facilities to make use of the systems provided by satellite operating companies. The companies wishing to receive signals can do so directly from a satellite station by using a small dish-shaped AERIAL placed on the roof of their office buildings.

One of the first commercial satellites (Early Bird) was launched in 1965 and it carried 240 separate channels.

It is probable that future satellite services will enable a great variety of information services to transmit directly into the home, possibly including personalized ELECTRONIC MAIL.

Community Access Television CATV makes it possible for geographical areas to receive more CHANNELS by means of directional ANTENNAS and a CABLE NETWORK. A networking scheme based on RADIO FREQUENCY transmissions and offering multiple frequency-divided channels, it allows simultaneous mixed data communications transmissions. Also called Community Antenna Television or cable television.

compatibility Pertaining to the degree of INTERWORKING possible between two devices or systems. If an element in a system is fully compatible with the functional and physical characteristics of a system, it can be placed into the system without any effect upon the grade of service experienced by USERS. See also TRANSPARENCY.

compiler A SOFTWARE program that converts statements written in a particular PROGRAMMING LANGUAGE into machine code instructions that can be recognized by a particular type of COMPUTER.

composite video signal A signal that includes video information, plus the SYNCHRONIZATION PULSES used to control the positioning of the RASTER in a TV RECEIVER or monitor used to play back a video MESSAGE. Also known as VISUAL MESSAGE SIGNAL. See also VIDEO SIGNAL.

composition coding A technique used for the display of CHARACTER SETS for languages that encompass diacritical marks, such as accents in Latin-based language forms. The technique requires the coded representations of the CHARACTER and the associated diacritical mark to be transmitted separately and composed together to form the desired composite character in the display terminal. This is a method recommended for use in VIDEOTEX SYSTEMS where the full range of character sets used in a particular country must be displayed. Compare with DYNAMICALLY REDEFINABLE CHARACTER SETS.

computer Any machine that can accept DATA in a certain form and process the data to supply results or to control a process. Generally, an electronic device in which inputs and outputs may be in DIGITAL or ANALOG form and in which the program controlling the operation of the COMPUTER may itself be modified by logical actions taken under program control.

A program for a DIGITAL COMPUTER is a set of instructions that can be interpreted by the central processing unit in the computer resulting in data being manipulated as required to produce a desired result. A typical computer will respond to a hundred or more basic types of commands such as Add, Subtract, Compare. Each of these commands may refer to items of data in specified storage locations. The USERS who wish to make the computer perform a specific task have to write their programs as a series of step-by-step instructions. In practice, few programmers write their programs directly in the language that the computer understands. Instead, various levels of other programs, known as system software, are available that act as translators between the machine and the end user's program. Computers perform instructions in millionths of a second, and a complete program can be performed in a very short time. Because a computer can store very large amounts of information and because it can, under program control, modify its action to react to changes in external events, it has become a predominant tool in the modern world and of particular influence in the increasing efficiency and functioning of modern communications systems.

computer aided design (CAD) A COMPUTER capability that assists industrial designers in their work, allowing designs to be constructed and visualized on display screens. Used in diverse industries, including automobile manufacturing, aircraft design, town planning and civil engineering.

Computer Inquiry An FCC study of DATA PROCESSING and DATA COMMUNICATIONS. Computer Inquiry III, issued in 1986, is the most recent. It specifies that FCC regulation of a CARRIER's services be in accordance with OPEN NETWORK ARCHITECTURE. Computer Inquiry II, issued in 1980, distinguishes between basic and enhanced services: the former regulated, the latter unregulated by the FCC. According to Computer Inquiry I, issued in 1971, data processing was an unregulated service, which meant that the BELL TELEPHONE SYSTEM could not offer it.

computer networking The use of NETWORKS to link COMPUTERS together so that they can share a workload or allow USERS connected via TERMINALS to a particular computer to have access to facilities and services provided by other computers in the network.

COMSAT Abbreviation for Communications Satellite Corporation.

concentrator 1. A device that enables a number of CALLS arising on individual LINES to be concentrated onto a single line using MULTIPLEXING techniques.

2. Equipment in a TELEPHONE EXCHANGE that receives calls arising on LOCAL LINES in a particular area and directs the calls to a DISTRIBUTOR for transmission to OUTGOING TRUNKS or outgoing LOCAL LINES.

In a CIRCUIT SWITCHING system it has to be possible to switch every INCOMING LINE of an exchange to every OUTGOING LINE. For an exchange with 1,000 incoming and outgoing lines, this would entail a matrix of 1,000,000 CROSSPOINTS at which switching could take place. However, more efficient internal ARCHITECTURES are possible that reduce the number of crosspoints while maintaining a low probability of CALL BLOCKING. A typical design might reduce the number of crosspoints in the example above to 30,000. This improvement in efficiency can be achieved by having three stages of switching: (a) CONCENTRATOR, (b) DISTRIBUTOR, (c) EXPANDOR.

The first stage concentrates the incoming lines onto a smaller number of internal links before passing calls to the distributor.

The second stage switches calls and then passes them to an expandor or to an outgoing TRUNK ROUTE.

The expandor accepts the switched calls from the distributor and connects them to the appropriate outgoing lines in the LOCAL NETWORK. See also GROUPING.

conditioning See LINE CONDITIONING.

conductor An element used to carry an electrical current, e.g., a pair of copper wires used to carry an electrical MESSAGE SIGNAL from a TERMINAL to an EXCHANGE.

Conference of European Postal and Telecommunications Administrations (CEPT) An organization formed by the European PTTs to facilitate talks regarding TELECOMMUNICATIONS services: for example, their TARIFFS and operations.

configuration control A set of functions performed at a NETWORK MANAGEMENT CENTER to control the availability of paths and resources in the overall NETWORK in an orderly fashion. For example, some new TRANSMISSION PATHS and NODES may be attached to the network, and some may be temporarily withdrawn for maintenance purposes. A set of complex facilities provided by HARDWARE and SOFTWARE are usually available to a human operator to effect configuration control procedures.

confusion signal A SIGNAL passed on a BACKWARD CHANNEL to indicate that a NODE in a NETWORK is unable to act upon a signal received because the signal is not a reasonable request.

congested system If a system has insufficient capacity to carry the TRAFFIC required in a given period of time, it is said to be congested.

connect charge A charge made to a USER as part of the TARIFF for utilization of a service in which the user pays a fee for each minute (or part of a minute) of connection to a PORT in the system.

connect signal A SIGNAL transmitted in the FORWARD DIRECTION at the beginning of a CALL to secure a CIRCUIT to switch the call.

connection charge A single payment charge made by a new SUBSCRIBER for being connected to a communications service provided by an operator.

connection in progress In a DATA NETWORK, a CONTROL signal from a MODEM (or DCE) to a DATA TERMINAL to advise the TERMINAL that the connection is about to be made and that the READY-FOR-DATA SIGNAL will follow.

contention A situation that arises when two MESSAGE SIGNALS attempt to use the same physical resources, e.g., a TIME SLOT or a physical CIRCUIT at the same instant. In some systems it may be a deliberate policy to allow contention, and a formal procedure may be established to allocate the LINE temporarily to TERMINALS on a first-entry basis. See COLLISION, and contrast with POLLING.

contention resolution A procedure that is observed automatically by a system to deal with situations in which two MESSAGES attempt to use the same physical resources or TIME SLOTS simultaneously.

continental circuit Any INTERNATIONAL CIRCUIT between two EXCHANGES in different countries but in the same continent.

continuity check A check made upon a CIRCUIT, or series of circuits, to verify that a particular TRANSMISSION PATH is not broken.

continuity-failure signal A SIGNAL that is passed in the BACKWARD DIRECTION indicating that a CALL cannot be completed because a continuity check has revealed an interrupted CIRCUIT.

continuous receiver Any device, such as a TELEPRINTER, that can record a series of MESSAGES received line by line without the need for operator intervention between messages.

control This is a role performed by an EXCHANGE or a NODE in a communications NETWORK and is concerned with the functions that govern the orderly selection and maintenance of paths through the NETWORK to allow a CALL to take place. These functions include:

recognizing a CALL REQUEST from a TERMINAL
receiving the ADDRESS INFORMATION
translating the ADDRESS to identify a route
selecting a specific path
sending CONTROL signals to the LINE
monitoring the CALL ANSWERED SIGNALS
clearing the connection

In the interest of efficiency, control equipment is usually shared over several lines.

control character Any CHARACTER occurring as a SIGNAL in a context that causes a procedure or operation to be stopped, started or modified.

control circuit Any CIRCUIT used to convey supervisory information to coordinate transmission taking place on another circuit. For example, in transmitting television pictures from an outside broadcast event to a studio, one or more control circuits may be used.

control information DATA or SIGNALS carried in a NETWORK to support the CONTROL functions.

control input A SIGNAL provided by the action of a USER, SUBSCRIBER or operator in a communications system and having significance in respect to the recognition of a CALL REQUEST or the setup, maintenance and termination of a CALL.

control procedure In any communications service, a method by which SIGNALS are sent in a FORWARD or BACKWARD DIRECTION in accordance with a predetermined order to ensure coordination between USERS and the NETWORK.

controlled maintenance A systematic method of maintenance using sampling and analysis techniques to reduce CORRECTIVE MAINTENANCE and improve efficiency in PREVENTIVE MAINTENANCE.

controller A device at the heart of a communications system that is responsible for coordination of the system by receiving, interpreting and transmitting SIGNALS, e.g., responsible for switching CALLS in a controlled manner.

controlling exchange A designation given by telephone administrations when participating in international CALLS. The EXCHANGE that sets up calls and decides the sequence in which they are connected is the controlling exchange, and usually it is the INTERNATIONAL EXCHANGE to which a CALLING PARTY is connected.

conversation The process that takes place when two DATA TERMINALS exchange information; a period of activity that is preceded by the CALL ESTABLISHMENT process, and followed by call clearing.

conversation state The STATE that exists in a TELEPHONE NETWORK when a CALLED TERMINAL has responded to a CALLING SIGNAL and a CIRCUIT is made to enable a conversation to take place.

conversation time In the operation of a public TELEPHONE SYSTEM, the time interval between the ANSWER SIGNAL and CLEAR-FORWARD SIGNAL being recorded, at the point where the recording of the CALL DURATION takes place.

conversational mode A method of communication involving two-way communication between two TERMINALS in which both USERS may act as a MESSAGE SOURCE and a MESSAGE DESTINATION. The dialogue is carried out in accordance with a PROTOCOL that serves to ensure that the terminals are coordinated and give appropriate responses to one another to secure the safe and intelligible transmission of MESSAGES.

correct bit A BIT (BINARY DIGIT) of information correctly received over a CIRCUIT as compared to an ERROR BIT in which the significance of the bit has been reversed, i.e., a 0 becomes a 1 or a 1 becomes a 0. See TRANSMISSION ERRORS.

corrective maintenance Work carried out to repair any device that has failed, such that the device is considered to be unsuitable for maintaining the operation of the system to the level of quality required.

counter A device that records a number of events to assist in the control and coordination of a logical process. For example, a device that records the number of BLOCKS of DATA sent to a distant TERMINAL.

country code A CODE used to prefix a telephone number and to designate the country in which that particular SUBSCRIBER is situated. The code is used to facilitate INTERNATIONAL TRUNK DIALING.

CPE See CUSTOMER PREMISES EQUIPMENT.

CR See CARRIAGE RETURN.

cradle switch The contacts that are activated when a telephone HANDSET is raised or put down. Sometimes called a SWITCH HOOK.

CRC See CYCLIC REDUNDANCY CHECK.

crossbar exchange An EXCHANGE in which a bar rotated by a SOLENOID is used to make switched connections between CIRCUITS to connect INCOMING CALLS to OUTGOING LINES. Typically, a single CROSSBAR SWITCH provides a matrix of 10 by 20 individual switches, which are contact points activated by a complex arrangement of levers. The selection of a particular path is achieved by rotating the bar. Based upon the operation of electromechanical devices, these exchanges are being gradually superseded by ELECTRONIC EXCHANGES, which are faster in operation and easier to maintain. See SWITCHING EQUIPMENT.

crossbar switches An electromechanical device used in TELEPHONE EXCHANGES that carry VOICE ANALOG SIGNALS. It consists of contacts arranged in a matrix, which are activated by a metal bar that is, in turn, rotated by the action of a SOLENOID. These devices are constructed in large matrixes to connect INCOMING LINES and OUTGOING LINES to establish CALLS in a CIRCUIT SWITCHED EXCHANGE. These are being replaced in the present generation of exchanges by ELECTRONIC EXCHANGES, which are more efficient used in conjunction with digital forms of transmission.

cross-office check A CONTINUITY CHECK made through an EXCHANGE to verify that a TRANSMISSION PATH exists.

crosspoint A switch forming part of a matrix to switch CIRCUITS in an EXCHANGE. Originally, crosspoints were electromechanical switches but have progressed through to REED-RELAYS and now to ELECTRONIC CROSSPOINTS with the advance of switching technology.

crosstalk An undesirable condition in which MESSAGE SIGNALS from one CHANNEL are overlaid on another, physically adjacent channel. This condition is caused by stray electric and magnetic FIELDS, which are generated when AC SIGNALS are transmitted along a LINE. See also TRANSMIT-TO-RECEIVE CROSSTALK.

crosstalk, intelligible CROSSTALK that results in intelligible SIGNALS being transferred from one CIRCUIT to intrude on another.

crosstalk, possible CROSSTALK components that exist but do not intrude on the USER to the point at which they have been measured—but may intrude at another point.

crosstalk, unintelligible CROSSTALK that results in intrusive unintelligible speech components being transferred from one CIRCUIT to another.

CRT See CATHODE RAY TUBE.

CSMA/CD See CARRIER SENSE MULTIPLE ACCESS/COLLISION DETECTION.

CSU See CHANNEL SERVICE UNIT.

CUG See CLOSED USER GROUP.

cursor control In any system that uses VISUAL DISPLAY units for the presentation of information, control CODES are used to govern the positioning of CHARACTERS and to control the format of documents presented on display screens. The position for the next character to be displayed is always indicated by the movement of a character known as the cursor, and formats are effected by cursor control instructions.

customer premises equipment (CPE) The TELECOMMUNICATIONS and DATA COMMUNICATIONS equipment that is situated on the premises of the service provider's customer is called CPE. It is distinguished from equipment that is located in the CENTRAL OFFICE. CPE ranges from TELEPHONES to MULTIPLEXERS and SWITCHES.

customer reference number A reference number that is unique to each USER of a service. It enables USAGE CHARGES and utilization statistics to be attributed to individual users.

customer's loop See LOCAL LINE.

cyclic code A coding system used for ERROR DETECTION in which a calculation is performed upon each BLOCK of DATA to be transmitted and a remainder is derived to be appended to the data as a CHECK CHARACTER. The same calculation is performed at the RECEIVING STATION, and a comparison is made to see that BITS have not been lost or inverted during transmission. The method relies upon treating the bits of the data as a pure BINARY NUMBER, and the remainder is produced by dividing by a GENERATING POLYNOMIAL. A CCITT recommendation (V.41) advocates a 16-bit polynominal of the form $x^{16}+x^{12}+x^{5}+1$. See also CYCLIC REDUNDANCY CHECK.

cyclic redundancy check (CRC) A procedure used in checking the accuracy of information FRAMES transmitted over a DATA LINK, in which a series of BITS known as the FRAME CHECK SEQUENCE (FCS) is derived and appended to each frame. The FCS is computed as a function of all the FIELDS contained in the particular frame prior to transmission. A RECEIVING STATION then checks the accuracy of the frame by attempting to derive the same FCS from the received information. If the procedure fails to validate the FCS field, a retransmission of the frame is requested.

D

D channel The D channel of ISDN carries CONTROL SIGNALS and low-speed DATA. It can transmit 16 kbps or 64 kbps.

dark fiber FIBER OPTIC CABLE that has been installed but remains unused until the light source is activated.

data Any values, NUMBERS, CHARACTERS or symbols that have been arranged to represent information in accordance with predefined rules. The word "data" is used often as a singular noun.

data channel A TRANSMISSION CHANNEL used to carry DATA to provide a means of communication between two points.

A data channel may be an ANALOG DATA CHANNEL, i.e., providing a path for alternating current SIGNALS that are converted at each end of the CIRCUIT into DIGITAL SIGNALS for a TERMINAL by a MODULATOR/DEMODULATOR (MODEM).

A data channel may alternatively be a DIGITAL DATA CHANNEL, i.e., providing a path for signals made up of discrete pulses, with a NETWORK INTERFACE UNIT at each end to INTERFACE to the terminal.

In strict definition, a CHANNEL provides a means of one-way transmission and two channels are required to form a means of two-way communication known as a DATA CIRCUIT.

data circuit A two-way means of transmission, consisting of two CHANNELS, allowing for the transfer of DATA between two TERMINALS. A data circuit may carry DIGITAL OF ANALOG SIGNALS. In the former case, the DATA TERMINAL (DTE) at each end of the CIRCUIT is interfaced to it by a NETWORK INTERFACE UNIT. In the latter case, the DTE is interfaced by a MODEM. See also DATA CHANNEL.

data circuit terminating equipment (DCE) The equipment installed to INTERFACE A user's DATA TERMINAL EQUIPMENT (DTE) to a communications line. It is not necessarily freestanding equipment. The DCE provides for the establishment, maintenance and termination of a call and the signal conversion necessary between the DTE and the LINE.

A MODEM is an example of a DCE, but, when connecting a terminal to a specialized DATA NETWORK, a device known as a NETWORK TERMINATING UNIT or NETWORK INTERFACE UNIT is used. In general, modems are used for connection to telephone networks where ANALOG SIGNALS are used in transmission, and a network interface unit is used to connect to a PUBLIC DATA NETWORK (PDN) where digital signals are used.

data collection The process entailed in collecting information about events and ENCODING them for transmission and reception prior to subsequent processing to achieve an end objective of an information system.

data communications The whole range of practice concerned with the transmission of information that has been encoded specifically for the purpose of transmission (e.g., in the form of a DATA COMMUNICATIONS CODE) and including the encoding, transmission, ROUTING, monitoring, checking and correction of errors in the process of transmitting and receiving DATA.

data communications code A CODE used to represent CHARACTERS of information as groups of BINARY DIGITS (BITS) and containing a system of BINARY NOTATION to represent the 26 characters of the alphabet, numerals 0 to 9 and a range of special symbols and punctuation characters. There are a variety of codes in use, but there is a movement toward international standardization of such codes, e.g., see INTERNATIONAL ALPHABET CODE NO. 5. The codes are designed for transmission of digital information for telegraphic or DATA TRANSMISSION purposes and also include a number of codes to perform special functions, including: TRANSMISSION CONTROL, FORMAT EFFECTORS, INFORMATION SEPARATORS, DEVICE CONTROL.

Most systems use 6 bits to represent each character, but some use 8-bit codes. Most data communication codes have been developed from the TELEGRAPH CODES, which preceded the evolution of computer-based systems.

data communications system Any system for communication in which information is sent between locations in the form of a DIGITAL DATA TRANSMISSION.

data compression A technique used to improve the efficiency of transmission by reducing the number of information BITS that need to be transmitted. For example, in some graphics display systems, arcs and lines can be transmitted as coordinates that are expanded in the

RECEIVING TERMINAL to recreate images stored at the TRANSMITTING TERMINAL.

data connection The process entailed in switching to connect together a number of DATA CIRCUITS to provide a path for DATA TRANSMISSION. The term also refers to the set of physical resources used in making a connection between two DATA TERMINALS.

data element A FIELD in an information record, or part of a MESSAGE SIGNAL, having a logical relationship to other items of information, e.g., account number, customer name, price, quantity ordered.

data encapsulation The functions in a communications system concerned with control of DATA in a TRANSMISSION LINK, e.g., establishing the boundary of FRAMES, handling the generation and recognition of source and DESTINATION ADDRESSES and the detection of TRANSMISSION ERRORS in the PHYSICAL CHANNEL.

data encoding Any process by which DATA is converted from one form to be represented in another form for the purpose of transmission.

data encryption standard (DES) An ALGORITHM specified by NIST to encipher and decipher DATA for security during TRANSMISSION, DES uses a 64-bit cryptographic key.

data entry terminal A terminal specifically designed to enable DATA to be collected and prepared for transmission over a CIRCUIT. It is usually equipped with a KEYBOARD, a printer or display screen and a MODEM or NETWORK INTERFACE UNIT to enable it to send and receive information over a NETWORK.

data flow control (DFC) An element in a PACKET SWITCHING NETWORK that has responsibility for regulating the direction and flow of PACKETS by end USERS. It manages the relationship between the users to ensure that an appropriate CONVERSATION (pattern of intermittency) takes place and maintains the relationships of MESSAGES to the separate PACKETS of which messages are comprised.

data link The set of physical resources that are connected together to form a path for communication of DATA including the DATA TERMINALS and all interconnecting resources.

data link control (DLC) A device and associated PROTOCOL that ensures error-free DATA TRANSMISSION. In its simplest form, it examines groups of BITS arriving at a RECEIVING TERMINAL and checks against a predetermined DLC protocol to see whether the bits in the group have been misplaced or dropped. A group of bits is referred to as a FRAME. If a frame is found to be in error, a retransmission is automatically requested.

As each frame is initially transmitted, bits are added to form a certain parity in the BIT STREAM in accordance with the DLC protocol, and the receiving DLC checks against this protocol. See also HIGH LEVEL DATA LINK CONTROL.

data link controller That part of a communications device that is responsible for DATA LINK CONTROL, i.e., for ensuring error-free DATA TRANSMISSION.

data link escape (DLE) An international TRANSMISSION CONTROL CODE that changes the significance of other CHARACTERS that follow after it in a transmission sequence.

data link layer In a NETWORK ARCHITECTURE, this level of control includes functions that are independent of the physical medium used for the CHANNEL but define the basic procedures for DATA ENCAPSULATION and LINK MANAGEMENT. This corresponds to the second level in the ISO MODEL OF ARCHITECTURE FOR OPEN SYSTEMS INTERCONNECTION.

data network A communication system used for DIGITAL DATA TRANSMISSION.

It may use PRIVATE NETWORKS or PUBLIC DATA NETWORKS, but has the potential to provide multiple ACCESS PATHS between USERS.

data PBX Users whose equipment is linked to CIRCUITS that are attached to a data PBX can connect to other attached circuits via digital, not analog, transmission. Compare with PBX.

data phase That period of time during a CALL in which DATA may be exchanged between DATA TERMINALS interconnected over a NETWORK, i.e., excluding time for CALL ESTABLISHMENT and CALL DISESTABLISHMENT.

data printer Any form of TERMINAL used for printing a HARD COPY of information received over a COMMUNICATIONS NETWORK.

data processing system Any system designed to perform operations upon DATA by some form of automatic processing and control. Designed to produce an ordered result from raw data.

data processing terminal A device used to transmit or receive DATA over a NETWORK usually in the form of DIGITAL SIGNALS.

data rate A term that relates to the speed at which CIRCUITS or devices operate when handling digital information. For example, a particular TRANSMISSION CHANNEL might be rated at 2,400 BITS per second, where a bit is a pulse representing a BINARY DIGIT. See also MODULATION RATE, DATA SIGNALING RATE, and DATA TRANSFER RATE.

data security Procedures established to protect a system and its USERS against the intentional or unintentional misuse of DATA, e.g., disclosure of confidential details or the modification or destruction of information. See also VIRUS and ENCRYPTION.

data segment The part of a PACKET or any MESSAGE SIGNAL that contains DATA rather than ADDRESS or CONTROL INFORMATION.

data service unit (DSU) A simplified high-speed MODEM for transmission of DIGITAL DATA over a PRIVATE LINE or for limited distance communication in which it is not necessary to comply with all the requirements for a HIGH SPEED MODEM using the PUBLIC SWITCHED TELEPHONE NETWORK. Other names given to such devices include BASEBAND MODEM, LINE DRIVER, LINE ADAPTOR and LIMITED DISTANCE MODEM.

data set ready A SIGNAL sent by a MODEM or NETWORK INTERFACE UNIT (DCE) to the LINE to inform a CALLING TERMINAL that the DCE has received a DATA TERMINAL READY signal from its associated DTE.

data signal Any SIGNAL that consists of DATA arranged to represent information. The signal may include CHECK DIGITS added to the data to provide ERROR CONTROL facilities.

data signaling rate A term used to express the rate at which information can be transmitted over a CIRCUIT. In most digital systems, the information is transmitted as a series of pulses having the significance of BINARY DIGITS 0 or 1, according to the polarity of each pulse. In such a case, the INFORMATION RATE and the DATA SIGNALING RATE are the same.

In some systems, the AMPLITUDE of pulses may be varied to represent different values, even though the duration of pulses remains constant. Thus, for example, a pulse may have the value of 00, 11, 01 or 10 according to amplitude. This is an example of MULTI-STATE SIGNALING. If the duration of each pulse is 20 milliseconds, the modulation rate is 1×0.02 BITS per second, i.e., 50 BAUDS. But the data signaling rate in this example is 100 bits per second. See also DATA TRANSFER RATE.

data signaling rate transparency Refers to the capability of a NETWORK to provide compatibility between TERMINALS operating at different DATA RATES.

data sink A term referring to a device (e.g., a PAPER TAPE PUNCH or a line printer) that receives information over a CIRCUIT from a DATA SOURCE.

data source Any device that generates DATA SIGNALS to be transmitted as information over a CIRCUIT or NETWORK. Compare with DATA SINK.

data switching exchange A set of equipment designed to make connections to switch DATA TRAFFIC from one TERMINAL to another. It may be a CIRCUIT SWITCHING system and/or a PACKET SYSTEM.

data terminal Any device capable of sending and/or receiving information over a communications NETWORK. Generally speaking, a device capable of sending or receiving digital information; but ANALOG devices, used to measure phenomena remotely, also can be classed as data terminals. A data terminal can range from a simple terminal to a very complex COMPUTER. See also DATA TERMINAL EQUIPMENT (DTE).

data terminal equipment (DTE) A TERMINAL or COMPUTER attached to a DATA NETWORK as an end USER NODE. Such a device must operate in accordance with the defined PROTOCOL for the NETWORK. For example, under X.25 NETWORK ARCHITECTURES, it must INTERFACE with PACKET LEVEL PROTOCOLS, which govern the size, sequence and format of PACKETS, and with FRAME LEVEL PROTOCOLS, which manage error-free transmission of packets to and from the network.

The DTE is responsible for these HIGH LEVEL FUNCTIONS rather than PHYSICAL LEVEL functions, which are performed by the DATA CIRCUIT TERMINATING EQUIPMENT (DCE). The DCE is a MODEM or NETWORK INTERFACE unit which connects the DTE to the network.

data terminal ready An INTERCHANGE SIGNAL between a DATA TERMINAL (DTE) and its DCE that signifies that the DTE is operable and ready to receive DATA. See also CALLING INDICATOR SIGNAL.

data traffic MESSAGE SIGNALS that represent information pertaining to a DATA PROCESSING SYSTEM rather than SPEECH SIGNALS, and implying the use of DIGITAL TRANSMISSION.

data transfer The process of transferring information from one location to another in a communication system and often cited to distinguish between other phases in a CALL sequence, including CALL ESTABLISHMENT and CALL CLEARING.

data transfer phase The period in which a USER'S DATA is transferred between two TERMINALS in making a CALL over a SWITCHED CIRCUIT network. It is distinguished from the CALL ESTABLISHMENT phase, in which an ACCESS PATH is created from the CALLING to the CALLED TERMINAL, and CALL CLEARING phase, in which the CIRCUIT is released.

data transfer rate A term used to express the rate at which information is received over a CIRCUIT, excluding such signal elements as are used to synchronize transmission, e.g., excluding START BITS or STOP BITS used in telegraphic transmission to denote the beginning and end of characters. The data transfer rate is thus less than the DATA SIGNALING RATE possible over the circuit. Another factor to be discounted in arriving at the data transfer rate is the number of redundant CHARACTERS and extra transmission sequences required as the result of the ERROR CONTROL procedures operated over the circuit.

The term transfer rate is used as an accurate statement of the performance of a circuit in transferring information and is related to a particular method of transmission under given conditions. The rate may be expressed in BITS, CHARACTERS, WORDS or BLOCKS received per unit of time. Also known as INFORMATION RATE.

data transfer requested signal A CONTROL signal from DATA CIRCUIT TERMINATING EQUIPMENT (DCE) to its associated DTE indicating that a distant TERMINAL has requested to transfer DATA.

data transmission The process of techniques concerned with transmitting information as DIGITAL PULSES. See also DIGITAL DATA TRANSMISSION.

database In DATA PROCESSING, a FILE (or files) organized in such a way that a variety of USERS can update or inquire of the file for different purposes, using COMPUTER procedures, which to the user appear to be independent of the file structure. A file that is not designed to satisfy a specific limited application.

database management Relating to a COMPUTER system operation to control the recording, analysis, indexing, storage and retrieval of DATA. Implying a method of FILE organization that allows for the efficient production of required results in response to both standard and ad hoc requests.

datagram In a PACKET SWITCHING SYSTEM, the simplest form of transmission that can occur is the transmission of a single PACKET from one USER to another, requiring no response. It is sometimes referred to as a datagram.

Datex The name given by the Deutsche Bundespost to a range of PUBLIC DATA TRANSMISSION SERVICES available to SUBSCRIBERS in West Germany. The specific service is denoted by a suffix, e.g., Datex—P represents the PACKET SWITCHING SERVICE.

dB Abbreviation of DECIBELS.

DC See DIRECT CURRENT.

DCE Same as DATA CIRCUIT TERMINATING EQUIPMENT, it corresponds functionally to a MODEM or NETWORK INTERFACE UNIT, and its purpose is to handle all CONTROL activities entailed in connecting DATA TERMINAL EQUIPMENT to a network.

DC1, DC2, DC3 and DC4 See DEVICE CONTROL CODES.

decentralized control signaling A system of CONTROL in which control SIGNALS related to DATA TRANSMISSION on a particular CIRCUIT must be carried on that circuit.

Also known as CHANNEL ASSOCIATED SIGNALING. Contrast with CENTRALIZED CONTROL SIGNALING.

decibels A unit of measure for the power of a SIGNAL or a measure of the ATTENUATION produced upon a signal in any part of a communication system.

It is usual to relate power levels to a standard point. These points vary and are defined by the particular system or particular measuring device being used.

As an example, a reference of one milliwatt may be taken, and power levels would be described as P dBm, where P is positive for power in excess of a milliwatt and negative for less.

decimal digit A DIGIT in decimal notation, i.e., from the set of digits 0, 1, 2, 3, 4, 5, 6, 7, 8 and 9.

decision feedback system A system based on the ERROR CONTROL principles of ARQ or AUTOMATIC REPEAT REQUEST.

decoder A device that interprets information represented in a defined CODE and generates output into a form required for another processing operation. For example, the reconstruction of samples from CHARACTER SIGNALS in PULSE CODE MODULATION. Also a device that converts ELECTRICAL SIGNALS received at a RECEIVING STATION into the form required by the DATA LINK CONTROL in the RECEIVING TERMINAL.

dedicated line See LEASED LINE.

deference A procedure by which a DATA LINK CONTROLLER delays its transmission to a CHANNEL to avoid CONTENTION with other transmissions using the same channel. This technique is sometimes used in LOCAL AREA NETWORKS.

DEL See DELETE.

delay distortion A form of signal impairment that arises because of a variation in the propagation time for different frequencies in a CIRCUIT.

delay equalizer A device used to overcome distortion arising from the differential effect of a TELEPHONE CHANNEL upon the propagation of DATA SIGNALS in different parts of the BANDWIDTH. The delay equalizer delays the more advanced frequencies to coincide with delayed frequencies; it therefore introduces an overall delay of a few microseconds, which is not significant.

delay time The ANSWERING TIME, i.e., the interval that elapses between the completion of a CALLING SIGNAL and the response by the operator or automatic equipment at the CALLED LOCATION.

delayed delivery A facility that is available in certain DATA NETWORKS to allow DATA to be stored temporarily until a particular DESTINATION TERMINAL is available.

delete (DEL) A special function used in a DATA COMMUNICATIONS CODE to allow USERS to overwrite an erroneous CHARACTER. For example, in connection with information punched in PAPER TAPE, a DEL is represented by a complete row of holes in every position of a character.

delivery confirmation A notification passed to a DATA TERMINAL that has used a DELAYED DELIVERY facility, confirming that the NETWORK has now delivered the MESSAGE to the DESTINATION TERMINAL.

democratic network A NETWORK in which each NODE or EXCHANGE has CLOCKS of equal status, i.e., no one clock has control over the whole network and the clock rate is defined as the mean of the clocks involved. Contrast with DESPOTIC NETWORK.

demodulation The process by means of which a MESSAGE SIGNAL is extracted from a CARRIER SIGNAL, which has been used to transmit the message signal over a NETWORK or as a RADIO TRANSMISSION. See also MODULATION.

demodulator 1. A device that receives DATA SIGNALS in ANALOG form and converts them into the form of DIGITAL SIGNALS representing BINARY DIGITS suitable for processing in DATA TERMINAL EQUIPMENT.

2. A device that analyzes a SIGNAL consisting of a CARRIER WAVE modulated by a MESSAGE SIGNAL and reconstructs the original message signal for further processing at a RECEIVING STATION. See also MODULATION.

demultiplexed A MESSAGE SIGNAL is said to be demultiplexed when it has been separated from a CARRIER SIGNAL with which it had originally been combined for efficient transmission. See also MULTIPLEXER, FREQUENCY DIVISION MULTIPLEXING and TIME DIVISION MULTIPLEXING.

demultiplexer A device used to separate individual MESSAGE SIGNALS that have been combined onto the same TRANSMISSION CHANNEL by using the techniques of FREQUENCY DIVISION MULTIPLEXING (FDM) or TIME DIVISION MULTIPLEXING (TDM).

demultiplexing The process of separating MESSAGE SIGNALS that have been combined for the purpose of transmission onto the same physical TRANSMISSION PATH using the techniques of TIME DIVISION MULTIPLEXING (TDM) or FREQUENCY DIVISION MULTIPLEXING (FDM).

demux See DEMULTIPLEXER.

de-packetizing The process that arises in receiving and handling an element of a MESSAGE SIGNAL over a PACKET SWITCHING NETWORK. The element is stripped of CODES that have been added to it to assist in transmission and is combined in correct sequence with other elements of the same MESSAGE that have been transmitted as separate PACKETS.

DES See DATA ENCRYPTION STANDARD.

deserializer A device that accepts a series of pulses one after another and groups them into required patterns according to the coding structure required for output. For example, it receives BITS in SERIAL MODE and outputs groups of bits in PARALLEL MODE to represent each CHARACTER CODE.

despotic network A NETWORK in which the timing of all operations is governed by one master CLOCK. Also known as SYNCHRONIZED NETWORK and contrasted with DEMOCRATIC NETWORK.

destination address The STATION designated to receive a specific MESSAGE SIGNAL or that part of a message signal that defines the ADDRESS of the CALLED LOCATION.

destination address field A FIELD of information within a FRAME that identifies the ADDRESS of the STATION to which that particular PACKET or frame of DATA is routed.

destination terminal The TERMINAL designated to receive a specific MESSAGE SIGNAL. Same as CALLED TERMINAL.

detection The process used in a DEMODULATOR to reconstruct an original MESSAGE SIGNAL from a MODULATED CARRIER WAVE. See ENVELOPE DETECTION, SYNCHRONOUS DETECTION and COHERENT DETECTION. See also MODULATION.

device control Processes or SIGNALS concerned with the physical activation of remote equipment rather than the information being carried in a communications system.

device control codes (DC1, DC2, DC3 and DC4) Special CODES occurring within the character set of standard DATA COMMUNICATIONS CODES and used to represent instructions to activate certain specified functions on a TERMINAL device (e.g., to switch it on or off).

DFC See DATA FLOW CONTROL.

dial tone The PROCEED-TO-SEND SIGNAL observed by the USER to a TELEPHONE when connected to an available LINE.

dialogue A process consisting of a series of SIGNALS passing between two TERMINALS that are in contact with each other over a NETWORK in order to perform a two-way sequence of communication. The dialogue proceeds according to a defined PROTOCOL, which is designed to ensure an orderly exchange of information and the correct initiation and termination of the CALL.

dialogue management Once an ACCESS PATH has been established between two USERS in a PACKET SWITCHING NETWORK, a DIALOGUE between the two users may take place. The access path has to be retained, by a VIRTUAL CIRCUIT, to suit the PATTERN OF INTERMITTENCY of the CALL.

In the simplest case, a single PACKET of information may travel from one user to another; or there may be a CONVERSATION allowing a TRANSACTION to be progressed, in which packets transmitted from one user result in several packets in response from the other.

Also, a so-called SESSION may take place in which a number of related transactions are progressed.

Such a dialogue has to be managed under control of SOFTWARE at each STATION. While the dialogue is taking place, it is necessary to associate related packets being transmitted and received and to control the dialogue so that the stations send and receive packets in a coordinated manner as though it were a rational exchange between two people.

dial-up connection A connection made via a switching operation in an EXCHANGE by a SUBSCRIBER who is able to dial a connection to a required destination. Any connection made by automatic means at the time required, rather than one effected by a permanent point-to-point circuit.

dibit Used to refer to two BITS of information.

differential echo suppressor A device that suppresses reflected SIGNALS in a long distance telephone CIRCUIT by monitoring the difference in levels between signals on the two SPEECH CHANNELS of a 4-WIRE CIRCUIT.

differential phase modulation A method of PHASE MODULATION in which no particular value is attributed to PHASE INVERSION in a certain direction. A change in PHASE simply indicates a change from a previous value to another, e.g., a change from 0 to 1 or from 1 to 0.

digit A numeric element selected from a finite set of elements and in DATA TRANSMISSION represented by a pulse (or a group of pulses) of a certain AMPLITUDE, timing, duration or PHASE. The term should be used to indicate in context the radix of notation, e.g., a DECIMAL DIGIT, or a BINARY DIGIT.

digit position The space or TIME SLOT into which a particular DIGIT is positioned.

digit pulse A pulse corresponding to a specific DIGIT POSITION in a transmission sequence representing a BINARY NUMBER or corresponding to a specific TIME SLOT.

digit rate The number of DIGITS transferred in a given time interval. Care is to be exercised in the use of this term to define the radix of notation, e.g., BINARY DIGIT. See also MODULATION RATE, DATA SIGNALING RATE and DATA TRANSFER RATE.

digit signal In TELEPHONY, a SIGNAL generated by dialing and representing a specific DIGIT forming part of a series giving the ADDRESS of a CALLED TERMINAL.

digit time slot The TIME SLOT allocated to a particular DIGIT POSITION.

digital computer A COMPUTER that operates using a stored program of instructions in which information to be processed and the instructions are represented by DIGITAL PULSES. The information is usually recorded in BINARY NOTATION. Such devices range in size from SMALL MICROCOMPUTERS to large MAINFRAME COMPUTERS and can handle millions of operations per second.

digital connection A DIGITAL PATH between two TERMINALS operating at a specified BIT RATE and using a switched connection through a DIGITAL SWITCH.

digital data channel A CHANNEL used to carry information recorded as discrete pulses representing BINARY DIGITS rather than ANALOG SIGNALS. It is possible today to convert VOICE SIGNALS into digital form by using PULSE CODE MODULATION techniques.

digital data link A set of resources used for the transmission of information recorded in digital form at a specified BIT RATE between two locations. See also DIGITAL DATA TRANSMISSION.

digital data transmission Digital transmission is used for the transmission of DATA (e.g., information recorded in a form recognized by COMPUTERS), and DIGITAL TECHNIQUES have been designed to provide for very low ERROR RATES, which are not available using ANALOG TECHNIQUES over a normal TELEPHONE CHANNEL. A DIGITAL SIGNAL deriving from a computer or DTE that is compatible with a computer will produce a SIGNAL at discrete voltage levels as a series of pulses, e.g., at two levels, representing the 1 or 0 condition associated with BINARY NUMBERS.

To transmit digital signals, it was common, prior to 1960, to convert this simple digital signal into an ANALOG SIGNAL by means of a MODEM. The signal could then be transmitted by FREQUENCY DIVISION MULTIPLEXING as though it were a VOICE SIGNAL to be converted back to digital form by a modem at the RECEIVING TERMINAL.

At a later stage, TIME DIVISION MULTIPLEXING techniques were introduced on TRUNK ROUTES to enable signals to be transmitted in digital form, and NETWORK INTERFACE UNITS were used to INTERFACE each terminal to the digital NETWORK, thus allowing digital transmission throughout the network.

These techniques enable a simple VOICE CHANNEL to support more than 20 digital channels operating at 2,400 BITS per second. Therefore, a much greater efficiency is realized in line utilization.

Another advantage of digital transmission is that digital signals can be easily regenerated as they pass through the network. This allows error rates typically of 1 bit in 10^7 versus 1 bit in 10^5 by analog techniques. Another benefit is the reduction in complexity required for interfacing a terminal to a digital transmission network.

Other techniques have been developed to transmit digital data, and examples are given under FREQUENCY SHIFT KEYING and PHASE MODULATION.

digital error An error detected as a discrepancy between a SIGNAL as it is transferred and received over a LINE, e.g., the displacement of a DIGIT from one position to another.

digital exchange An EXCHANGE in which the MESSAGE traffic is transported as DIGITAL SIGNALS and the connections for incoming and outgoing TRAFFIC are achieved by DIGITAL SWITCHES. See also SWITCHING EQUIPMENT.

digital filling The insertion of a defined number of DIGITS into a DIGITAL SIGNAL to increase the DIGIT RATE. These inserted digits do not contribute to the information transferred but are used to alter the timing of SIGNALS on a CHANNEL relative to certain TIME SLOTS. Sometimes referred to as BIT STUFFING.

digital leased circuit A private CIRCUIT hired by a user from a CARRIER and providing a permanent connection for point-to-point DATA TRANSMISSION between two TERMINALS using DIGITAL SIGNALS in the TRANSMISSION PATH. See also PUBLIC DATA NETWORKS.

digital multiplex equipment Equipment used for combining several DIGITAL SIGNALS onto a single digital CIRCUIT using the techniques known as TIME DIVISION MULTIPLEXING (TDM). The equipment also allows the reconstruction of the original SIGNALS at a distant location by demultiplexing.

digital multiplexer A MULTIPLEXER that operates in accordance with the principles of TIME DIVISION MULTIPLEXING (TDM).

digital path A complete set of physical resources used to create a two-way link between two TERMINALS for the transmission of DIGITAL SIGNALS at a specified BIT RATE. If digital paths are linked through a DIGITAL SWITCHED CIRCUIT, the term DIGITAL CONNECTION is frequently used.

digital pulses Electronic SIGNALS that represent information in binary coded form as a finite number of pulses, e.g., at two levels that correspond to the BINARY NOTATION 0 and 1. Numeric information can be transmitted in this way, but also groups of digital pulses may represent alphabetic characters, numerals or special symbols. This is the primary way in which information is represented in COMPUTERS and other electronic systems. See also BINARY DIGITS.

digital radio path A two-way TRANSMISSION PATH for DIGITAL SIGNALS at a specified BIT RATE made up of several DIGITAL SECTIONS, where each section comprises two radio terminal stations and their interconnecting TRANSMISSION MEDIUM.

digital repeater An amplifier designed to regenerate a DIGITAL SWITCH and used at regular intervals along a TRANSMISSION PATH to overcome the problem of ATTENUATION. See also ANALOG REPEATER.

digital section A term used in line transmission systems to refer to a segment in a DIGITAL PATH that provides a means for two-way transmission of DIGITAL SIGNALS between two locations at a specified BIT RATE.

digital signal An ELECTRICAL SIGNAL made up of discrete pulses coded to represent information and contrasted with an ANALOG ELECTRICAL SIGNAL, which is a continuous waveform. A digital signal is of a noncontinuous form and is made up of discrete pulses that take specific values, e.g., in BINARY NOTATION, pulses representing 0 and 1.

digital speech interpolation (DSI) Often a feature of SWITCHING EQUIPMENT that is used with DIGITAL CIRCUITS, DSI improves line efficiency by sending no BITS when the speaker is silent.

digital sum A sum created by adding a series of PULSE AMPLITUDES over a given period of time to find a difference in a coded sequence.

digital switch A device for making SWITCHED CONNECTIONS between CIRCUITS to establish TRANSMISSION PATHS for DIGITAL DATA TRANSMISSION and in which the connections are made by processing DIGITAL SIGNALS rather than ANALOG SIGNALS.

digital switched circuit A CIRCUIT provided by a CARRIER for the transmission of digital data, which can be utilized by USERS by dialing a connection from a CALLING TERMINAL to a CALLED TERMINAL. The circuit is only in use and charged to the user for the period involved in CALL ESTABLISHMENT, MESSAGE TRANSFER and CALL CLEARING.

Strictly speaking, a digital switched circuit is one using digital switching, i.e., the connections between circuits are established by operating on DIGITAL SIGNALS rather than ANALOG SIGNALS. In some systems, digital signals are converted to analog signals for transmission purposes. See also PUBLIC DATA NETWORKS.

digital techniques Pertaining to the recording, transmission and processing of information recorded as DIGITAL SIGNALS. See also BINARY DIGIT and DIGITAL TRANSMISSION.

digital terminal A device connected to a NETWORK for the purpose of transmitting or receiving DIGITAL SIGNALS.

digital traffic Information transmitted over a CIRCUIT in which each MESSAGE is transferred as a DIGITAL SIGNAL rather than an ANALOG SIGNAL.

digital transmission See DIGITAL DATA TRANSMISSION.

digitization The process involved in converting DATA or SPEECH SIGNALS into digital form for transmission or for subsequent processing.

direct call A facility provided to allow fast setup times in establishing a SWITCHED CONNECTION in which the NETWORK interprets a CALL REQUEST as an instruction to establish a connection with a predetermined ADDRESS, i.e., the selection of the address does not require a dialing operation.

direct current (DC) An electrical current in which the direction and value of the current remains constant.

direct service circuit Any CIRCUIT that directly links two SUBSCRIBERS or TERMINALS and is reserved exclusively for that purpose.

directional antenna An ANTENNA used in point-to-point radio communication and designed to send or receive RADIO WAVES in a particular direction.

director exchange In the early Strowger-type TELEPHONE EXCHANGES, the SELECTORS that set up connections were controlled directly by SIGNALS originating from the telephone dial. At a later stage of development, special units were introduced to translate the signals from the dial. The purpose of this development was to reduce the number of DIGITS the SUBSCRIBER had to dial. EXCHANGES adapted for this later development were called director exchanges, and the former type were known as NONDIRECTOR EXCHANGES.

distortion An impairment of a MESSAGE SIGNAL caused by the characteristics of the TRANSMISSION LINK and having different effects at different frequencies. For example, the GAIN or LOSS of a SIGNAL in a system may vary with frequency, so that the various frequencies that make up a signal are not reproduced at correct relative strengths. In an audio system, this would be observed as impaired tone.

Another kind of distortion is known as NONLINEARITY DISTORTION; its effect is to cause the AMPLITUDE of signals to be reproduced out of proportion in different FREQUENCY BANDS. It is a factor to be considered in planning MULTIPLEXING links that use AMPLIFIERS to increase the gain (i.e., signal strength) of complex signals. Unwanted harmonics are generated through the nonlinearity of the amplifiers and will cover a wide frequency band and occur as NOISE.

To avoid the effects of nonlinear distortion in TRANSMISSION LINKS, it may be necessary to limit AMPLIFIER GAIN and thus position repeaters at more frequent intervals. An alternative is to compensate by the use of EQUALIZATION techniques.

distributed data processing (DDP) Many of the early COMPUTER systems installed in industrial organizations were based on central computer installations, and very often DATA collected at distant locations was physically transported to the computer center for processing. The need to link remote locations to central computers was envisaged from the beginning, but PUBLIC DATA NETWORKS were not extensively available. At first, MESSAGES were transferred in batches at convenient times using TELEX facilities or over PRIVATE LEASED CIRCUITS. Then on-line interactive systems developed where TERMINALS from remote locations could communicate with central systems over great distances.

With the advent of public data networks in the 1960s and PACKET SWITCHING in the 1970s, it became possible to install NETWORKS in which computer centers were linked. Large volumes of data and programs could be transferred automatically, between computer centers. The idea of a single dominant central computer began to give way to a concept in which both the intelligence and the data FILES are distributed over several distant locations.

This decentralizing process provided greater responsiveness and efficiency to organizations and has become known as distributed data processing. Like many terms in the computer field, it is not always used in the same context. Sometimes the term is used simply to signify a situation where processing takes place independently at different locations, but it should be used to denote a situation in which computing power and data are shared.

DDP TRANSMISSION lines connect equipment that is located in various geographical sites, tying together input/output functions with DATA PROCESSING, storage and CONTROL operations that may be widely dispersed.

distributed frame alignment signal A FRAME ALIGNMENT SIGNAL that is distributed over a number of nonconsecutive TIME SLOTS.

Distributed Queue Dual Bus (DQDB) See METROPOLITAN AREA NETWORK.

distributed system Relates to any system in which CONTROL does not reside at one point but is distributed throughout the NETWORK. For example, in a DISTRIBUTED DATA PROCESSING system, intelligent functions are carried out at remote locations using TERMINALS with local processing power. There may be a need to communicate with a NODE, or other terminals via a node, but the terminals can function autonomously in the interests of overall efficiency and to eliminate the dependence upon key nodes.

distribution point The point at which a number of LINES in a TELEPHONE SYSTEM are radiated out to different SUBSCRIBERS in a locality.

distributor Equipment switches INCOMING CALLS to appropriate OUTGOING LINES in a CIRCUIT SWITCHING system.

In a circuit switching system, it has to be possible to connect every INCOMING LINE of an EXCHANGE to every outgoing line. For an exchange with 1,000 incoming and 1,000 outgoing lines, this would entail 1,000,000 CROSSPOINTS at which switching can take place.

More efficient internal ARCHITECTURES can be used to reduce the number of crosspoints while maintaining a low probability of CALL BLOCKING. For example, a three-stage exchange could reduce the number of crosspoints in the DISTRIBUTOR to 30,000. The three stages of switching entail: (a) CONCENTRATOR, (b) DISTRIBUTOR, (c) EXPANDOR.

The concentrator receives the incoming LOCAL LINES and passes CALLS via a smaller number of internal links to the distributor.

The distributor switches the calls received from the concentrator or INCOMING TRUNKS and passes them to OUTGOING TRUNKS or to an expandor.

The expandor accepts the switched calls and makes final connection to the appropriate local lines. See also GROUPING.

district switching center A term used in the British TELEPHONE SYSTEM to describe a TRUNK EXCHANGE at the level known as a SECONDARY CENTER. This is somewhat confusing, since in North America the term PRIMARY CENTER is used at this level. See also EXCHANGE HIERARCHY.

divestiture The process of the breakup of AT&T into AT&T plus the REGIONAL BELL HOLDING COMPANIES is known as divestiture. It is a legal agreement between AT&T and the U.S. Justice Department that was reached in 1984.

DLC See DATA LINK CONTROL.

DLE See DATA LINK ESCAPE.

document facsimile system A form of TELEGRAPHY in which documents, but not photographs, are transmitted over a NETWORK, but not necessarily maintaining the original density scale.

document facsimile telegraphy A system of TELEGRAPHY in which documents other than photographs are transmitted over a communications CIRCUIT and in which there is no guarantee of the faithful recreation of the original density scale. Compare with PHOTOGRAPH FACSIMILE and ALPHABETIC TELEGRAPHY.

double current circuit A CIRCUIT used for DATA TRANSMISSION in which voltages are applied directly to a LINE to represent BINARY NUMBERS, e.g., positive voltage for "1" and a negative voltage for "0." This definition is contrasted with a SINGLE CURRENT CIRCUIT in which a current is made to flow from 1 but is interrupted for 0. Either system can be used for transmission over short distances (a few kilometers) but, for connection to a NETWORK for long-distance communication, a DCE or NETWORK INTERFACE UNIT is needed. Such circuits are often used between a DTE and DCE, when they are referred to as INTERCHANGE CIRCUITS.

double ended control A system of CONTROL in which SYNCHRONIZATION between CLOCKS in two communicating EXCHANGES (or NODES) is achieved by monitoring the PHASE of incoming SIGNALS and the phase of the clocks in each exchange.

double sideband modulation A form of AMPLITUDE MODULATION in which both the SIDEBAND signals produced in the modulation ENVELOPE are transmitted and detected. The CARRIER WAVE is not always transmitted in such transmission systems, and it has to be reintroduced at the RECEIVING TERMINAL. See also MODULATION.

downlink A COMMUNICATIONS SATELLITE CIRCUIT is divided into UPLINK and downlink segments. The portion extending from the satellite to Earth is the downlink.

DRCS See DYNAMICALLY REDEFINABLE CHARACTER SET.

DS-0 (digital signal level 0) A class of digital transmission at 64 kbps, which is the standard for digitizing one voice conversation.

DS-1 (digital signal level 1) A class of digital transmission that includes 24 voice channels multiplexed onto one 1.544-Mbps digital channel. In Europe, the rate is 2.048 Mbps, including 30 channels.

DS-1C (digital signal level 1C) A 3.152-Mbps DIGITAL SIGNAL carried on a COMMON CARRIER'S T1 facility.

DS-2 (digital signal level 2) A 6.312-Mbps DIGITAL SIGNAL that is carried on a COMMON CARRIER'S T2 facility.

DS-3 (digital signal level 3) A SIGNAL of approximately 44 Mbps that is carried on a COMMON CARRIER'S T3 facility.

DS-4 (digital signal level 4) A SIGNAL of approximately 273 Mbps that is carried on a COMMON CARRIER'S T4 facility.

DSI See DIGITAL SPEECH INTERPOLATION.

DSU See DATA SERVICE UNIT.

DTE See DATA TERMINAL EQUIPMENT.

DTE clear request A CONTROL signal sent by a DATA TERMINAL (DTE) to clear a CALL.

DTE waiting A CONTROL signal between a DATA TERMINAL (DTE), indicating that the DTE is waiting for a further control signal from the DCE.

dumb terminal A VISUAL DISPLAY unit used to display information. It has little or no intelligent functions to enable it to be connected to a communications CIRCUIT. The normal mode of use requires such a TERMINAL to be connected to a local CONTROLLER, which provides the intelligence to connect several dumb terminals to the TRANSMISSION SYSTEM.

duplex system A system of operation in which transmission between two TERMINALS can take place simultaneously in both directions.

duration of a call The time interval between the completion of CALL ESTABLISHMENT and the CALL being cleared.

dynamic bandwidth allocation The process whereby BANDWIDTH is made available to a TRANSMISSION device on demand, that is, only when there is DATA to be sent, rather than in a fixed amount for a continuous period.

dynamic equalizer A device that counteracts DELAY DISTORTION affecting ANALOG SIGNALS in transmission CIR-

CUITS. It is constructed to respond appropriately at different speeds and operating conditions. See also EQUALIZATION.

dynamic port allocation Any device that is capable of allocating access PORTS to incoming CHANNELS automatically in response to operating conditions. For example, some HIGH SPEED MODEMS can automatically switch channels when a channel becomes inoperative and automatically switch channels to higher speeds of operation to make use of the full BANDWIDTH on a CIRCUIT provided.

dynamic range The range of acoustic SIGNALS produced by a MESSAGE SOURCE in terms of frequency and loudness.

dynamic test set Test equipment used to test the performance of MODEMS and other line equipment, enabling the operator to create a wide range of operating conditions to test the efficiency of the equipment at various operating speeds and for various functions. Such test sets are usually portable and help to rapidly isolate faults in complex communication NETWORKS.

dynamically redefinable character set (DRCS) A technique used to enable a TERMINAL to be used alternately to display different CHARACTER SETS (e.g., English, Arabic, French, etc.). In most terminals, the display character set is stored in a READ ONLY MEMORY (ROM) where it cannot be changed readily by the USER. Although it is possible to store more than one character set, it may not be practicable to store all the character sets possible.

A practical method is to store character sets centrally on the DATABASES that the TERMINAL must access. In this way, the required character set can be downloaded into terminals as required and stored in RANDOM ACCESS MEMORY (RAM), ready to operate in a particular language.

E

earth network A network based upon installations on the ground rather than upon atmospheric reflections and including cable or direct ground-to-ground radio links.

earth station A TRANSMITTING and/or RECEIVING STATION designed to send or receive RADIO SIGNALS in the form of ELECTROMAGNETIC WAVES to and from the atmosphere, i.e., waves reflected from an orbiting COMMUNICATIONS SATELLITE.

EBCDIC A DATA COMMUNICATION CODE much used by IBM and offering 256 unique 8-BIT character combinations. The term is pronounced as "ebbseedik" and is a contraction of EXTENDED BINARY CODED DECIMAL INTERCHANGE CODE. See also ASCII.

echo A delayed version of a MESSAGE SIGNAL produced by reflections in the CHANNEL, which could impair the quality of the signal. On certain channels, particularly intercontinental telephone links, special echo-suppressing devices are used.

echo cancellation A technique that helps provide DIGITAL TRANSMISSION service over a single TWISTED WIRE PAIR line, echo cancellation subtracts the ECHO (or an approximate estimate of its value) that is produced when send and receive SIGNALS travel simultaneously on the same BANDWIDTH.

echo effect A condition that arises in long-distance communication over LINES; it appears to USERS of a TELEPHONE as an echo of the speaker's VOICE. It is, in fact, caused by reflections created by variations in the CIRCUIT (e.g., a TWO-WIRE CIRCUIT connected to a FOUR-WIRE CIRCUIT). On intercontinental circuits, ECHO SUPPRESSORS are often fitted to permit only one pair of wires to transmit speech at a time. If simultaneous transmission is required on such circuits, special tones have to be transmitted to disable the echo suppressors.

echo suppressor A device used on a CIRCUIT to suppress unwanted SIGNALS that are delayed versions of MESSAGE SIGNALS and that arise due to reflections in circuits over long distances. It is activated by a speech detector and reduces the ECHO on the return path of a roundtrip transmission. It must be disabled to permit bidirectional high-speed data transmission.

EDI See ELECTRONIC DATA INTERCHANGE.

EDIFACT (EDI for Administration, Commerce, and Transport) An international standard for EDI that is used in international trade, EDIFACT focuses on business functions. It was developed jointly by the ANSI X12 subcommittee, various European EDI interest groups and subcommittees of the United Nations.

editing terminal A TERMINAL designed for the preparation of TEXT and GRAPHICS by an INFORMATION PROVIDER. See also TELETEXT EDITING TERMINAL and VIDEOTEX TERMINAL.

effective call A CALL that is established so that CONVERSATION may take place between two people or two TERMINALS.

effectively transmitted signal A definition used in the transmission of SOUND PROGRAMS, in which the NOMINAL OVERALL LOSS at any specified frequency must not exceed the nominal overall loss at 800 Hz by more than 4.3 DB. A SIGNAL at a frequency outside this limit is not effectively transmitted.

EFT See ELECTRONIC FUNDS TRANSFER.

800 service A billing arrangement with a U.S. TELECOMMUNICATIONS service provider whereby CALLS placed to a given location are not charged to the CALLING PARTY but to the recipient. Alternatively, the arrangement can specify that calls placed going out from a given location are billed according to a prespecified agreement. The three-digit prefix "800" is added to the SUBSCRIBER'S phone number.

80-column display standard Pertaining to a TERMINAL and associated transmission system that will allow a display of information containing 80 columns of CHARACTERS on each page. For example, in a WORD PROCESSOR.

electrical analog The representation of a phenomenon as an ELECTRICAL SIGNAL, e.g., the representation of SOUND WAVES as AUDIO FREQUENCY magnetic waves.

electrical interface The specification of the electrical requirements for communication between two devices and encompassing the SIGNALS that must pass between the devices to transfer CONTROL or MESSAGE INFORMATION. For example, the duration, frequency, AMPLITUDE, direction, encoding and significance of ELECTRICAL SIGNALS.

electrical signal Any SIGNAL by means of which information is conveyed from one location to another and in which the information is represented by variations either in PHASE, frequency, AMPLITUDE or duration of the electrical current. See also ANALOG ELECTRICAL SIGNAL and DIGITAL SIGNAL.

electrical telegraph The system originally developed by Samuel Morse in which information is represented by interrupting the electrical current in a CIRCUIT to transmit information as a series of pulses representing ALPHANUMERIC characters. The later development of this system resulted in telegraphic communication using TELETYPEWRITERS.

electromagnetic radiation The transmission of energy resulting from charged particles undergoing acceleration and arising as magnetic FIELDS known as ELECTROMAGNETIC WAVES, which are propagated through free space with a constant velocity of 2.998×10^8 meters per second—the velocity of light.

electromagnetic waves Both RADIO WAVES and LIGHT WAVES are examples of electromagnetic waves, which can be propagated by a transmitter and BROADCAST through the atmosphere. Such waves can also be transmitted along cables or WAVEGUIDES. Unlike SOUND WAVES, they can be propagated in space and need not be carried in air.

The early research into electromagnetic waves was conducted by Heinrich Hertz, who is attributed with the discovery of electric waves in the RADIO FREQUENCY SPECTRUM and who established that such waves could pass through materials opaque to light. Today, the hertz is a unit used to define frequency: 1 hertz is 1 cycle per second and thus, 2 kHz is 2,000 cycles per second or 2×10^3 cycles per second.

All systems of communication must generate signals that can in the end be detected by the human ear or eye. Human ears are sensitive to air waves in a frequency range from about 20 cycles per second to 17,000 cycles per second (20 Hz to 17 kHz).

Human eyes respond to waves within a narrow band of frequency around 5×10^{14} cycles per second; i.e., frequencies of about 420 to 790 terahertz, where 1 THz $= 10^{12}$ Hz. These light waves are carried as electromagnetic waves that travel in space.

RADIO FREQUENCIES occupy a lower frequency spectrum, and the useful radio frequencies are:

low frequency (LF)	30 kHz to 300 kHz
medium frequency (MF)	300 kHz to 3 MHz
high frequency (HF)	3 mHz to 30 MHz
very high frequency (VHF)	30 MHz to 300 MHz
ultra high frequency (UHF)	300 MHz to 3 GHz
1 MHz (megahertz)	$= 1 \times 10^6$ cycles per second
1 GHz (gigahertz)	$= 1 \times 10^9$ cycles per second

In most forms of long-distance communication, audible or visible waves are "translated" into radio frequencies for transmission purposes and translated back to their audible or visible forms at the RECEIVING STATION for the USER.

All electromagnetic waves travel through space at approximately the same speed of 300,000,000 meters per second, and the WAVELENGTH in meters can be calculated by dividing this number by the frequency in hertz. (See Appendix 3.)

The wavelength determines the size of the TRANSMITTING AERIALS and RECEIVING AERIALS required to propagate and receive SIGNALS. If the frequency is low approaching audibility, the aerials have to be immense; if the frequencies are above the UHF BAND, they are easily obstructed. Thus, the radio frequency spectrum provides a choice of characteristics that include:

LF and MF—used for radio broadcasting by the propagation of SURFACE WAVES that are guided over the earth's surface.

HF—used for radio broadcasting by reflecting waves from the IONOSPHERE—known as SKY WAVE propagation. Used for long-distance communication.

VHF and UHF—both used for radio and television broadcasting as SPACE WAVES ranging up to 300 kilometers, depending upon the geography and positioning of the aerial. See also AUDIO SIGNALS, VIDEO SIGNALS and RADIO SIGNALS.

electron beam A stream of elementary particles of negative charge emitted from a particular source and directed at an object, e.g., emitted from the cathode of a CATHODE RAY TUBE (CRT) and directed at a luminiscent display screen.

electron gun A device used to generate a beam of electrons, a most common application being in the construction of COLOR TELEVISION RECEIVERS.

electronic bulletin board See BULLETIN BOARD SERVICE.

electronic crosspoint A microelectronic device used in the present generation of ELECTRONIC EXCHANGES for handling VOICE and DATA TRAFFIC. It consists of a simple AND GATE, which, when combined into a matrix with many other such devices, forms a highly efficient method for SPACE SWITCHING and TIME SWITCHING of DIGITAL SIGNALS. Same as ELECTRONIC DIGITAL CROSSPOINT.

electronic data interchange (EDI) The communication of DATA that represents business transactions, EDI TRANSMISSIONS are sent between the COMPUTERS of different companies and conform to a standard data format. The syntax of EDI messages is standardized by X12, an accredited subcommittee of ANSI.

electronic digital crosspoint A device for switching CIRCUITS in DIGITAL EXCHANGES used for VOICE or DATA TRAFFIC. The MESSAGE SIGNALS are represented as DIGITAL SIGNALS, and switching operations take place by synchronizing TIME SLOTS. See also SWITCHING EQUIPMENT.

electronic exchange An electronic exchange is the term applied to a TELEPHONE EXCHANGE that uses electronic switching components rather than electromechanical components such as STROWGER SELECTORS or CROSSBAR SWITCHES. The evolution of electronic switches has advanced with the introduction of PULSE CODE MODULATION (PCM) techniques, which allow VOICE ANALOG SIGNALS to be converted to DIGITAL SIGNALS. Prior to this development, problems existed with exchanges that carried ANALOG SIGNALS; with such signals, it is necessary to have a very high OFF RESISTANCE to prevent a signal leakage, which otherwise appears as NOISE generated in the switching matrix. Electronic switches with this characteristic are difficult to design; in addition, harmonic DISTORTION is difficult to avoid.

With BINARY DIGITAL SIGNALS, these characteristics are not important and the CROSSPOINT is achieved by simple AND GATES, one of the inputs of which is a signal input and the other is a control input. With a control signal 1 applied to the gate, the crosspoint is set on and allows the signal input to pass; with a control signal 0, the crosspoint is set off.

These ELECTRONIC CROSSPOINTS can operate at very high speeds and allow compact switching matrixes to be created using SPACE SWITCHING and TIME SWITCHING methods. The great benefits of such exchanges include a very high degree of TIME SHARING, allowing TRANSMISSION PATHS to be used for hundreds of CHANNELS at high speed, and the NETWORK can be expanded and controlled much more easily.

electronic funds transfer (EFT) The processing of financial transactions via computerized systems.

electronic mail A STORE AND FORWARD SYSTEM providing person-to-person communication of MESSAGES using electronic means for entry transmission and delivery of information in a visual form. Messages can be addressed to an unlimited number of multiple recipients and predefined groups of recipients. See also X .400.

electronic mail box A system that allows MESSAGES to be placed into a storage medium, such as a DIGITAL COMPUTER, so that a particular SUBSCRIBER can retrieve the message by LOGGING ON to the system and requesting to inspect the FILE of received messages.

electronic switching system (ESS) Referring to a computerized TELEPHONE EXCHANGE, the term electronic switching system was originally specific to the BELL SYSTEM but is now used industrywide.

EM See END OF MEDIUM.

emergency restart A process involving the reestablishment of a system and its CONTROL PROCEDURES following a major failure in which SIGNAL communication has failed.

emergency routes TRANSMISSION PATHS designated for use in the event of a major breakdown of the main paths of communication.

Emile Baudot A pioneer in the field of DATA TRANSMISSION, after whom the rate of SIGNALING was named. Thus, we speak of transmission speeds in BAUDS, meaning pulses per second. See also MODULATION RATE.

en-bloc address signaling A SIGNALING system in which an address is transmitted as an entity, and transmission from one stage to the next does not start until the complete ADDRESS has been received.

encoder 1. An encoder is used in DATA TRANSMISSION systems to convert SIGNALS within a TRANSMITTING STATION into a form required to translate physically separate signals of SYNCHRONIZATION PULSES and DATA into a single SERIAL BIT STREAM. At RECEIVING STATIONS, a DECODER is situated to convert signals from the form required on the LINE to the form needed by the DATA LINK CONTROL at the RECEIVING TERMINAL.
2. Any device for the generation of CHARACTERS or BITS to a defined CODE.

encoding law The rules established to define the QUANTIZATION LEVELS and their relative values in the process known as PULSE CODE MODULATION.

encryption Scrambling DATA by using calculations that start with a secret key, or CODE. The recipient of encrypted messages uses the same calculations to unscramble the data.

end of medium (EM) A special CHARACTER used in a DATA COMMUNICATIONS CODE to signify the completion of a sequence of information recorded in BINARY CODED form, e.g., the last column from a PUNCHED CARD or the last row in a PAPER TAPE.

end of message (EOM) A TRANSMISSION CONTROL character indicating the conclusion of transmission of one or more TEXTS forming a complete MESSAGE.

end of selection Similar in meaning to END-OF-PULSING SIGNAL, indicating in a SWITCHED SYSTEM that the ADDRESS component needed to select a CIRCUIT has been completed.

end of text (ETX) A TRANSMISSION CONTROL CODE used to terminate a TEXT.

end of transmission (EOT) An international TRANSMISSION CONTROL CODE that terminates a transmission sequence and restores the TERMINALS concerned to a quiescent condition.

end of transmission block (ETB) An international TRANSMISSION CONTROL CODE used to denote the end of a BLOCK forming part of a MESSAGE, where the overall message has been subdivided into two or more blocks for the convenience of transmission.

end office The point at which a SUBSCRIBER'S COMMUNICATIONS CHANNEL terminates, the end office is categorized as OFFICE CLASS 5.

end-of-address signal A SIGNAL that informs the control system in a NETWORK (e.g., a TELEPHONE or TELEX system) that the preceding CHARACTERS were ADDRESS DIGITS used to ROUTE a CALL, thus allowing the CONTROL to isolate and identify the particular ROUTING information.

end-of-block signal A predefined SIGNAL or CHARACTER that indicates the end of a BLOCK of DATA.

end-of-message identification A SIGNAL or CHARACTER that defines the completion of DATA related to a MESSAGE.

end-of-pulsing signal A SIGNAL in a TELEPHONE NETWORK indicating that an ADDRESS is complete and no more ADDRESS DIGITS are to follow.

end-to-end layer See TRANSPORT LAYER.

end-to-end protocol A PROTOCOL that provides for the management of the ACCESS PATH for a MESSAGE SIGNAL from the TRANSMITTING STATION to the RECEIVING STATION through any intermediate NODES in the NETWORK. May be contrasted with a system known as NODE-TO-NETWORK PROTOCOL in which access path management is from one node to the next adjacent node in the network.

ENQ See ENQUIRY.

enquiry (ENQ) An international TRANSMISSION CONTROL CODE used in POLLING to enquire of a distant TERMINAL its status with respect to being available to send or receive information. This code may be prefixed by ADDRESS characters to define a specific STATION.

envelope Information recorded to encapsulate an item of USER DATA and required to ensure the effective operation of the DATA NETWORK. For example, the envelope may contain information used to control communication between MODEMS or NETWORK INTERFACE UNITS at each end of a CIRCUIT.

envelope detection DETECTION is the process by which an original MESSAGE SIGNAL is derived from a MODULATED CARRIER WAVE. It is part of the process known as DEMODULATION. In a MODULATION system in which the complete SPECTRUM ENVELOPE is transmitted (i.e., no suppression of the SIDEBANDS or CARRIER), the method of detection is known as envelope detection. See also MODULATION.

EOM See END OF MESSAGE.

EOT See END OF TRANSMISSION.

equal access A ruling by the Department of Justice effective 1984 that requires the RBHCs to offer an equal quality of connection at equal rates to all COMMON CARRIERS. Equal access pertains to RBHCs that have ESS equipment and serve at least 10,000 access lines.

equalization A technique used to overcome DELAY DISTORTION affecting ANALOG SIGNALS. Delay distortion arises due to line characteristics that permit some frequency components of such a signal to arrive at a point ahead of other components. This phenomenon creates serious distortion of signals. An equalizer is effectively a FILTER that has characteristics that are the opposite (or inverse) of those exhibited by the LINE. Equalizers can be constructed to have different characteristics at different operating conditions, and these are able automatically to adjust to different operating speeds. They are known variously as AUTOMATIC EQUALIZERS, DYNAMIC EQUALIZERS or ADAPTIVE EQUALIZERS.

equalizing repeaters REPEATERS that overcome the DISTORTION effects of NONLINEARITY in a TRANSMISSION CHANNEL.

equivalent bit rate The number of BINARY DIGITS that can be transmitted over a CIRCUIT in a given time interval and related to the information content of a SIGNAL rather than to the CONTROL INFORMATION required to handle the signal on the particular TRANSMISSION PATH. See also DATA SIGNALING RATE and DATA TRANSFER RATE.

erlang A unit used to denote the utilization of a TELECOMMUNICATIONS system, named after a Danish engineer (Agner Erlang) who was a leader in the development of TRAFFIC THEORY. An erlang is not a precise volume of information but a measure of the traffic experienced, e.g., an INSTANTANEOUS TRAFFIC of 10 erlangs means that ten CALLS are in progress at a defined time. See also TRAFFIC VOLUME.

erroneous bit/block An erroneous BIT is a BINARY DIGIT signal that is not correctly received. An erroneous BLOCK is a unit of DATA containing one or more erroneous bits.

error bit A BIT (BINARY DIGIT) of information incorrectly received, i.e., the significance of the bit has been reversed: a 0 becomes a 1, or a 1 becomes a 0.

error blocks BLOCKS of DATA in which errors have been detected, e.g., by means of a CYCLIC REDUNDANCY CHECK.

error burst A sequence of BITS in which errors occur and where the ERROR BITS are not separated by a given number of CORRECT BITS as required by a CIRCUIT of the specified standard. Also known as BURST ERROR.

error checking A function performed automatically in nearly all forms of DATA TRANSMISSION to ensure that information transferred from one location to another is accurate. This is achieved by simple techniques, of which there are a number of variations in use.

A BINARY DIGITAL SIGNAL, for example, can be considered as a number of CODED characters to which PARITY BITS are added, so that each extended CHARACTER thus formed will consist of a column of BITS which must consist of an odd number of 1 bits. By checking parity along each row and column, SINGLE BIT ERRORS can be automatically detected and corrected.

Another form of checking requires information received to be retransmitted back to the TRANSMITTING STATION on a separate CHANNEL where it is compared with the original transmission.

In all forms of error checking, it is usual for the device to automatically retransmit FRAMES when errors occur, and this would not be apparent to the USER at a terminal unless the LINE was of very bad quality, causing transmission to be noticeably delayed. See also REDUNDANCY CHECKING, CYCLIC REDUNDANCY CHECKING, FORWARD ERROR CORRECTION and LONGITUDINAL REDUNDANCY CHECKING.

error control Related to the procedures concerned with the automatic detection and correction of errors in DATA TRANSMISSION. See also ERROR CHECKING and HIGH LEVEL DATA LINK CONTROL (HDLC).

error correcting code A CODE used in DATA COMMUNICATIONS which includes rules of construction so that CHARACTERS or BLOCKS of information received over a communication LINE can be checked. Departures from the rules will be detected, permitting automatic correction of some, or all, of the errors. See also REDUNDANCY CHECKING.

error correcting system Any system which uses an ERROR DETECTING CODE and allows for the automatic correction of errors before the MESSAGE concerned is accepted by a DATA TERMINAL. This may or may not involve retransmission of ERROR BLOCKS.

error correction The rules and techniques defining the way in which errors detected in BLOCKS of DATA may be corrected. In most DATA TRANSMISSION systems, REDUNDANCY CHECKING is performed to detect errors. Correction is then performed by retransmitting ERROR BLOCKS or by FORWARD ERROR CORRECTION. See also AUTOMATIC REPEAT REQUEST.

error correction, forward See FORWARD ERROR CORRECTION.

error detecting and feedback system A system which uses an ERROR DETECTING CODE to identify BLOCKS of DATA containing errors and automatically requests retransmission of the blocks concerned. Also known as AUTOMATIC REPEAT REQUEST system, or ARQ.

error detecting code A CODE used in DATA COMMUNICATIONS which conforms to rules of construction such that errors in received DATA can be identified automatically.

error detecting system Any system using an ERROR DETECTING CODE but not one able to correct errors automatically. Errors may be delivered to the DATA TERMINAL with indication of an error. Contrast with ERROR CORRECTING SYSTEM.

error detection In DATA TRANSMISSION, the DETECTION of lost or inverted BITS by automatic means. See also ERROR CHECKING.

error peak A period during the day when the frequency of ERROR BITS is at its highest. For example, in systems using the PUBLIC SWITCHED TELEPHONE NETWORKS, error peaks arise at the BUSY HOUR due to IMPULSIVE NOISE created by automatic SELECTORS in EXCHANGES. Systems using older mechanical selectors are particularly prone to such error peaks. See TRANSMISSION ERRORS.

error protocol That part of a PROTOCOL dealing with the DETECTION and correction of errors. See also HALF-DUPLEX ERROR PROTOCOL and FULL-DUPLEX ERROR PROTOCOL.

error rate The error rate is given as an average rate of the occurrence of errors for a given volume of bits transmitted, e.g., 1 error in 10^7 bits transmitted. Transmission CIRCUITS are never entirely free of NOISE and other impairments, and it is expected that errors resulting in the corruption of BITS will occur from time to time. Circuits are constructed to conform to international standards, and the ERROR RATE is one of the factors used to designate the quality of a circuit.

Equipment used to transmit and receive digital information contains ERROR CHECKING facilities to seek automatic retransmission of FRAMES containing errors.

ESC See ESCAPE CODE.

escape code A CHARACTER in a DATA COMMUNICATIONS CODE that changes the meaning of a group of ensuing characters. The use of an ESC character extends the range of meanings possible from a finite set of character codes.

ESF See EXTENDED SUPERFRAME FORMAT.

ESPRIT European Strategic Programme for Research and Development in Information Technologies, an organization of the European Community that studies developments in data communications and telecommunications.

ESS See ELECTRONIC SWITCHING SYSTEM.

ETB See END OF TRANSMISSION BLOCK.

Ethernet This system was one of the first products intended as a basis for LOCAL AREA NETWORKS. Ethernet was developed jointly by Digital Equipment Corporation, Intel Corporation and the Xerox Corporation and based upon prototype work at Xerox. It is included here as an example of the objectives sought in such networks, but other products have followed different principles.

Ethernet is intended to provide for communication between up to 1,024 STATIONS, at the DATA RATE of 10 million BITS per second, over distances around 2.5 kilometers. It is one of the implementations of the IEEE 802.3 standard.

The TRANSMISSION PATH is provided by a COAXIAL CABLE LOOP to which all USER terminals are INTERFACED. Ethernet transmitted over a TWISTED WIRE PAIR is a recent development.

Its specification includes the definition of the two lowest levels of an overall NETWORK ARCHITECTURE up to what is known as the LINK LEVEL facility. Thus, higher level facilities are to be provided by structures built into the user devices (COMPUTERS and TERMINALS). Local area networks of this type exhibit very low ERROR RATES, and their main objective is to carry BURSTY TRAFFIC at HIGH PEAK DATA RATES between a group of users wishing to share facilities in an economical way.

The users all share the same transmission path, and communication is achieved by loading information with appropriate ADDRESS codes for the user destination on to the CABLE LOOP, with special features designed to prevent COLLISION of data and to ensure that over a given time all users have equal access to the NETWORK. Compare with TOKEN RING. See also CSMA/CD.

ETX See END OF TEXT.

Euronet This is a Europeanwide PACKET SWITCHING service that has been developed by the European Economic Community (EEC) with the cooperation of the PTTs of member countries. It is based upon an implementation of X.25 and includes 5 PACKET SWITCHING EXCHANGES (PSE) located in Frankfurt, London, Paris, Rome and Zurich. There are also 5 REMOTE ACCESS POINTS (RAP) located in Amsterdam, Copenhagen, Brussels, Luxembourg and Dublin, and a NETWORK MANAGEMENT CENTER (NMC) in London.

The system is designed to meet the growing need for public DATA COMMUNICATIONS services in Europe and for Europeanwide INFORMATION RETRIEVAL services.

even parity A condition that is said to exist when all the BITS in a particular row or column of a BLOCK of digital DATA add up to an even number. PARITY CHECKS are made as part of standard ERROR CHECKING procedures and, where even parity checking is used, the occurrence of ODD PARITY signifies an error in a block of received data.

exchange 1. The geographical area, regardless of political boundaries, that is billed by a TELEPHONE company according to a single charge rate, which has been approved by a government regulatory body. Often synonymous with OFFICE. For the five categories of offices, see OFFICE CLASS.

2. The place where TELECOMMUNICATIONS lines terminate and may be interconnected via manual or automatic SWITCHING EQUIPMENT. See also ELECTRONIC SWITCHING SYSTEM.

exchange hierarchy A NETWORK arrangement including the interlinking of TRUNK EXCHANGES by TRANSMISSION PATHS to provide a SUBSCRIBER SWITCHING service. In any communication system involving a large number of USERS, it would be impractical to have a separate pair of wires to connect each TERMINAL to every other in the system. If one were to attempt to construct a system in this way, it would be necessary to provide $(N(N-1) \div 2)$ separate line pairs, where $N =$ the number of terminals.

In modern communication systems, it is usual to establish a number of central switching points (EXCHANGES or NODES) that have high capacity TRANSMISSION LINKS (known as TRUNKS) between them. These TRUNK CIRCUITS are normally MULTIPLEXED so that a particular circuit can handle several hundred MESSAGES at any one time, i.e., these links are shared by many concurrent CALLS.

The terminals in the system are all wired into a particular exchange by LOCAL LINES. Each terminal thus has a specific TRANSMISSION PATH to its own LOCAL EXCHANGE. In the TELEPHONE SYSTEM, a SUBSCRIBER is usually directly connected to the local exchange by lifting the HANDSET from the terminal. Dialing a number generates CODES that are interpreted by the local exchange. If the subscriber being called is on the same local exchange, the dialing signal is switched automatically to call the appropriate terminal. If the subscriber called is not on the local exchange, the local lines from the CALLING TERMINAL are automatically switched to a trunk exchange.

Trunk exchanges carry out the necessary switching to route messages that must pass through the TRUNK NETWORK. It is not usual to have a direct connection between every trunk exchange. To fully interlink N trunk exchanges in a network to every other would require $(N(N-1) \div 2)$ trunks. In practice, an exchange hierarchy usually exists, which provides a more economical use of trunks.

There are many possible routes for a particular call, and the combination of trunks and exchanges to make a call is known as its ROUTING.

The routing that uses the least number of TRUNK ROUTES is known as the BASIC ROUTING for a call; other routings are known as ALTERNATIVE ROUTINGS.

expandor Equipment that accepts CALLS on the internal links of a CIRCUIT SWITCHING EXCHANGE and passes them to the appropriate lines. See also CONCENTRATOR and DISTRIBUTOR.

extended control set A set of CONTROL codes (e.g., CURSOR CONTROL) that provide for TRANSMISSION CONTROL and display functions over and above the CODES contained in the basic set of a DATA COMMUNICATION CODE.

extended superframe format (ESF) A diagnostic technique that enables USERS and CARRIERS to obtain performance information about T1 lines. ESF extends the FRAMING pattern in a T1 BIT STREAM from 12 DS-1 frames to 24.

extension circuit Any CIRCUIT that is used to provide a permanent connection to connect a TERMINAL, or NODE, to some other facility or location, e.g., to give access to a particular NETWORK.

extension codes A range of CHARACTERS that can be available as an extension of a basic CHARACTER SET in a DATA COMMUNICATION CODE. Here the basic set represents the minimum requirement for compliance with a particular code standard.

F

facility request Part of a SIGNAL to be sent over a PUBLIC DATA NETWORK and used to select the NETWORK FACILITIES required. See also SELECTION SIGNALS.

facsimile A branch of TELEGRAPHY concerned with the reproduction of images over a TELECOMMUNICATIONS system. The reproduction is in a permanent form (e.g., recorded on paper) and may include photographs, monochrome images, color or intermediate shades. The term DOCUMENT FACSIMILE is sometimes used to imply the reproduction of documents without the ability to recreate photographic images, and the term PHOTOGRAPHIC FACSIMILE is applied in the latter case. The CCITT standardizes four categories for facsimile equipment.

facsimile apparatus A device used to transmit documents by FACSIMILE methods and which may or may not use special techniques to compress the BANDWIDTH of the SIGNAL to achieve a particular transmission time. Such devices are rated according to the transmission time into groups. The transmission time is based upon a standard ISO A4-size document using the public telephone network as a TRANSMISSION MEDIUM:

Group 1 apparatus	3 to 6 minutes
Group 2 apparatus	3 minutes
Group 3 apparatus	1 minute

Such devices use DOUBLE SIDEBAND MODULATION and, in the case of Group 3, include means for reducing redundant information in the SIGNAL prior to MODULATION. Standardized in 1984, Group 4 specifies transmission over public digital networks at up to 64 kbps with resolutions of 200 to 400 picture elements that contain black and/or white, but no gray-scale, values.

facsimile baseband The name given to ELECTRICAL SIGNALS generated directly as an output from the scanning process in a FACSIMILE system. These signals constitute the primary MESSAGE SIGNAL that is usually MODULATED onto a CARRIER WAVE for transmission.

facsimile telegraphy A system of TELEGRAPHY that permits the reproduction of images in permanent form over a communications NETWORK. Each image is captured by a scanning process that generates ELECTRICAL SIGNALS to represent the image. These signals are transmitted to allow reproduction (e.g., as a photograph or printed page) at a distant STATION.

facsimile transceiver A device used to transmit or receive SIGNALS using the techniques of FACSIMILE TRANSMISSION.

facsimile transmission More strictly known as FACSIMILE TELEGRAPHY, a method for transmitting and receiving GRAPHICS images to reproduce an image at a distance. The process entails scanning a picture or image to create ELECTRICAL SIGNALS that can be transmitted over a NETWORK. These signals are often known as the FACSIMILE BASEBAND and, in many systems, MODULATION techniques are used to transmit the signals onto a CARRIER WAVE to a distant STATION. At the distant station, a FACSIMILE TRANSCEIVER demodulates the incoming SIGNAL, and the derived signal is used to modulate the intensity of a light source in order to reproduce the black and white shades of the original image. The technique has also been adapted to the reproduction of photographic images containing continuous tonal densities that are faithfully reproduced. This is known as PHOTOGRAPH FACSIMILE TELEGRAPHY.

The transmission of images other than photographs, entailing a lesser degree of accuracy in the reproduction of the density scale, is known as DOCUMENT FACSIMILE TELEGRAPHY.

fast circuit switching A method of providing DATA TRANSMISSION facilities in which a USER dials a connection to another, using a DATA CIRCUIT provided by a COMMON CARRIER for the duration of the CALL. The availability of such circuits (providing CALL SET-UP TIMES in fractions of a second and BILLING increments in fractions of a second) provides attractive economic solutions to intermittent communication requirements where a LEASED CIRCUIT would be too costly. See also PUBLIC DATA NETWORKS.

fast packet switching A version of PACKET SWITCHING that exploits the characteristics of, and hinges on the presence of, high-speed digital transmission lines for WIDE AREA NETWORKS. The processing speed of fast packet switching results in part from the reduction of processing on a link-by-link basis within the SWITCH FABRIC. The CCITT's I.121 recommendation outlines an emerging standard for fast packet switching. Compare with ASYNCHRONOUS TRANSFER MODE and CELL RELAY. See also FRAME RELAY.

fault Any condition in equipment or SOFTWARE that causes a system to operate below the level of service specified for USERS.

fault detection See FAULT DIAGNOSIS.

fault diagnosis The practice and procedures involved in determining the particular conditions causing errors or interruptions to a communications service. Usually the responsibility of an engineer or NETWORK MANAGER but often aided by complex test equipment that is able automatically to detect component failures.

fault rate An expression used in assessing the reliability of a system, or system component, and referring to the average number of faults occurring in a given period of time. See also MEAN DOWN TIME.

fault report point The location or organizational entity to which faults in a system are to be notified. Sometimes highly automated procedures using special CIRCUITS are provided.

fault tolerance In DATA COMMUNICATIONS, fault tolerance is a NETWORK'S capability of protecting itself from faulty INTERFACES. It requires, for example, REDUNDANCY and ALTERNATE PATH ROUTING.

fax A nickname for FACSIMILE.

FCC See FEDERAL COMMUNICATIONS COMMISSION.

FCS See FRAME CHECK SEQUENCE.

FDDI See FIBER DISTRIBUTED DATA INTERFACE.

FDM See FREQUENCY DIVISION MULTIPLEXING.

Federal Communications Commission (FCC) The U.S. regulatory body responsible for governing interstate communications and COMMON CARRIER services.

FEP See FRONT END PROCESSOR.

FF See FORM FEED.

fiber See FIBER OPTIC CABLE, OPTICAL FIBERS.

fiber distributed data interface (FDDI) A 100-Mbps access method defined by ANSI for sharing FIBER OPTIC CABLE on a LAN, FDDI specifies TOKEN PASSING technology and two counter-rotating RINGS, where DATA travels over one while the other acts as a backup. Stations can be attached to both rings (dual-attached) or to a CONCENTRATOR (single-attached) that is itself attached to both rings. Research on running FDDI over TWISTED WIRE PAIRS is in progress.

fiber optic cable A type of TRANSMISSION medium that is replacing COAXIAL CABLE in many regions, fiber optic cable is made of thin filaments of glass or plastic through which a light beam is transmitted. The use of multiple internal reflections helps extend the transmission distance. See also OPTICAL FIBERS.

field A unit of DATA in a RECORD or MESSAGE and designated for a particular purpose. For example, an ADDRESS FIELD containing ROUTING information or a data field used in a particular application such as job number, staff number, quantity in stock, name and address field.

field flyback An interval during the scanning operation of a television picture in which the ELECTRON BEAM is blocked off and the RASTER is repositioned to begin a new scanning operation. See also VIDEO SIGNAL.

field frequency The frequency with which a complete sequence of scanning operations takes place in the creation of a television picture. Measured in cycles per second or HERTZ (Hz): typical frequencies are USA 60 Hz and CCIR-625 lines systems 50 Hz. See also INTERLACED SCANNING and VIDEO SIGNAL.

field scan The vertical movement of the RASTER during the scanning operation to create a television picture. See also VIDEO SIGNAL.

15-supergroup An assembly of equipment carrying fifteen separate SUPERGROUPS in a FREQUENCY DIVISION MULTIPLEXING system and providing a means of transmission for up to 900 separate SPEECH CHANNELS along a single COAXIAL TUBE. Also known as a HYPERGROUP.

50 percent duty cycle In TIME DIVISION MULTIPLEXING systems, DIGITAL SIGNALS are transmitted as waveforms that, due to line conditions, become more rounded than the square pulses originated by the digital source signal to represent 0's and 1's. Sometimes it is arranged that pulses delivered to the LINE occupy only half the duration of the TIME SLOT allocated to the DIGITAL PULSE. This creates a sharply defined waveform, which assists in the identification of pulses.

figures shift A special CHARACTER in a TELEGRAPH CODE or DATA COMMUNICATION CODE that has the function of designating all subsequent codes in a transmission sequence as being numbers (0 to 9) or characters from a secondary group of codes. The figures shift remains in force until a LETTERS SHIFT occurs.

file An accumulation of RECORDS in a DIGITAL COMPUTER or on any device capable of storing digital information. The file will be structured to permit individual records or groups of related records to be selected and processed. Records may be selected or sequenced according to the content of FIELDS within the records.

file separator (FS) A special CODE under the general classification known as INFORMATION SEPARATORS and used in a DATA COMMUNICATIONS CODE to denote the boundary of a specific FILE of BINARY CODED INFORMATION.

file server See SERVER.

filter A device used to control the frequencies that can pass along a CIRCUIT, enabling selected frequencies to pass without significant ATTENUATION but blocking frequencies that are not desired. See also LOW PASS FILTER, BAND PASS FILTER and HIGH PASS FILTER.

first exchange Refers to the EXCHANGE closest to a CALLING PARTY or to the first exchange in any connection that utilizes a specific SIGNALING system, e.g., the first NO. 6 EXCHANGE. See also LAST EXCHANGE and INTERMEDIATE EXCHANGE.

first-party clearing A method of CALL CLEARING in which the CALL is cleared when either party places the HANDSET on the SWITCH HOOK. Contrast with CALLING PARTY CLEAR.

5-bit code A DATA COMMUNICATIONS CODE in which each CHARACTER is represented by a combination of five signal elements, thus allowing 2^5 (or 32) characters, each formed of unique code combinations, to be used.

fixed path protocol (FPP) A method used to transmit information over a PACKET SWITCHING NETWORK in which a VIRTUAL CIRCUIT is established such that all PACKETS relating to a CALL use that identical path. The path is released when either party hangs up. Contrast with PATH INDEPENDENT PROTOCOL.

fixed reference phase modulation A method of PHASE MODULATION in which the BINARY DIGITS 0 and 1 are indicated by a UNIT SIGNAL ELEMENT beginning with a PHASE INVERSION in a specific direction. With this method, a REFERENCE WAVE is required in the DEMODULATOR to provide DETECTION of the PHASE of the DATA SIGNAL.

fixed virtual circuit Same as PERMANENT VIRTUAL CIRCUIT.

flicker effect An effect perceived when a person looks at a television picture (or some form of visual display) in which the interval between successive pictures being presented is too long, relative to the rapid decay of LUMINANCE generated by the ELECTRON BEAM on the tube surface. The frequency below which this effect becomes apparent varies with individual people, but a FIELD FREQUENCY of 60 per second is used in North America and 50 per second is common in Europe. See also INTERLACED SCANNING.

floppy disk A medium for storing digital information which is recorded as magnetized FIELDS. A floppy disk is so called because the material from which it is made is not rigid. Such disks are readily handled by operators and are in common use for small office COMPUTERS and WORD PROCESSORS.

floppy disk drive A mechanism for handling FLOPPY DISKS during the operation of a system consisting of a drive mechanism to revolve the disk and magnetic read/write heads that record or retrieve information.

flow control The process that takes place in a DATA NETWORK to regulate the transfer of DATA between any two points. Since different DATA TERMINALS (DTE) and NODES in a network may operate at different speeds, CONTROL has to be exercised to store FRAMES OR PACKETS at various points to prevent BUFFERS at other points becoming overloaded.

flow control information In any PACKET SWITCHING or MESSAGE SWITCHING system, the rate of packet flow has to be regulated so that BUFFERS at RECEIVING STATIONS or intermediate NODES do not overflow. To avoid overloading parts of the system, queues may be formed at intermediate buffers, and alternative ACCESS PATHS may be chosen to avoid bottlenecks. To achieve CONTROL, flow control information has to be fed back along the system to advise the TRANSMITTING STATIONS of the current capacity and status of RECEIVING STATIONS.

fluorescence Light radiation produced from certain materials, e.g., the light energy produced when an ELECTRON BEAM strikes phosphor materials coated on the surface of a TV tube. See also PHOSPHORESCENCE.

flyback An event during the scanning operation that takes place to create a television picture and relating to the movement of the SCANNING BEAM back to a point at which the next scanning movement can commence. There are two kinds of flyback, LINE FLYBACK and FIELD FLYBACK. See also VIDEO SIGNAL.

flyback periods The intervals of time during which the SCANNING BEAM is blocked out to enable it to be repositioned to begin the next LINE or FIELD SCANNING operation in a television system. See also VIDEO SIGNAL.

FM See FREQUENCY MODULATION.

FM broadcast A radio broadcast using the techniques of FREQUENCY MODULATION.

footprint In SATELLITE communications, the footprint refers to the area of the earth's surface that the satellite TRANSMISSION reaches. Also refers to the amount of floor space or desktop space required to accommodate COMPUTER equipment.

form feed (FF) A function represented as a special FORMAT EFFECTOR in a DATA COMMUNICATION CODE and serving as an instruction to move a PRINT MECHANISM or the CURSOR of a VISUAL DISPLAY UNIT ready to print or display a new form.

format effectors Special symbols forming part of a DATA COMMUNICATIONS CODE and used to control ancillary devices such as printers connected to a communications line. Examples include:

BS BACK SPACE
CR CARRIAGE RETURN
FF FORM FEED
HT HORIZONTAL TABULATION
LF LINE FEED
VT VERTICAL TABULATION

forward channel A CHANNEL in a DATA NETWORK in which the direction of transmission is from a TRANSMITTING TERMINAL to a RECEIVING TERMINAL. This is to be contrasted with a BACKWARD CHANNEL in which supervisory information and CONTROL signals will flow in the opposite direction to the USER information on the forward channel. It should be noted that DATA COMMUNICATIONS systems can transfer user information in both directions, and the terms "forward" and "backward" channel are related to the DATA SOURCE at any instant.

forward direction A term used in TELEPHONY and in DATA COMMUNICATIONS to denote the direction of information flow as distinct from the BACKWARD DIRECTION in which supervisory and ERROR CONTROL information may flow. It is important to note that information may flow in either direction, and so this term is used relative to the information flow at any instant.

forward error correction A method of ERROR DETECTION and CORRECTION based upon REDUNDANCY CHECKING techniques in which a high volume of redundant BITS is computed and added to transmitted DATA. The redundancy is such that the RECEIVING TERMINAL is able to automatically correct and not simply to detect errors.

Fourier components Fourier was an early researcher into complex waveforms, and he determined that each such waveform is composed of fundamental frequencies and harmonics that are exact multiples of their fundamental frequency.

In dealing with the design of physical devices to handle such waveforms, engineers are able to perform an analysis to identify these so-called Fourier components and deal with them separately on the basis of simple sine wave theory. Fourier analysis is a technique widely used in communications involving ELECTRICAL SIGNALS.

40-column display standard Pertaining to a TERMINAL and the associated transmission system that will allow up to 40 columns of CHARACTERS on a single PAGE of information. Examples include VIDEOTEX and TELETEXT systems.

four-wire channel A TRANSMISSION PATH in which two pairs of wires are used, one pair for each direction of transmission. Strictly speaking, a CHANNEL provides a one-way path and the term FOUR-WIRE CIRCUIT is more correct.

four-wire circuit A TRANSMISSION PATH between two TERMINALS in which there are two separate CHANNELS. For example, in DATA COMMUNICATIONS, one channel may be used to transmit information and the other may be a return channel used for supervisory or ERROR CONTROL data. Four-wire circuits are also used to provide for MULTIPLEXING or AMPLIFICATION of SIGNALS on SPEECH CHANNELS.

four-wire link This form of LINK refers to a TRANSMISSION SYSTEM that uses separate pairs of wires for each direction of transmission. A four-wire link is usually created to allow AMPLIFICATION in an ANALOG circuit or to permit MULTIPLEXING of several CHANNELS onto a single physical channel.

FPP See FIXED PATH PROTOCOL

frame 1. Generally used in DATA TRANSMISSION to denote a unit of information used in transmission and upon which various automatic ERROR CHECKING operations are performed to ensure correct and error-free transmission. In ASYNCHRONOUS DATA TRANSMISSION, a frame is a sequence of contiguous BITS that has a start bit at the beginning and a stop bit at the end. In TIME DIVISION MULTIPLEXING, a frame is a complete cycle of events including TIME SLOTS that represent subchannels of the multiplexed system.

2. A frame in a VIDEOTEX or TELETEXT system is equivalent to one screen display of information, and there may be 26 such frames to a designated PAGE.

3. In television broadcasting, a frame is a unit of transmission equivalent to a screen, e.g., in the United Kingdom, 625 lines make up one picture or frame; in the United States, 525.

4. In a TIME DIVISION MULTIPLEXED system, a set of TIME SLOTS in which the DIGIT POSITION of each time slot is defined in relation to a FRAME ALIGNMENT SIGNAL.

frame alignment A process in which the timing of a RECEIVING TERMINAL is correctly adjusted to the alignment of FRAMES in a received SIGNAL.

frame alignment signal A part of a MESSAGE SIGNAL that serves to identify the boundary of a FRAME and assists to create SYNCHRONIZATION between a RECEIVING TERMINAL and an incoming SIGNAL.

frame check sequence A sequence of BITS attached to a FRAME to provide for the DETECTION and correction of errors in a DATA LINK. See also CYCLIC REDUNDANCY CHECK.

frame format A definition of the structure of an indivisible unit of information transmitted in a DATA COMMUNICATIONS system, including DESTINATION ADDRESS, SOURCE ADDRESS, frame type, the DATA and FRAME CHECK SEQUENCE. The structure of the FRAME is an important part of the specification for a DATA LINK.

frame grabber An element in a RECEIVING STATION that inspects ADDRESS INFORMATION in FRAMES passing along a CHANNEL to detect whether the frame should be received by the particular STATION. This technique is sometimes used in CABLE LOOPS used for LOCAL AREA NETWORKS where all TRANSMITTING STATIONS and receiving stations may be connected to the same channel and where all frames transmitted include DESTINATION ADDRESSES. It is also used in TELETEXT systems to grab specific frames transmitted as part of a general BROADCAST.

frame level functions Processes performed in a PACKET SWITCHING SYSTEM to check the transmission of DATA to ensure that LINE errors have not occurred, and to retransmit FRAMES automatically when errors are detected. It is the main purpose of the HIGH LEVEL DATA LINK CONTROL (HDLC) to be responsible for these functions.

frame level protocols In DATA COMMUNICATIONS, using HIGH LEVEL CONTROL FUNCTIONS, CONTROL is exercised by procedures and rules that enable small units of information known as FRAMES to be transmitted and received securely with automatic ERROR CHECKING. The control procedures exist at various levels and those concerned with the identification sequencing, ROUTING and checking of frames are referred to as frame level protocols. See also PACKET SWITCHING NETWORK and X .25.

frame relay One implementation of FAST PACKET SWITCHING, frame relay uses a unit of DATA called a FRAME, which has a variable length. At the periphery of the SWITCHED NETWORK, data coming from, for example, BRIDGES and ROUTERS communicates with the network via a frame relay interface defined by ANSI and the CCITT. Within the SWITCH FABRIC, the functions performed by frame relay on a node-by-node basis are minimal: 7 basic tasks versus 20 with the X.25 PROTOCOL. Hence, frame relay is faster. The emerging CCITT I.122 Frame Relay recommendation, at this time, does not include voice or video services. See also CELL RELAY, ASYNCHRONOUS TRANSFER MODE.

frame store A MEMORY UNIT capable of storing a display of information for a PAGE (or FRAME) of TEXT and GRAPHICS. For example, the memory unit in a VIDEOTEX TERMINAL. Also known as PAGE STORE.

frame (videotex system) In VIDEOTEX SYSTEMS, as exemplified by the British system known as PRESTEL, the DATABASE consists of individually numbered PAGES, each page being the equivalent of one screen display of 960 CHARACTERS. Each page can include up to 26 continuation pages (identified by letters a to z); each of which is termed a FRAME.

framing bits Extra BINARY DIGITS attached specifically to TIME DIVISION MULTIPLEXED signals to provide CONTROL INFORMATION for the correct transmission and separation of individual FRAMES. The framing bits identify both individual TERMINALS concerned with particular MESSAGES and the start of MESSAGE CHARACTERS. See also TIME DIVISION MULTIPLEXING.

frequency band A range of frequencies that can be propagated through a particular CIRCUIT or a range assigned for any designated purpose. For example, RADIO FREQUENCY SIGNALS exhibit different characteristics according to the point in the FREQUENCY SPECTRUM at which they occur. SIGNALS in the HIGH FREQUENCY band (HF) from 3 MHz to 30 MHz are able to be deflected off the

IONOSPHERE and can be bounced around the world. They are suitable for all kinds of long-distance radio communication.

ELECTROMAGNETIC WAVES higher than 30 MHz are not reflected and can only travel between points in direct line of contact. They are suitable for short-distance radio communication, e.g., television, RADAR, radio broadcast communication.

Within any particular frequency band there are further subdivisions or BANDS allocated for specific purposes. For example, in the United Kingdom, the various TELEVISION CHANNELS in the ULTRA HIGH FREQUENCY (UHF) spectrum occupy frequencies from 470 MHz to 940 MHz; in the United States, 470 MHz to 890 MHz. See also FREQUENCY SPECTRUM and BANDWIDTH.

frequency division multiplexing (FDM) In a MULTIPLEXING system, a single CHANNEL of suitable BANDWIDTH is used to carry a number of TRANSMISSION CHANNELS of narrower bandwidth. In frequency division multiplexing, a technique that is used for analog SPEECH CHANNELS, this is achieved by modulating each MESSAGE SIGNAL onto a separate CARRIER WAVE. Thus, the resulting signals are separated from one another by a frequency displacement that ensures that there is not mutual interference.

In a typical FDM system for transmission of telephone signals, each channel is created by means of SINGLE SIDEBAND MODULATION of separate carrier waves, and the resulting signals are combined. In the modulation process, the message signals are limited by means of FILTERS to a bandwidth of 3 kHz. The carriers are separated in steps of 4 kHz to provide an assembly of 12 channels known as a GROUP in the BAND from 60 to 108 kHz. The group, thus, has a bandwidth of 48 kHz.

A second stage of multiplexing allows five groups to be used to modulate carriers in steps of 48 kHz between 420 kHz and 612 kHz. The LOWER SIDEBANDS are selected to provide an assembly of 60 channels known as a SUPERGROUP in the band 312 to 552 kHz, i.e., a bandwidth of 240 kHz.

Further stages of multiplexing to combine supergroups may take place. For example, a combination of 900 channels created in this way is sometimes referred to as a HYPERGROUP. When the groups have been assembled into a single band, they are transmitted over the TRANSMISSION PATH (e.g., a COAXIAL TUBE) and then DEMULTIPLEXED by a reverse process.

The number of channels that can be carried over an FDM channel in this way depends upon the TRANSMISSION MEDIUM. The maximum FREQUENCY BAND of a MULTIPLEXED CHANNEL, using 2.6/2.9 mm coaxial tube with REPEATERS staged at 4-kilometer intervals, is in the region of 12 MHz. This would sustain approximately 2,700 TELEPHONE CHANNELS using the techniques mentioned above.

This form of multiplexing is known as frequency division multiplexing because each signal occupies a different frequency band when transmitted. For the transmission of DIGITAL SIGNALS, a different technique known as TIME DIVISION MULTIPLEXING (TDM) is used.

frequency error An error arising to affect the stability of the frequency of a SIGNAL or CARRIER WAVE in a MULTIPLEXING system. Usually this sort of error must be kept within a BAND of ±2 Hz. Also known as FREQUENCY OFFSET.

frequency modulation (FM) A method for carrying a MESSAGE SIGNAL imprinted upon another CARRIER SIGNAL that is at a selected frequency to suit the particular mode of transmission. The technique is used in RADIO TRANSMISSION, also in transmission of telephone signals over a TRANSMISSION PATH used to carry many simultaneous messages. See also MODULATION and FREQUENCY DIVISION MULTIPLEXING.

frequency offset An error condition affecting the stability of the frequency of a SIGNAL. For example, the CARRIER SIGNALS in a MULTIPLEXING system. Such frequency variations have usually to be contained to ±2 Hz. Also known as FREQUENCY ERROR.

frequency response The ability of a particular CIRCUIT or device to carry SIGNALS of different frequencies is known as its frequency response.

frequency shift keying (FSK) A method of FREQUENCY MODULATION used for the transmission of binary information, in which the frequency of a CARRIER SIGNAL is changed to represent the BINARY DIGITS 0 and 1. The occurrence of several contiguous cycles at a particular frequency equals 0, and the occurrence of a similar set of cycles at another frequency equals 1. Thus, the carrier will be seen to vary between two frequency levels without a change in the PHASE of the signal. See also UNIT SIGNAL ELEMENT and MODULATION. Compare also with PHASE MODULATION.

frequency shifting A technique used so that several thousand CALLS can be carried simultaneously on the same TRANSMISSION CHANNEL. This process is achieved by MULTIPLEXING, i.e., each MESSAGE SIGNAL is modulated onto a different CARRIER SIGNAL for transmission, and the frequency of each carrier signal is chosen such that each multiplexed signal occupies a different FREQUENCY BAND from all the others. See also MODULATION and FREQUENCY DIVISION MULTIPLEXING.

frequency spectrum ELECTROMAGNETIC WAVES and LIGHTWAVES can be grouped into BANDS that provide convenient classifications for the purpose of considering their characteristics for propagation and use as communication vehicles. Some examples are listed below:

VOICE FREQUENCY—the band of frequencies used to carry a human voice ANALOG SIGNAL in a telephone NETWORK. From 300 to 3,300 cycles per second (300 to 3,300 HERTZ).

AUDIO FREQUENCY—the band of frequencies used to carry an analog signal equivalent to the range of sounds perceived by human ear. From 20 cycles per second to 20,000 cycles per second (20 kilocycles, written as 20 kHz).

The RADIO FREQUENCY spectrum includes a great range of frequencies, among which the more useful are in the range from 20,000 to 20,000,000,000 cycles per second. All forms of electromagnetic and light waves travel through space at the same speed of 300,000,000 meters per second. In radio broadcasting and communications, it is useful to consider the following frequency bands:

LOW FREQUENCY (LF)—a range of signals from 30 kHz to 300 kHz. They are suitable for long-distance radio communication and are often used for military or transoceanic services. At the lower frequencies, a large ANTENNA is needed to propagate and receive signals.

HIGH FREQUENCY (HF)—a range of signals from 3 million cycles per second to 30 million cycles per second, 3 to 30 megahertz (MHz). Used for long-distance communication, but the quality is dependent upon ionization in the upper atmosphere.

VERY HIGH FREQUENCY (VHF)—a range of signals from 30 MHz to 300 MHz. Used for short-distance radio communication.

ULTRA HIGH FREQUENCY (UHF)—a range of signals from 300 MHz to 3,000 MHz. Often used for television broadcasts, and covering FREQUENCY BANDS from 470 MHz to 940 MHz.

SUPER HIGH FREQUENCY (SHF)—a range of signals from 3,000 MHz to 30,000 MHz, otherwise expressed as from 3 gigahertz to 30 gigahertz (GHz). See also FREQUENCY BAND and BANDWIDTH.

front-end processor A computer subsystem used mainly to INTERFACE a main COMPUTER or HOST PROCESSOR to a communication NETWORK. It takes responsibility for the COMMUNICATION CONTROL activity rather than the APPLICATION PROGRAMS, which are run in the host system. See also COMMUNICATIONS CONTROLLER.

FS See FILE SEPARATOR.

FSK See FREQUENCY SHIFT KEYING.

full availability transposition Full availability transposition is said to exist when the pattern of interconnection is such that every switching group in one stage has a connection to every group in the previous stage. It is an objective in designing EXCHANGES to minimize the number of CROSSPOINTS while at the same time reducing the probability of CALL BLOCKING. A method to achieve this optimization consists of arranging the crosspoints in stages in which a number of matrixes known as switching groups occur.

full duplex A TRANSMISSION CHANNEL in which simultaneous two-way transmission is available. See also HALF DUPLEX and SIMPLEX.

full duplex error control A system of ERROR CORRECTION used in DATA TRANSMISSION over LINKS that have a long transmission delay time, such that a TRANSMITTING TERMINAL transmits a whole series of BLOCKS without waiting for the RECEIVING STATION to acknowledge correct acceptance of each block separately. If an error is detected, individual ERROR BLOCKS are retransmitted or all blocks commencing with an error block are retransmitted. These techniques require blocks to be numbered, and the latter method is also referred to as GO BACK TO N technique.

full echo suppressor An ECHO SUPPRESSOR in which the SPEECH SIGNALS on each path are used to control the suppression loss in the other path of a FOUR-WIRE CIRCUIT used for long-distance communication. Contrast with HALF ECHO SUPPRESSOR.

fully provided route A TRANSMISSION PATH designed to handle all the OFFERED TRAFFIC without relying on any ALTERNATIVE ROUTE in times of PEAK LOAD. See also HIGH-USAGE ROUTE.

functional compatibility Most modern communication systems are of modular design, i.e., it is possible to extend the capacity of the system by adding additional equipment components. Additional equipment must be capable of supporting all the logical functions of the existing system and must also exhibit INTERFACE COMPATIBILITY (e.g., electrical and physical compatibility).

functional specification A document describing the attributes of equipment and/or SOFTWARE systems. The emphasis is on what the equipment does rather than how it does it and should explain how the inputs and outputs are related.

functional test A test to determine whether a device or a CIRCUIT will operate correctly under working conditions to fulfill the specification for the quality of service defined for a system.

G

gain The term used to describe the increase in the power of a MESSAGE SIGNAL during the process of AMPLIFICATION. Compare with the LOSS of power in a message signal passing through a cable.

AMPLIFIERS are introduced into communication CIRCUITS to overcome cable losses and to deliver message signals to the message destination at an appropriate MINIMUM SIGNAL LEVEL.

gaussion noise A form of interference that manifests itself as a hiss on telephone or radio CHANNELS and is caused by the natural movement of electrons in CIRCUITS, which varies with temperature. Also known as WHITE NOISE and RANDOM NOISE.

generating polynomial A mathematical expression used in the creation and checking of CYCLIC CODES used for ERROR CHECKING in DATA NETWORKS. The method relies upon any element of DATA being regarded as a pure BINARY NUMBER. The generating polynomial is used as a means of calculating a remainder that is attached to each BINARY STRING prior to transmission. The same formula is used at the RECEIVING STATION to derive the remainder once more, and a check against the transmitted remainder is performed.

geosynchronous orbit When the path of a COMMUNICATIONS SATELLITE meets certain conditions, it is said to be in geosynchronous orbit. This is 22,300 miles above Earth, at which height the satellite takes exactly 24 hours to travel around the planet—the same time as Earth's rotation cycle. A satellite in geosynchronous orbit over the equator traveling in the same direction as Earth appears to hang stationary over one point on Earth.

gigabit One billion (ten to the ninth power) BITS.

go back to N A TRANSMISSION CONTROL signal that acts as an instruction to repeat a transmission from a specific BLOCK OF DATA.

go path A TRANSMISSION PATH from a TERMINAL or NODE used for outgoing SIGNALS and MESSAGES. Compare with RETURN PATH, which relates to a CHANNEL used to transmit supervisory or ERROR CONTROL information.

G1 code set A set of GRAPHICS CHARACTERS forming part of a standard for display of ALPHAMOSAIC GRAPHICS in a VIDEOTEX system.

GOSIP Government Open Systems Interconnection Profile, an emerging standard for DATA NETWORKS.

grade of service A measure of user service expressed as a probability. For example, on lifting a telephone receiver, the probability that the DIAL TONE will not be received or the probability that a BUSY TONE may be received due to system congestion. See also PROBABILITY OF CALL BLOCKING and PROBABILITY OF EXCESSIVE DELAY.

graphic character In some forms of graphics presentation, illustrations to be displayed upon screens are realized by combining individual CHARACTERS to form an overall picture. These characters are themselves composed of a number of individual dots (PIXELS), which, when resolved together on the screen, form the shape of the character. An example is provided in the ALPHAMOSAIC GRAPHICS used in certain VIDEOTEX systems.

graphical processing Some forms of communication allow drawings to be conveyed over CIRCUITS. This function is important in training, management and operational applications. A variety of devices are used, but essentially it must be possible to scan a drawing displayed on a pad or display screen and to create DIGITAL SIGNALS representing the features of the illustration. These signals are transmitted and retained in a store which is a map of the display screen at the RECEIVING TERMINAL. The store at the receiver can be used to refresh the screen so that stored pictures can be displayed for as long as required.

graphics Any DATA presented to end USERS as an illustration rather than as pure TEXT may be referred to as graphics. Certain COMPUTER applications are of value only if data in the form of illustrations, charts or graphs can be presented, along with text, to end users.

graphics display standards Pertaining to the way in which GRAPHICS INFORMATION is stored and transmitted in a system to be displayed on a screen. The possible fineness of the illustrations is governed by the techniques adopted within the display terminal. Some standards do not allow for fine illustrations and are known as LOW RESOLUTION display standards; others do allow for fine illustrations and are known as HIGH RESOLUTION display standards. See also VIDEOTEX STANDARDS.

graphics information Digitally encoded information that represents a description of a drawing. In many GRAPHICAL PROCESSING applications, the information actually transmitted is highly condensed to provide for rapid transmission of a detailed picture. For example, straight lines and corners are represented by reference coordinates and the interpretation and plotting of the desired pictures is achieved by programs in the RECEIVING TERMINAL.

ground waves Radio broadcast signals used in short-range HIGH FREQUENCY communication, consisting of SURFACE WAVES plus waves reflected from the ground.

group In relation to FREQUENCY DIVISION MULTIPLEXING, an assembly of equipment providing a means of transmission for 12 separate VOICE CHANNELS along a single TRANSMISSION PATH with 48 kHz BANDWIDTH.

group delay/frequency response An effect experienced when transmitting DATA SIGNALS over TELEPHONE CHANNELS. This term is used to describe the difference in the delay of different frequencies due to circuit conditions that affect the propagation time of different frequencies. The delay factor is dependent upon the signal frequency and the length of the CIRCUIT. This phenomenon is not generally noticeable to a USER in SPEECH COMMUNICATION but may be significant in DATA COMMUNICATIONS. The problem can be overcome by the use of DELAY EQUALIZERS, which effectively slow down the advanced signals.

group link The complete means of transmission for a group of 12 SPEECH CHANNELS using a BANDWIDTH of 48 kHz over a NETWORK. See also GROUPING.

group 1/2/3/4 facsimile apparatus See FACSIMILE APPARATUS.

group separator (GS) A special CODE under the general classification known as INFORMATION SEPARATORS and used in a DATA COMMUNICATIONS CODE to denote the boundary of groups of RECORDS in binary coded form.

grouping This term is used to define the way in which a number of separate MESSAGE SIGNALS can be combined for transmission over a single COAXIAL TUBE using techniques of FREQUENCY DIVISION MULTIPLEXING. Each message signal is used to modulate a different CARRIER WAVE using SINGLE SIDEBAND MODULATION and the derived signals are combined into groups. Usually groups of 12 CHANNELS are chosen, each occupying 4 kHz within the BAND from 64 kHz to 108 kHz.

Further stages of multiplexing may be used to combine groups in 48 kHz steps within the band from 420 kHz to 612 kHz, resulting in a 60 channel group known as a SUPERGROUP. Further extensions of the grouping principle allow 16 supergroups to be combined to form a HYPERGROUP of 960 channels.

GS See GROUP SEPARATOR.

G2 code set A set of CHARACTERS and their means of representation in a VIDEOTEX system and covering a range of special symbols and diacritical marks used in different languages.

guard band An unused portion of a FREQUENCY BAND used to separate different CHANNELS in the BANDWIDTH to prevent mutual interference between adjacent channels.

gun See ELECTRON GUN.

H

half duplex 1. Sometimes used to indicate a TRANSMISSION CHANNEL in which two-way transmission is available but only one way at a time. See SIMPLEX 2.

2. The CCITT definition describes a half duplex CIRCUIT as allowing a two-way transmission but the TERMINALS connected can only receive or transmit at any one time. See also FULL DUPLEX.

half duplex error protocol A system in DATA TRANSMISSION in which the TRANSMITTING TERMINAL waits for a response from the RECEIVING TERMINAL after a BLOCK has been transmitted. This is done so that the transmitting terminal may know whether to retransmit the block because of an error or to send the next block. Compare with FULL DUPLEX ERROR PROTOCOL.

half echo suppressor An ECHO SUPPRESSOR in which the SPEECH SIGNALS on one path only are used to control the suppression loss in the other. Contrast with FULL ECHO SUPPRESSOR.

Hamming distance The number of DIGIT POSITIONS that differ between two WORDS of the same length and radix. For example, in 3789124 and 2719124, the Hamming distance is 2.

handset That part of a telephone TERMINAL which the USER lifts to speak and hear through when making a CALL.

handshake A procedure followed to interconnect two DATA TERMINALS to initiate a CALL prior to an exchange of information known as a CONVERSATION. The handshaking procedure effectively establishes the TRANSMISSION path for the CALL and is also known as CALL ESTABLISHMENT.

hang-up signal A SIGNAL sent to an EXCHANGE to indicate that a CALLED PARTY has cleared by replacing his HANDSET to terminate a CALL. The exchange must then clear the call and stop the charging process.

hard copy Describes any form of ouput from a system in which MESSAGES or commands are displayed in some more or less permanent form (e.g., printed on paper), rather than in a transient form (e.g., displayed on a screen of a VISUAL DISPLAY unit).

hard copy printer Any printing device that produces a printout of information from a COMPUTER or TERMINAL on paper, as distinct from a device that displays information on a screen as a transient record.

hard disk storage A data storage device used in COMPUTERS to retain files of information and in which DATA is recorded on tracks on both sides of a magnetized disk. The term "hard disk" is used to distinguish such devices from FLOPPY DISKS, which work on the same principle but are made of less rigid material.

hardware A term used to define the physical components of a machine, particularly COMPUTER equipment, and devices containing logic elements used in DATA PROCESSING or communications machines. To be contrasted with SOFTWARE, which defines logical functions implemented as coding in a program.

HDB3 (high-density bipolar three zeros) A coding scheme, HDB3 is used with the 2.048-Mbps version of the primary rate interface of ISDN to facilitate SYNCHRONIZATION between the sender and receiver communications devices. See also B8ZS.

HDLC SEE HIGH LEVEL DATA LINK CONTROL.

HDTV See HIGH-DEFINITION TELEVISION.

header Information attached to a MESSAGE or PACKET to provide for control of delivery to the appropriate RECEIVING STATION or for its management at the receiving station.

For example, in a PACKET SWITCHING network, a unit of application information is referred to as a REQUEST/RESPONSE UNIT; it would be common to attach the following headers to it:

RESPONSE HEADER—identifies the packet to the TRANSMISSION CONTROL and DATA LINK CONTROL (DLC) elements in the NETWORK;

TRANSMISSION HEADER—identifies the ROUTING of the packet for ACCESS PATH CONTROL purposes;

LINK HEADER AND TRAILER—contains information relevant to checking and controlling transmission to overcome line errors. See also DATA LINK CONTROL.

The precise titles and functions of headers may vary from one PROTOCOL to another, but the same principles apply.

header information Information attached to a MESSAGE (or to a unit of DATA forming part of a message) and intended to impart information for use by the COMMUNICATIONS CONTROL features in a communications system. For example, header information may be used to: identify DESTINATION ADDRESSES, select TRANSMISSION PATHS, determine PACKET SEQUENCE, provide ERROR CHECKING and manage the dialogue between communicating TERMINALS.

head-on collision An event that can arise in a two-way DATA NETWORK when two NODES secure the opposite end of a DATA CIRCUIT at the same instant.

hertz The definition of the frequency of a SIGNAL in cycles per second, e.g., a 50 kHz signal is an AC SIGNAL at 50,000 cycles per second.

The definition is named after Heinrich Hertz, a scientist who contributed to the discovery of the nature of ELECTROMAGNETIC WAVES.

hierarchic network A network in which some NODES exert more control than others, i.e., their CLOCKS are more dominant than others.

Hi-Fi See HIGH FIDELITY.

high definition television (HDTV) A television system in which a large number of lines are drawn to make a picture on a screen, e.g., more than the standard number of lines recommended by the ITU (525 lines in the United States; 625 lines in Great Britain). The amount of detail conveyed in a picture is increased by increasing the number of lines. However, increasing the number of lines also increases the requirements for SIGNAL BANDWIDTH. The amount of detail that can be perceived by humans is another factor to be considered.

The expression HIGH DEFINITION DISPLAY is used in relation to TV as well as VISUAL DISPLAY units used in TEXT, DATA and GRAPHICAL PROCESSING. The term is not precise, and what may be considered high definition in one situation may not be so for another. A CCITT category, high definition television specifies a service quality for video images. Its resolution is comparable to 35-mm film projection, and the TRANSMISSION rate using compression is from 92 Mbps to more than 200 Mbps. See also VISUAL ACUITY.

high fidelity Relating to the processing of SOUND SIGNALS as an ELECTRICAL ANALOG of SOUND WAVES and the reproduction of sound waves as a faithful representation of the original sound field. Systems that reproduce sound are never perfect, but those that can satisfy human requirements under controlled listening conditions are referred to as Hi-Fi or high fidelity systems.

high frequency (HF) A range of frequencies in the BAND from 3 to 30 MHz. See also FREQUENCY SPECTRUM.

high level control functions A concept related to PACKET SWITCHING SYSTEMS in which CONTROL is exercised by pairs of elements; one element of a pair is stationed at each end of the TRANSMISSION PATH. The functions controlled by these elements include:

error-free transmission—*high level data link control (HDLC)* element;

addressing, routing, packetizing—*access path control* element;
DIALOGUE MANAGEMENT—*data flow control* element

These so-called high level functions are performed by operating upon information conveyed as HEADERS to TEXT information and are recorded and transmitted in the form of BIT PATTERNS. The use of such functions has been made possible by high-speed DIGITAL TRANSMISSION facilities.

high level data link control (HDLC) A COMMUNICATIONS CONTROL standard developed by the International Organization for Standardization. The term also refers to a device and the associated communications PROTOCOL by means of which checking is undertaken to ensure that a transmission has taken place successfully. Under this standard, a MESSAGE is transmitted as a series of FRAMES that contain BITS specifically added to the MESSAGE SIGNAL. Checks are performed on frames as they arrive at the RECEIVING TERMINAL. These checks ensure that all INFORMATION BITS are present and include examination of redundant bits that have been added to frames at the TRANSMITTING TERMINAL. Error frames are automatically detected and retransmitted.

Early forms of DATA LINK CONTROL (DLC) use different CHARACTERS to represent LINE CONTROL, DEVICE CONTROL and TEXT but might use the same positions in a frame for such purposes. A disadvantage of this method is that corruption during transmission can convert a text character into a CONTROL CHARACTER.

With modern high-speed communications protocols, line control information always occurs at a specified place in a frame, and distinctive BIT PATTERNS that have no relation to ALPHABET sets are used for control purposes. With this standard, line errors are much less likely to cause confusion, and greater efficiency arises in line utilization.

high level language A PROGRAMMING LANGUAGE used to give instructions to a COMPUTER and having a resemblance to a natural language such as English or to mathematical notation. Compare with LOW-LEVEL LANGUAGE.

high pass filter A FILTER that allows all frequencies above a particular cutoff point to pass along a CIRCUIT while blocking all frequencies below that point. Contrast with LOW PASS FILTER and BAND PASS FILTER.

high peak data rate The rate of traffic flow that arises when the TRAFFIC offered to a NETWORK approaches the maximum level planned in the design of the network.

high resolution A system for displaying information and graphics images is said to be of high resolution when fine details can be resolved upon a screen. There is no absolute definition of high resolution, but one might expect the number of PICTURE ELEMENTS making up the image to be of the order of a 500×500 matrix. See also RESOLUTION.

high resolution display A VISUAL DISPLAY system capable of resolving a picture containing great detail. A relative expression for which no general standards can be given. See also RESOLUTION.

high resolution graphics A standard for displaying GRAPHICS INFORMATION. It allows fine lines and details to be resolved. See also ALPHAGEOMETRIC CODING.

high-speed modem A device for connecting DATA TERMINAL EQUIPMENT to a communications LINE and capable of operating at speeds up to 9,600 BITS per second and faster. See also MODEM.

high-usage route A TRANSMISSION PATH designed to take a high volume of TRAFFIC. It may be supported during periods of excessive traffic by auxiliary ROUTES. See also FULLY PROVIDED ROUTE.

highway A TRANSMISSION PATH in which a number of DIGITAL SIGNALS may pass, but each is separated in different TIME SLOTS.

holding time The period during which a particular CALL occupies a CHANNEL or some part of a TELECOMMUNICATIONS system.

horizontal resolution A definition of the number of PICTURE ELEMENTS that can be resolved along a horizontal line drawn upon a display screen, e.g., in the British 625-line television system, 572 picture elements; in the U.S. 525-line system, 522 picture elements. See also RESOLUTION.

horizontal tabulation (HT) A function represented as a special FORMAT EFFECTOR in a DATA COMMUNICATIONS CODE and serving as an instruction to move a PRINT MECHANISM or the CURSOR of a VISUAL DISPLAY unit to the next predetermined position along a line of a document.

host processor A COMPUTER that runs APPLICATION PROGRAMS and exerts the primary level of control over activities in a DATA NETWORK. Until the 1970s, most data networks were dominated by the host processor, which invariably appeared at the apex in a TREE NETWORK hierarchy. Developments since then have tended to pass more control over communications activities to other NODES of the network so that the host may be primarily noted for its control over APPLICATIONS and for its storage and processing capacity, which are interfaced to the network by a COMMUNICATIONS CONTROLLER.

hostile user A USER who is intent on creating confusion or interruption of a NETWORK. Most networks, particularly public service networks, take measures to prevent unauthorized access to, or use of, the network. See also VIRUS.

housekeeping information Information recorded, transmitted and processed in a communications system to enable the system itself to perform its function in the handling of USER INFORMATION.

HT See HORIZONTAL TABULATION.

hub In a multipoint NETWORK, the hub is the device at which branch NODES interconnect. A number of geographically dispersed hubs may be linked in a network.

hub polling A system of POLLING in which the CONTROLLER activates the most distant TERMINAL to inquire if it wishes to send or receive information, and that terminal responds accordingly before activating its neighboring terminal directly, and so on until the polling cycle is complete.

hybrid A device in a speech transmission system consisting of transformers that are arranged to convert a TWO-WIRE CHANNEL into a FOUR-WIRE CHANNEL. It thus creates a separate wire pair for each direction of transmission. The separation of the two directions permits separate AMPLIFICATION of the GO and RETURN PATHS. Hybrids are also associated with REPEATERS used to amplify MESSAGE SIGNALS. See also HYBRID REPEATER.

hybrid repeater In a speech transmission system, an arrangement of a HYBRID and amplifying REPEATERS which permits a TWO-WIRE LINK to be converted to a FOUR-WIRE LINK for AMPLIFICATION and then reconverted to a two-wire link.

hypergroup An assembly of 960 SPEECH CHANNELS delivered over a single COAXIAL TUBE without loss of identity, using techniques of FREQUENCY DIVISION MULTIPLEXING. See also GROUPING.

hypothetical reference circuit A CIRCUIT specification designated by the CCITT for reference purposes to enable design and operational issues to be expressed. There are many such recommendations, including those required for TELEVISION, SOUND, TELEPHONY, TELEGRAPHY and DATA NETWORKS.

I

IA2 Abbreviation of INTERNATIONAL TELEGRAPH ALPHABET NO. 2, also known as INTERNATIONAL ALPHABET NO. 2.

IA5 See INTERNATIONAL ALPHABET NO. 5.

idle bytes Redundant units of DATA sent to a LINE when there are gaps in the sequence of data to be transmitted.

idle character A CHARACTER inserted into a sequence of MESSAGE characters to occupy particular TIME SLOTS and to maintain timing, e.g., in a TIME DIVISION MULTIPLEXER.

idle state The condition that exists when a LINE or TERMINAL is unused and awaiting a CALL to COMMENCE.

IEEE Abbreviation for Institute of Electrical and Electronics Engineers.

IEEE 802.3 A standard PROTOCOL specifying a CSMA/CD LAN. It was originally based on 10-Mbps ETHERNET but also describes a range of CSMA/CD systems running at speeds from 1 to 10 Mbps. The maximum cable length permitted by 802.3 is 500 meters, which can be extended by repeaters. The collision detection process requires an ANALOG component in the network. Compare IEEE 802.4, IEEE 802.5.

IEEE 802.4 A standard PROTOCOL specifying a TOKEN BUS LAN. Physically, it uses a linear or TREE-shaped cable, but logically the stations form a RING and are aware of the ADDRESSES of the neighboring STATIONS. The TOKEN passes around the logical ring granting permission to transmit and thereby preventing collisions. It uses BROADBAND COAXIAL cable and is often found in factory environments, which require the combined characteristics of 802.3's robustness and the predictability found with ring TOPOLOGIES where it is possible to know the time a station may have to wait before sending a FRAME.

IEEE 802.5 A standard PROTOCOL specifying a TOKEN RING LAN at 1, 4 or 16 Mbps. It describes a collection of POINT-TO-POINT LINKS and does not broadcast in the manner of IEEE 802.3. Instead, a 3-byte TOKEN travels on the ring continuously until a STATION that wants to transmit takes it. Usually a WIRING CENTER is installed with 802.5 LANs to avoid network failure if a cable should break.

IEEE 802.6 See METROPOLITAN AREA NETWORK.

impulsive noise A form of interference arising in a CIRCUIT from electrical activity in adjacent equipment and which can be detected as a clicking noise in a radio or telephone CHANNEL.

in-band signaling Any form of SIGNALING in which CONTROL signals to set up, progress and CLEAR a CALL are associated with the CHANNEL in which the MESSAGE SIGNAL is transmitted and occur in a designated section of the BANDWIDTH. Contrast with OUT-BAND SIGNALING.

incoming buffers Storage space allocated to maintain a copy of incoming MESSAGE SIGNALS until the particular TERMINAL EXCHANGE or COMPUTER is able to process the signals.

incoming call Any MESSAGE SIGNAL being received by a TERMINAL, or by an exchange, to be switched to an appropriate terminal ADDRESS over OUTGOING LINES.

incoming call rate The rate at which CALLS are received at a particular TERMINAL or NODE in a system over a particular period.

incoming lines The communications CIRCUITS that are being used to bring MESSAGE SIGNALS into an EXCHANGE or NODE, to be switched to appropriate ADDRESSES over OUTGOING LINES.

incoming trunks The TRUNK LINES connected to an EXCHANGE for the purpose of receiving incoming TRAFFIC from another exchange.

inductance A property that links the magnetic flux in a CIRCUIT to the current flowing in the circuit or in an adjacent CONDUCTOR. This phenomenon has to be considered in the design of circuits used for transmission of MESSAGE SIGNALS.

information A nonspecific term meaning any SIGNALS transmitted or stored in a NETWORK. The term should be qualified, e.g., USER information implies information required by the users of a system rather than HOUSEKEEPING INFORMATION generated to allow the communications system to function correctly.

information bearer channel A CHANNEL provided for communication in a DATA NETWORK that is able to carry all information to allow communication, including, in addition to the USER DATA, certain CONTROL INFORMATION and data synchronizing signals. The information bearer channel may, therefore, operate at a DATA SIGNALING RATE higher than that required solely for transmission of user data.

information bits This term is frequently used to denote USER information in BINARY CODED form, as distinct from SYNCHRONIZATION bits or CHECK BITS, which may be added to allow a system to handle the user information correctly.

information content That part of a CHARACTER or MESSAGE containing pulses representing USER information rather than SIGNALING or ADDRESSING information required by the NETWORK.

information feedback system A system in which the RECEIVING STATION always returns BLOCKS of DATA to the TRANSMITTING STATION to allow the TRANSMITTING TERMINAL to check whether there has been an erroneous transmission. Blocks designated as errors are retransmitted.

information provider (IP) The generic title given to persons or organizations who supply information to be made available to USERS in a VIDEOTEX service.

information rate A term referring to the speed with which information is transferred over a CIRCUIT.

Synonymous with DATA TRANSFER RATE and contrasted with DATA SIGNALING RATE and MODULATION RATE.

information retrieval Pertaining to a DATA PROCESSING SYSTEM specifically designed to provide search and retrieval facilities in response to random requests by USERS for responses from a DATABASE.

information security Relating to the extent to which procedures are established to prevent purposeful or accidental access to information held in a system and to prevent disclosure, modification or destruction of USER information.

information separators Special symbols forming part of a DATA COMMUNICATIONS CODE and used to separate FIELDS of INFORMATION as required by an APPLICATION.

Examples include: FS (FILE SEPARATOR), GS (GROUP SEPARATOR), RS (RECORD SEPARATOR) and US (UNIT SEPARATOR).

information transfer The end result that occurs in sending information from one TERMINAL to another over a NETWORK.

infrared light Radiation beyond the VISIBLE LIGHT SPECTRUM covering a range from about 730 nanometers to about one millimeter in WAVELENGTH. See also ELECTROMAGNETIC RADIATION and Appendix 5.

initial signal unit The first SIGNAL of any SIGNAL MESSAGE that uses more than one SIGNAL UNIT.

in-plant communication Relating to the use of PRIVATE NETWORKS for communication within a building or group of buildings without utilization of facilities and CIRCUITS provided by a COMMON CARRIER.

in-plant equipment A term used to describe the internal facilities for communication within an organization. Such equipment may serve internal communication functions, without access to COMMON CARRIER facilities provided by the public service authority, or may connect to common carrier facilities for external communications.

input channel Any COMMUNICATION CHANNEL that provides input SIGNALS to a device or process.

input data signaling rate The rate at which a device can receive information transmitted to it; usually expressed in BITS-per-second.

insertion loss The overall LOSS of power that arises in a CIRCUIT attributable to the losses introduced by each and every circuit component. The insertion loss is usually measured in BELS or DECIBELS end to end, using a test frequency of 800 Hz. Also known as OVERALL LOSS.

in-slot signaling SIGNALING information associated with a CHANNEL and transmitted at a predetermined position within the TIME SLOT allocated to the channel.

instantaneous traffic The average number of concurrent CALLS in progress in a given system is known as the instantaneous traffic and is expressed in ERLANGS, e.g., 24 concurrent calls is 24 erlangs of TRAFFIC.

instantaneous traffic level The number of CALLS in progress at a particular moment in time. See also TRAFFIC VOLUME and INSTANTANEOUS TRAFFIC.

integrated digital exchange An EXCHANGE using digital technology and in which all TRAFFIC is received and distributed as DIGITAL TRAFFIC. VOICE SIGNALS are converted from ANALOG to digital form using PULSE CODE MODULATION (PCM) techniques and are transmitted using TIME DIVISION MULTIPLEXING (TDM) techniques. Exchanges using this technology are said to be integrated because it is possible to handle all basic services (e.g., TELEPHONE, DATA, TELEX, VIDEOTEX and FACSIMILE) using the same exchanges and TRUNK NETWORK.

integrated digital transmission and switching system A NETWORK in which connections are made by using DIGITAL SWITCHES. With this type of system, speech, DATA and other SIGNALS are transmitted as DIGITAL SIGNALS, using the techniques of TIME DIVISION MULTIPLEXING in both the transmission and the SWITCHING EQUIPMENT. In such a system, SPEECH SIGNALS are converted to digital signals by analog-to-digital converters at the TRANSMITTING and RECEIVING STATIONS. Speech is then transmitted digitally over a FOUR-WIRE CIRCUIT and the TRANSMISSION LOSS is independent of the distance used to carry the CALL. See also SWITCHING EQUIPMENT, INTEGRATED SERVICES DIGITAL NETWORK.

Integrated Services Digital Network (ISDN) An emerging set of standards that defines a type of telecommunications service. Some industry experts envision it will be the standard service provided on the LOCAL LOOP. The key CCITT recommendations for the ISDN data communications standard were approved in 1984 and refined in 1988. They reflect the objective of redesigning the worldwide telephone system, which was created for ANALOG voice transmission and must now provide more modern communications services, such as DATA transmission, FACSIMILE and VIDEO. Deployment of ISDN hinges on the installation of DIGITAL SWITCHING systems that provide a physical layer digital bit pipe and support the ISDN ARCHITECTURE and USER-to-NETWORK INTERFACES as defined by the CCITT. The BANDWIDTH requirements of ISDN mean that the INTEREXCHANGE TRUNKS will have to be upgraded to FIBER OPTIC CABLE. ISDN uses OUT-OF-BAND signaling, which uses the D CHANNEL. The format of control packets on the D channel is specified by CCITT SS#7 (SIGNALING SYSTEM NO. 7). In ISDN the user DATA travels on the B CHANNELS (64 kbps each). See also BASIC RATE INTERFACE, PRIMARY RATE INTERFACE.

intelligent controller A device used to control a CLUSTER or remote TERMINALS, handling their CONTROL requirements for communication with a NETWORK or central NODE in a system. Such a device may be programmable to carry out specific APPLICATION tasks required by USERS.

intelligent terminal A TERMINAL that has storage capacity and processing power, thus enabling complex logical functions to be performed within the terminal in support of the USERS APPLICATION or to accommodate HIGH-LEVEL CONTROL FUNCTIONS required by the INTERFACE requirements of the NETWORK. Contrast with DUMB TERMINAL.

intelligent time division multiplexer A device that acts as a TIME DIVISION MULTIPLEXER (TDM) but contains a MICROPROCESSOR control device that allocates the available BANDWIDTH (i.e., TIME slots) dynamically to improve the utilization of the CHANNEL. With more conventional TDM devices, the time slots are allocated whether a particular channel is active or not, and IDLE CHARACTERS are inserted if the channel is not activated. Also known as STATISTICAL MULTIPLEXER.

intelligible crosstalk CROSSTALK that results in intelligible SPEECH SIGNALS being transferred from one CIRCUIT to intrude on another adjacent circuit.

Intelsat See INTERNATIONAL TELECOMMUNICATIONS SATELLITE CONSORTIUM.

interactive applications A DATA PROCESSING SYSTEM in which the USERS are directly connected, when required, to the COMPUTER, using a TERMINAL and communication lines and in which the computer program responds to events initiated by users to maintain an accurate up-to-date record of the events or objects being controlled.

interchange circuit A CIRCUIT between two devices over which SIGNALS are exchanged to allow communication to take place, e.g., between a DATA TERMINAL (DTE) and a MODEM. See also COMMUNICATIONS INTERFACE.

interchange signals SIGNALS passed between two devices, or systems, that have separate functions. For example, between a MODEM and its associated DATA TERMINAL (DTE) to effect SIGNALING to a distant terminal. Examples are described under REQUEST TO SEND, READY FOR SENDING, CARRIER DETECTOR, CALLING INDICATOR and DATA TERMINAL READY. See also COMMUNICATIONS INTERFACE.

interchange specifications A specification defining the electrical and logical connection between any two devices, e.g., between a TERMINAL and a MODEM.

intercom A simple system to provide two-way communication between persons in different rooms. Each person is usually equipped with a MICROPHONE and a LOUDSPEAKER, and these are connected to the equipment at the remote location by a cable. VOICE SIGNALS are amplified to pass from one location to the other.

interexchange carriers Private companies, regulated by the U.S. government, that provide DATA COMMUNICATIONS services between different LOCAL ACCESS AND TRANSPORT AREAS.

interexchange signals The signals that are passed between TELEPHONE EXCHANGES (OFFICES) in setting up, maintaining and clearing a trunk CALL. See also SIGNALING.

interface A specification of the rules by which interaction between two separate functional units can be made to operate to conform with overall system requirements. Since most modern systems are modular in nature, with perhaps several hundred units in any one overall system, there are many levels of interface to be considered. An interface specification may include logical, electrical and mechanical specifications. Many standard interface specifications exist for different classes of systems or devices, and international organizations such as the CCITT are responsible for producing standards for international compatibility.

interface compatibility When introducing a new item of equipment into an existing system of communication, it is necessary to ensure that its electrical and mechanical characteristics INTERFACE with existing components. See also FUNCTIONAL COMPATIBILITY.

interlaced scanning A technique used in television broadcasting to reduce the SIGNAL BANDWIDTH by limiting the PICTURE FREQUENCY and arranging for it to be a submultiple of the FIELD FREQUENCY. Usually there are two FIELDS per complete picture; thus a picture of 500 LINES, for example, can be achieved by interlacing two field sequences of 250 lines. The interlaced sequences are arranged so that one traces the odd number lines 1, 3, 5 . . . , and the other the even lines 2, 4, 6, etc.

The picture frequency under this arrangement is half the field frequency, and the FLICKER EFFECT is observed to affect small areas of the screen rather than the total picture.

inter-LATA Between one LOCAL ACCESS AND TRANSPORT AREA and another.

inter-layer interface A precise definition of the procedures and logical structures providing for interaction between the different layers of CONTROL in a NETWORK ARCHITECTURE. An example of such an architecture is provided by the ISO REFERENCE MODEL FOR OPEN SYSTEMS INTERCONNECTION.

intermediate exchange A TRANSIT EXCHANGE at a point in a NETWORK and part of a connection for a specific CALL.

International Alphabet No. 2 (IA2) A DATA COMMUNICATIONS CODE used primarily for TELEX communication in which up to 52 ALPHANUMERIC characters and symbols can be represented plus CARRIAGE RETURN, LINE FEED and FIGURES and LETTERS SHIFT characters.

International Alphabet No. 5 (IA5) This is a DATA COMMUNICATIONS CODE developed as an international standard to allow telegraphic and DATA TRANSMISSION. It originated from a standard, formulated by the American Standards Association, known as ASCII (American Standard Code for Information Interchange). The standard was further developed by the INTERNATIONAL ORGANIZATION FOR STANDARDIZATION (ISO) and the CCITT and was ratified by them in 1968.

The code is shown in Appendix 1.

international circuit Any CIRCUIT between INTERNATIONAL EXCHANGES situated in different countries.

international dialing prefix The set of DIGITS that has to be dialed by a USER wishing to make an international call and used to obtain access to the outgoing INTERNATIONAL EXCHANGE.

international exchange An EXCHANGE that provides connection for TRAFFIC onto INTERNATIONAL CIRCUITS.

international gateway An EXCHANGE used to switch TRAFFIC (VOICE, TELEX or DATA) between a national communications NETWORK and an international network.

international leased circuit The complete TRANSMISSION PATH from a TERMINAL in one country to a terminal in another country and reserved exclusively for the use of a particular organization or person.

international number A number that excludes the INTERNATIONAL PREFIX providing access to the international NETWORK but that includes the COUNTRY CODE and the national subscriber number for the SUBSCRIBER concerned.

International Organization for Standardization (ISO) An international body, including standards groups from many countries, that develops standards for goods and services to facilitate international trade and exchange. Particular standards for DATA COMMUNICATIONS are developed by ISO Technical Committee 97. See also OSI.

international prefix A combination of DIGITS that has to be dialed by any SUBSCRIBER to obtain access to the international NETWORK and is then followed by the full INTERNATIONAL NUMBER of the subscriber to be called.

international sound program center A center in which AUDIO CIRCUITS for SOUND PROGRAMS terminate and in which connections can be made to other sound CIRCUITS to allow for supervision and distribution of sound transmission between different countries.

international switching center An EXCHANGE for switching TRAFFIC between different countries over INTERNATIONAL CIRCUITS.

International Telecommunications Satellite Consortium (Intelsat) An international organization formed in 1964 with the goal of providing communications between many countries. Intelsat is managed by COMSAT.

International Telecommunications Union (ITU) See UNION INTERNATIONALE DES TÉLÉCOMMUNICATIONS.

International Telegraph Alphabet No. 2 (IA2) A DATA COMMUNICATIONS CODE used primarily for MESSAGE systems using the TELETYPEWRITER and the international TELEGRAPH NETWORK. It is a 5-BIT CODE that uses SHIFT CHARACTERS to permit up to 64 characters to be represented. The code was first ratified by the ITU in 1932.

International Telegraph and Telephone Consultative Committee (CCITT, or, Comite Consultaif Internationale de Telegraphique et Telephonique) An international advisory committee, sponsored by the United Nations, that recommends standards to be followed on a voluntary basis for international communications. With headquarters in Geneva, Switzerland, the CCITT has a plenary assembly every four years.

International Telegraph Convention An international body established under the auspices of the ITU to harmonize standards in telegraphic communication.

international television center A center in which TELEVISION CIRCUITS for carrying VIDEO SIGNALS terminate and in which connections can be made to other television circuits to allow for supervision and distribution of television programs between different countries.

international transit exchange A TELEPHONE EXCHANGE situated in one country but intended as a center for switching CALLS between other countries.

international trunk dialing The method for directly calling a telephone SUBSCRIBER in another country, in which the CALLING PARTY adds a PREFIX to the basic number of the CALLED PARTY. This prefix consists of a special code that connects the caller to the INTERNATIONAL GATEWAY plus a COUNTRY CODE. Standard country codes have been created by the CCITT.

Internet protocol (IP) The IP refers to the ROUTING and delivery of DATA between different NETWORKS. In the OSI model of the INTERNATIONAL ORGANIZATION FOR STANDARDIZATION, the Internet protocol describes operations that occur on top of the NETWORK LAYER but below the TRANSPORT LAYER.

interoffice A reference to transmission (and the related billing charges) that occurs between the CENTRAL OFFICES of a COMMON CARRIER that may have different rate structures in its various central offices.

interoffice signals The SIGNALS that are passed between TELEPHONE EXCHANGES in setting up, maintaining and clearing a trunk CALL.

interoffice trunk A direct communications CHANNEL between local CENTRAL OFFICES. See also JUNCTION CIRCUIT.

interrupted isochronous transmission The transmission of SYNCHRONOUS DATA in bursts over a PUBLIC DATA NETWORK where the rate of transmission on the INFORMATION BEARER CHANNEL is higher than the INPUT SIGNALING RATE of the receiving device. Also known as BURST ISOCHRONOUS TRANSMISSION.

interval A period of time selected for a specified purpose.

interworking The process by which two systems can interact. For example, a TERMINAL in one DATA NETWORK can interact with one in another network. Or the means by which dissimilar terminals can communicate through a network.

intra-LATA Within the boundaries of a single LOCAL ACCESS AND TRANSPORT AREA.

intranode addressing In a DATA NETWORK, the ADDRESSING INFORMATION concerned with USERS connected to the same NODE. The logical equivalent to a LOCAL NUMBER in a TELEPHONE NETWORK.

intranode routing The operations concerned with providing an ACCESS PATH for USERS connected to the same NODE in a DATA NETWORK.

ionosphere A layer of air, surrounding the planet Earth, which is ionized, i.e., it consists of charged gases that provide conducting layers. The layers vary in thickness from 50 to 400 kilometers above the earth, and they have different effects upon radio broadcasting in different BANDS of the RADIO FREQUENCY SPECTRUM. At very low frequencies, RADIO WAVES travel around the earth as though in a WAVEGUIDE between the earth and the ionosphere. However, at higher frequencies, waves are reflected from the ionosphere and are sometimes referred to as SKY WAVES. Both MEDIUM FREQUENCY and HIGH FREQUENCY broadcasting make use of sky waves. Transmissions in these bands are affected by variations in the ionosphere and by overcrowding of BROADCASTS, as well as atmospheric conditions such as are caused by sun spots. Above the high frequency band, RADIO SIGNALS are not affected by the ionosphere.

ISDN See INTEGRATED SERVICES DIGITAL NETWORK.

I-Series CCITT recommendations describing ISDN in terms of, for example, NETWORK characteristics, user-to-network INTERFACES and SERVICES.

ISO See INTERNATIONAL ORGANIZATION FOR STANDARDIZATION.

ISO reference model for open systems architecture See OPEN SYSTEMS INTERCONNECTION.

isochronous system A communication system in which timing information is transmitted on the CHANNEL, as well as DATA, to establish a common TIME INTERVAL for TRANSMITTING and RECEIVING STATIONS. More commonly referred to as SYNCHRONOUS SYSTEM. Contrast with ANISOCHRONOUS SYSTEM.

ISPC See INTERNATIONAL SOUND PROGRAM CENTER.

ITC See INTERNATIONAL TELEVISION CENTER.

ITDM See INTELLIGENT TIME DIVISION MULTIPLEXER.

ITU Abbreviation of INTERNATIONAL TELECOMMUNICATIONS UNION; also known as UNION INTERNATIONALE DES TELECOMMUNICATIONS (UIT).

J

jitter A signal impairment causing BITS of a DIGITAL SIGNAL to be advanced or retarded relative to the TIME SLOTS allocated. A timing fault of this nature would probably cause errors at the RECEIVING TERMINAL or NODE.

judder Related to FACSIMILE and describing a condition in which there is a lack of uniformity in the scanning of a picture resulting in overlapping of elements of the picture.

junction circuit A CIRCUIT provided between two LOCAL EXCHANGES in an EXCHANGE HIERARCHY. Such a circuit acts as a TRUNK CIRCUIT by connecting two local exchanges without ROUTING via a TRUNK EXCHANGE. In the United States, it is referred to as an INTEROFFICE TRUNK. In Great Britain, the term is also used to describe the link between a local exchange and a trunk exchange.

justification A process concerned with altering the BIT RATE of a DIGITAL SIGNAL on a CHANNEL so that it is brought to conformity with another rate in a controlled manner. A technique used in TIME DIVISION MULTIPLEXING. Also known as BIT STUFFING and DIGITAL FILLING.

justifying digit A digit inserted into a DIGIT TIME SLOT as part of the process of JUSTIFICATION and distinguished within the process from an INFORMATION BIT.

K

k Abbreviation for kilo, meaning a thousand, as in KILOCYCLES (K) or KILOBITS per second (kbps).

Ka band The Ka band portion of the electromagnetic spectrum spans the frequency ranges of approximately 20 GHz to 30 GHz and is specified for SATELLITE transmission.

kell factor A factor used in dealing with human perception of images in a VISUAL DISPLAY system, e.g., television. This factor has been derived from statistical tests to determine the ability of humans to resolve alternate black and white elements. There are a range of kell factors suggested by experiments, but a factor of 0.7 is used in television systems. Thus, if it is accepted that the average television viewer can resolve 425 lines (see VISUAL ACUITY), then 607 lines are required to produce this RESOLUTION; 607 × 0.7 gives 425 lines.

Kermit A FILE transfer PROTOCOL. The name Kermit also refers to a SOFTWARE program that runs on the sender's and receiver's COMPUTER or MINICOMPUTER. Kermit is available free of charge from Columbia University in New York City.

key A term used mostly in DATA PROCESSING to indicate a DATA ELEMENT that identifies a particular information record, e.g., a stock item number on a file containing inventory details.

keyboard A device for entering information in a DATA TERMINAL. For example, allowing for all the functions and CHARACTERS of the INTERNATIONAL ALPHABET NO. 5 to be controlled by the human operator of a TERMINAL.

keyboard send and receive (KSR) Pertaining to a TERMINAL used as a DATA PRINTER and having a KEYBOARD to enter ALPHANUMERIC information. It can be used as a REMOTE PRINTER or a DATA ENTRY TERMINAL.

keypad A device providing a limited set of CHARACTERS and functions to be entered into a DATA TERMINAL. See also VIDEOTEX TERMINAL.

key-to-tape machine A device that captures information to be transmitted at a later time. It consists of a KEYBOARD containing keys for ALPHANUMERIC characters. DATA entered through the keyboard is encoded on a storage medium such as PAPER TAPE or MAGNETIC TAPE.

kilobits A unit of DATA volume, i.e., one thousand BINARY DIGITS. For example, a particular CHANNEL may be said to handle 9.6 kilobits per second. It is sometimes referred to as two to the tenth power, which is actually 1,024 BITS, not 1,000.

kilocycle One thousand cycles per second.

KSR Abbreviation of KEYBOARD SEND AND RECEIVE. A type of DATA PRINTER used for REMOTE PRINTING or as a DATA ENTRY TERMINAL.

Ku band The portion of the electromagnetic spectrum that spans the frequency range of approximately 12 GHz to 14 GHz. The Ku band is used by many communications satellites.

L

label An element of information attached to a MESSAGE for some identification purpose, e.g., to identify a CIRCUIT with which the message is associated.

LAN See LOCAL AREA NETWORK.

LAP See LINK ACCESS PROCEDURE.

LAP-B See LINK ACCESS PROCEDURE B.

LAP-D See LINK ACCESS PROCEDURE D.

large scale integration (LSI) The application of MICRO-ELECTRONIC TECHNOLOGY to the integration of hundreds or thousands of components onto a single SILICON CHIP of small physical size. The design, manufacture and testing of such chips can be aided by automated techniques.

laser A device that generates a narrow beam of electromagnetic energy whose frequency falls in the visible light spectrum. Lasers emit light that is coherent, that is, having a fixed phase.

last exchange Refers to the EXCHANGE closest to a CALLED PARTY or to the last exchange in any connection that utilizes a specific SIGNALING system, e.g., the last NO. 6 EXCHANGE. See also FIRST EXCHANGE and INTERMEDIATE EXCHANGE.

LATA See LOCAL ACCESS AND TRANSPORT AREA.

layered architecture A NETWORK ARCHITECTURE in which the various levels of CONTROL are logically separated from one another and from the physical details of the communication medium. The ISO has produced a standard that defines a hierarchy of 7 levels of PROTOCOL. This is an example of a layered architecture. The virtue of implementing systems in accordance with standards of this nature is that USERS requiring more simple networking functions can implement the lower levels only, and those requiring increasing levels of complexity can progressively implement the higher levels. This also allows for the practical growth of facilities at successive stages of NETWORK IMPLEMENTATION. See also OPEN SYSTEMS INTERCONNECTION.

leased circuit A CIRCUIT hired by a particular person or organization to provide a connection between two locations with the circuit not being available for use by another party.

leased lines TRANSMISSION CHANNELS for VOICE or DATA that are used exclusively for a particular organization for communication between predetermined locations. The LINES are hired from the telephone company or transmissions authority to provide transmission facilities where the requirements are such that dependence upon a PUBLIC SWITCHED NETWORK is not cost-effective or not sufficiently reliable.

least significant bit In any BINARY NUMBER, or unit of BINARY CODED INFORMATION, the lowest order BINARY DIGIT. In a communications system this may not necessarily be the first BIT transmitted.

LED See LIGHT EMITTING DIODE.

letters shift A special CHARACTER in a TELEGRAPH CODE or DATA COMMUNICATIONS CODE that has the function of designating all subsequent codes in a transmission sequence as being letters (A to Z). The letters shift remains in force until a FIGURES SHIFT occurs.

LF See LINE FEED.

light emitting diode A device often used to provide a VISUAL DISPLAY on the front panel of communications devices.

light frequency Light is a form of ELECTROMAGNETIC RADIATION. INFRARED LIGHT, in the frequency from 1 THz to 100 THz, is today being used for data transmission in OPTICAL WAVEGUIDES. 1 THz (tera) is equal to 1,000,000,000,000 cycles per second. See also ELECTROMAGNETIC WAVES.

lightwaves ELECTROMAGNETIC RADIATION in the light spectrum. With the introduction of OPTICAL WAVEGUIDES, lightwaves are being increasingly used to carry communications TRAFFIC.

limit test 1. A test made to check the sensitivity of components in equipment in an attempt to isolate a possible cause of intermittent failure or poor service. For example, creating a temporary reduction in operating voltage.

2. A test made to ascertain if any measurable entity would appear outside of predetermined limits.

limited distance modem A simplified MODEM used over short distances or on PRIVATE LINES where it is not necessary to comply with the more stringent requirements for a modem approved for INTERFACING to the PUBLIC SWITCHED TELEPHONE NETWORK. Also known as a DATA SERVICE UNIT.

line Any CIRCUIT providing a connection between two points. It may consist of two wires only or of four wires. In TELEPHONY, a two-wire LINE is used to connect a TELEPHONE to a LOCAL EXCHANGE, but four-wire lines are used in the NETWORK to permit line AMPLIFICATION and MULTIPLEXING to take place.

line access point A physical point for connection of a TERMINAL to a LINE.

line adaptor A simplified form of MODEM that is used for connecting a DATA TERMINAL (DTE) to a PRIVATE NETWORK or certain PUBLIC DATA NETWORKS. Not generally acceptable for connection to the PUBLIC SWITCHED TELEPHONE NETWORK. See also DATA SERVICE UNIT.

line code A CODE used for transmission purposes. It may use pulses chosen to represent CHARACTERS that differ from the representation used in DATA TERMINALS (DTE).

line conditioning Line conditioning is a method for improving DATA throughput by controlling DISTORTION on leased voice-grade TRANSMISSION LINES. It can be done by equalizing the ATTENUATION and DELAY TIME that occur at different frequencies or by controlling the SIGNAL-TO-NOISE RATIO. HIGH-SPEED MODEMS can perform the former, otherwise the CARRIER can condition the lines, for which it charges a monthly fee.

line control Pertaining to the discipline and SIGNALING method that enables TERMINAL devices connected to a TRANSMISSION PATH to communicate with one another.

line driver A simplified MODEM for connecting a DATA TERMINAL (DTE) directly to a LINE and used for connection to PRIVATE NETWORKS or certain PUBLIC DATA NETWORKS. Not usually suitable where transmission is necessary using the PUBLIC SWITCHED TELEPHONE NETWORK. Also known as a DATA SERVICE UNIT.

line feed (LF) A function represented as a special FORMAT EFFECTOR in a DATA COMMUNICATIONS CODE and serving as an instruction to move a PRINT MECHANISM or the CURSOR of a VISUAL DISPLAY unit to the beginning of the next LINE.

line flyback An interval during the scanning operation of a television picture in which the ELECTRON BEAM is blocked off and the RASTER is repositioned to begin a new LINE SCAN. See also VIDEO SIGNAL.

line frequency The frequency of LINE SCANNING operations in the generation of a picture in a television system. The frequency is given by the number of LINES × the PICTURE FREQUENCY and is measured in cycles per second (Hz); typical values are: USA—525-line system, 15,750 Hz, and CCIR—625-line system, 15,625 Hz.

line isolator A device that connects a TERMINAL to a communications LINE to protect the NETWORK from high voltages or extraneous SIGNAL frequencies inside the terminal.

line link This term describes a TRANSMISSION PATH of uniform BANDWIDTH between any nominated points, including all LINES and equipment necessary to maintain the path.

line loop test A method of testing a LINE and its MODEM using test equipment. See also LOOP BACK TEST.

line period The time taken in the creation of a television picture to trace the RASTER movement, equivalent to a single horizontal LINE SCAN and the corresponding LINE FLYBACK. This entails a movement of the ELECTRON BEAM across the screen and back, including a downward movement ready to start the next forward stroke. See also VIDEO SIGNAL.

line scan The horizontal movement of the RASTER during the scanning operation to create a television picture. See also VIDEO SIGNAL.

line-out-of-service signal A SIGNAL sent on a BACKWARD CHANNEL to denote that the LINE to the CALLED PARTY is not in service.

line-up period The duration of time required to prepare a TELEVISION CIRCUIT by a communications authority before handing it over for operational use by a broadcasting authority.

link The complete assembly of circuit sections that make up a TRANSMISSION PATH for a particular purpose.

link access procedure (LAP and LAP-B) A procedure that operates in a PACKET SWITCHING NETWORK for data interchange and is responsible for functions involving framing, SYNCHRONIZATION control, ERROR DETECTION and for connections between the TERMINAL and a NETWORK NODE.

LAP-B is a standard version of this procedure recommended for the CCITT X.25 and uses a subset of the ISO HDLC (the HIGH LEVEL DATA LINK CONTROL specified by the INTERNATIONAL ORGANIZATION FOR STANDARDIZATION).

Link control procedures operate at level 2 of the seven levels defined by ISO for OPEN SYSTEMS INTERCONNECTION.

Link Access Procedure D (LAP-D) The procedure used for DATA being transmitted over the D CHANNEL according to INTEGRATED SERVICES DIGITAL NETWORK STANDARD, LAP-D specifies that USER information plus CONTROL information and parameters be transferred in FRAMES.

link control In managing the communication between two TERMINALS in a DATA NETWORK, certain procedures are operated to ensure that the DATA received is an error-free replica of the data transmitted. These procedures, known as LINK CONTROL, vary from one standard to another but usually employ the addition of redundant BITS to FRAMES of INFORMATION that are automatically checked. Automatic retransmission is requested if errors are detected at the RECEIVING STATION. Common standards include HIGH LEVEL DATA LINK CONTROL (HDLC), developed by the INTERNATIONAL ORGANIZATION FOR STANDARDIZATION, and ADVANCED DATA COMMUNCIATION CONTROL PROTOCOL (ADCCP) developed by the American National Standards Institute. Also known as DATA LINK CONTROL (DLC).

link header and link trailer In PACKET SWITCHING NETWORKS, the DATA LINK CONTROL (DLC) adds BITS to the beginning and end of each PACKET to assist in the ERROR CHECKING procedures that are performed to ensure that DATA is not lost or corrupted. See LINK CONTROL.

link level The procedures and functions in DATA COMMUNICATIONS concerned with LINK CONTROL, i.e., in managing the error-free transmission and reception of DATA. It relates to level 2 of the ISO REFERENCE MODEL FOR OPEN SYSTEMS INTERCONNECTION.

link management The procedures in a communications system concerned with allocation of CHANNELS and the RESOLUTION of CONTENTION for the available channels.

listening tests Tests conducted by a telephone company to establish the preference of USERS in regard to the loudness of the MESSAGE SIGNAL. Also used to test the sensitivity of human users to BANDWIDTH and SIGNAL-TO-NOISE RATIO. Such tests do not depend upon assumptions about the theoretical qualities of the human ear but require a large number of tests to be conducted to compile responses, known as PERCEPTION DATA. From these, statistical conclusions are derived.

loading A technique adopted to reduce the power loss that occurs in CIRCUITS due to the inherent CAPACITANCE between parallel wires in close proximity. Loading entails introducing coils that provide INDUCTANCE to counteract capacitance.

Local Access and Transport Area (LATA) A U.S. geographical designation within which the TELECOMMUNICATIONS services are provided by one of the BELL OPERATING COMPANIES.

local area network (LAN) A NETWORK designed to provide facilities for user communication within a defined building or plant. It does not necessarily use public service facilities. LANs generally have a DATA RATE of 2 Mbps or more and are owned by the organization that is going to use them. See also ETHERNET, TOKEN RING.

local call rate The *tariff* charged to a USER of a TELEPHONE NETWORK for a CALL within a local area. Usually a cheap charge (or sometimes no charge) compared to the tariff for a TRUNK call.

local central office A COMMON CARRIER'S facility that can be a termination point for LEASED LINES and provides service to local SUBSCRIBERS.

local circuit 1. In TELEPHONY a CIRCUIT between SUBSCRIBERS and a LOCAL EXCHANGE.

2. In DATA COMMUNICATIONS, a circuit forming part of an IN-PLANT network and not one provided by a communications CARRIER.

local exchange An EXCHANGE to which a population of people using TERMINALS in a particular geographic area are directly connected by means of LOCAL LINES. The exchange itself has access to other exchanges and to national TRUNK CIRCUITS. The term sometimes refers also to the site housing the CENTRAL OFFICE equipment.

local lines The LINES connecting a TERMINAL to a LOCAL EXCHANGE and providing a TRANSMISSION CHANNEL by which the terminal is able to connect with an EXCHANGE HIERARCHY forming an overall NETWORK.

local loop See LOCAL LINES.

local mode Certain communications devices can operate to provide useful functions when not connected to a COMMUNICATIONS CHANNEL. In this condition they are said to operate in local mode. For example, tests can be run on the local equipment, or DATA PROCESSING operations, such as collection and validation of DATA, can be performed.

local network 1. In TELEPHONY, that part of a TELEPHONE NETWORK that embraces the subscriber telephones, the LINES to LOCAL EXCHANGES and the local exchanges themselves. The term distinguishes these facilities from the TRUNK NETWORK, which includes the TRUNK EXCHANGES and TRUNK LINES.

2. The term is also applied in DATA COMMUNICATIONS to refer to IN-PLANT networks that do not depend upon PUBLIC SWITCHED or LEASED CIRCUITS to provide TRANSMISSION PATHS. See also LOCAL AREA NETWORK.

local number A NUMBER identifying a SUBSCRIBER on the same LOCAL EXCHANGE as another subscriber or an abbreviated TELEX number used for local TRAFFIC in a telex NETWORK.

local call A telephone CALL between two USERS whose TELEPHONES are connected to the same LOCAL EXCHANGE. The call thus uses LOCAL LINES but does not use TRUNK CIRCUITS which provide TRANSMISSION PATHS between distant TRUNK EXCHANGES.

local signals The SIGNALS that are passed between a TELEPHONE and the LOCAL EXCHANGE in setting up, maintaining and clearing a CALL. See also SIGNALING.

local telephone network Pertaining to the NETWORK involving the LOCAL CIRCUITS between SUBSCRIBERS and a TELEPHONE EXCHANGE but not including TRUNK CIRCUITS, which connect TRUNK EXCHANGES.

lockout facilities Facilities, usually implemented by SOFTWARE, that prevent interference between USERS who may be simultaneously trying to update the same records in a DATABASE or to make reservations upon the same objects. The system would automatically assign priority according to the sequence in which user requests are received, and the possible CONTENTION is not apparent to the users.

logical channel There are various techniques of MULTIPLEXING that enable several DATA CHANNELS to be available via a single physical TRANSMISSION LINK. The concept of a logical channel is used to identify each data channel within the NETWORK and to distinguish it from other channels sharing the same physical resources. See also LOGICAL CHANNEL NUMBER.

logical channel number In any form of MULTIPLEXING, it is possible to transmit hundreds or thousands of CALLS simultaneously over the same TRANSMISSION PATH. Each separate call is transmitted along a CHANNEL that occupies a particular frequency or a particular TIME SLOT. These channels are identified in the COMMUNICATION CONTROL system by unique numbers known as logical channel numbers. See also FREQUENCY DIVISION MULTIPLEXING and TIME DIVISION MULTIPLEXING.

logical interface The rules governing the way in which two devices must interact, including the identification of SIGNALS passing between the devices and the responses given by one to another under given conditions. Compare with ELECTRICAL INTERFACE and MECHANICAL INTERFACE.

log-off The act of a USER concluding a particular SESSION in a communication system, which for the time being terminates operations involving the use of system functions by that user.

log-on The act of a USER entering a communication system to conduct a particular SESSION, usually involving procedures to enable the system to check the authority of the particular user to perform allowable functions.

lone signal unit A SIGNAL UNIT consisting of only one unit of information rather than a MESSAGE consisting of several signal units.

long circuit A term used in TELEPHONY to define a CIRCUIT that requires ECHO SUPPRESSION.

long wave Radio broadcasts in the LOW FREQUENCY band, i.e., 30 to 300 kHz.

longitudinal judder A condition occurring in FACSIMILE devices in which a picture is reproduced with irregular lines due to inaccurate rotation of a scanning device.

longitudinal redundancy checking (LRC) One of the simplest forms of REDUNDANCY CHECKING in which a CHECK CHARACTER is added to each BLOCK of transmitted DATA. The check character is computed to make each row of BITS formed by the same bit positions in each successive character into a specific parity, e.g., an even number of 1-bits equals EVEN PARITY. Thus, using 8-bit characters, each block would consist of 8 strings of bits, the number of bits in each string being dependent on the block length. The parity of each string is checked at the RECEIVING STATION, and, if parity errors are detected, the block is classed as an error and retransmission is requested. When combined with PARITY CHECKING on each character position, LRC can achieve a powerful method of ERROR DETECTION. See also CYCLIC REDUNDANCY CHECKING.

long-term store A storage medium used to hold DATA that must be retained for a long time. For example, in a MESSAGE SWITCHING SYSTEM, to retain MESSAGES until they can be sent to the correct DESTINATION ADDRESS. Long-term store is usually a magnetic disk forming part of a COMPUTER system.

loop In COMPUTER programming a loop is a set of instructions that repeats continuously under certain conditions. In TELECOMMUNICATIONS the loop is the LINK between the CUSTOMER PREMISES EQUIPMENT and the CENTRAL OFFICE.

loop network A NETWORK in which the various NODES are interconnected along a TRANSMISSION LINK represented as the circumference of a wheel. The nodes appear as points along the circumference, and communication between two nodes must proceed via any intermediate nodes along the loop. Also known as RING NETWORK. See also NETWORK TOPOLOGIES

loopback test A test of the quality and performance of a LINE and/or its terminating equipment, achieved by looping the outgoing and incoming paths to an item of test equipment used to create operational conditions. The test equipment will generate test patterns, which are analyzed on receipt over the RETURN PATH.

loop-disconnect signaling A traditional method of SIGNALING in a TELEPHONE SYSTEM in which pulses representing the called ADDRESS are generated by disconnection of a CIRCUIT. A dial or push-button may be used for the purpose.

loop test See LOOP BACK TEST.

loss The loss of signal power caused by the characteristics of the cable, including energy consumed in overcoming resistance in the cable, and the effects of ATTENUATION.

loss/frequency response A term used to describe the variation in LOSS of power, which can be experienced at different parts of the BANDWIDTH of a given CIRCUIT. The figures quoted to describe this will be in DECIBELS and be expressed relative to the loss experienced for a given frequency, e.g., the INSERTION LOSS at 800 Hz. This phenomenon is not generally considered important in SPEECH COMMUNICATION over a TELEPHONE CHANNEL but may be significant in DATA COMMUNICATIONS.

loss-of-frame alignment An error condition arising in PULSE CODE MODULATION systems in which a receiving device is unable to determine the correct positioning of FRAMES in the incoming SIGNAL.

lost call A CALL that cannot be accepted by a NETWORK due to congestion of the available CIRCUITS.

loudspeaker A device that generates SOUND WAVES from ELECTRICAL ANALOG signals representing sound. A TRANSDUCER that converts electrical energy into sound energy.

low delay A quality desired in a NETWORK in which there should be as little delay as possible in the delivery of a FRAME of INFORMATION at any planned level of OFFERED TRAFFIC.

low frequency (LF) RADIO WAVES in the FREQUENCY BAND of 30 to 300 kHZ, sometimes known as the LONG WAVE.

low level language A PROGRAMMING LANGUAGE used to give instructions to a COMPUTER but having a form and structure convenient for representation within the machine and not designed to have a form easily understood by humans. Compare with HIGH LEVEL LANGUAGE.

low pass filter A FILTER used to allow all frequencies below a particular cutoff point to pass along a CIRCUIT without ATTENUATION while blocking all frequencies above the point. Contrast with HIGH PASS FILTER and BAND PASS FILTER.

low resolution Pertaining to a VISUAL DISPLAY system and defining one that cannot be used to present GRAPHICS INFORMATION in fine detail. An example would be the ALPHAMOSAIC GRAPHICS displays used in early VIDEOTEX SYSTEMS. Contrasted with HIGH RESOLUTION, but see also RESOLUTION.

low-speed modem A device for connecting DATA TERMINAL EQUIPMENT (DTE) to a communications LINE and capable of operating at speeds up to 1,200 BITS per second. See also MODEM.

lower sideband The process known as MODULATION (imprinting a MESSAGE SIGNAL onto a CARRIER WAVE) generates a series of harmonic frequencies known as the SPECTRUM ENVELOPE. The principal outputs generated are two SIDEBAND signals equally displaced in frequency about the CARRIER SIGNAL. One, the UPPER SIDEBAND, is above the frequency of the carrier; the other is below and is known as the lower sideband. See also MODULATION.

LRC See LONGITUDINAL REDUNDANCY CHECKING.

LSB See LEAST SIGNIFICANT BIT.

LSI Abbreviation of LARGE SCALE INTEGRATION. See also MICRO-ELECTRONIC TECHNOLOGY.

luminance A measure of the brightness of a light source, usually expressed in candelas per square meter.

luminous flux The total PHOTOMETRIC POWER generated by a source in all directions. See also VISIBILITY FUNCTION, WAVELENGTHS.

M

magnetic deflection coils Devices used to create movement of a SCANNING BEAM inside a television camera or TELEVISION RECEIVER. In a CATHODE RAY TUBE, they are positioned around the path from the ELECTRON GUN to the screen. They are activated to deflect the ELECTRON BEAM across and down the screen to trace out the RASTER movement required in a television system.

magnetic tape A medium for storing DATA in COMPUTERS in which DIGITAL SIGNALS are encoded on to a magnetizable strip of material. Once information has been recorded, it can be retrieved by reading the tape serially from the beginning—thus, information is stored on magnetic tape when it is to be archived for a time and is not expected to be immediately accessible to USERS.

main memory That part of a COMPUTER store into which programs and DATA must be transferred before processing can take place. The main memory consists of thousands of storage locations, which can be directly addressed by the central processing unit with very short access times. Contrast with BACKING STORAGE, which contains programs and data stored on a medium such as a magnetic disk. The access to main memory locations is measured in nanoseconds, whereas backing storage access is measured in milliseconds.

main network See TRUNK NETWORK.

main trunk A communications link providing a major route between EXCHANGES in a TRUNK NETWORK. Also known as TRUNK CIRCUIT.

mainframe A COMPUTER forming the central part of a DATA PROCESSING SYSTEM and usually a general-purpose computer able to run a mixed and heavy workload including ON-LINE SYSTEMS, BATCH SYSTEMS, PROGRAM DEVELOPMENT and DATABASE MANAGEMENT.

It is common to connect a main/frame computer to a NETWORK by a FRONT END PROCESSOR or COMMUNICATIONS PROCESSOR; thus, the communications aspects are handled by a specialized processor, while the mainframe runs the APPLICATIONS task.

A mainframe is usually much more powerful than a MINICOMPUTER, and the term is more commonly used to distinguish large general-purpose machines from minicomputers and MICROCOMPUTERS.

maintenance The operations concerned with setting up, monitoring, identifying the faults of and repairing HARDWARE, SOFTWARE, CIRCUITS and equipment within the limits intended to provide a service at a prescribed level of quality.

maintenance control system A subsystem in a DIGITAL EXCHANGE that diagnoses faults in the system and provides information to assist engineers to isolate and correct faults.

MAN See METROPOLITAN AREA NETWORK.

man/machine interface 1. A subsystem of a communications NETWORK that provides for interaction between the command center of the network and human operators responsible for NETWORK MANAGEMENT. The commands issued across the INTERFACE allow for monitoring, controlling and maintaining the network and its component parts.

2. Any procedure or PROTOCOL that allows a human operator to access and operate a system.

management signals SIGNALS concerned with the maintenance or operational management of a NETWORK.

management statistics A set of INFORMATION, usually gathered automatically by a system, to provide basic DATA needed for short- and long-term planning for the operation and enhancement of a NETWORK.

manual answer A facility in which a CALL can be established only if a human operator is in attendance to complete a manual operation to signify that the call will be accepted.

manual answering Pertaining to any system in which a human operator must be present to perform an operation in order to permit an INCOMING CALL to be accepted.

manual calling A system in which the ADDRESS of a CALLED TERMINAL is entered by a human operator, but the address CHARACTERS themselves may be generated by a DATA TERMINAL as a result of the operator action.

manual changeover An operation performed by a human operator to remove one set of equipment or LINES from operation and make another set available.

Manufacturing and Automation Protocol (MAP) A NETWORK communications PROTOCOL created by General Motors Corp. in the early 1980s, MAP was intended to be used in the factory environment. Although it is based on international standards and has no proprietary elements, it is not yet widely accepted. The specifications of MAP include a 10-Mbps BROADBAND CHANNEL DATA RATE, TOKEN PASSING and software suitable for message transfer.

many-to-many call A CALL in which there is more than one TERMINAL connected at each end of the CIRCUIT, thus allowing several USERS to speak and listen as though in conference. Contrast with ONE-TO-ONE CALL.

MAP See MANUFACTURING AND AUTOMATION PROTOCOL.

mark In TELEGRAPHY, one of two possible line conditions occurring in a SIGNAL; the other condition being known as SPACE. All CHARACTERS in ALPHABETIC TELEGRAPHY are made up of combinations of marks and spaces, i.e., patterns of BITS representing the BINARY DIGITS 0 and 1.

In a transmission sequence, the first bit of each character is always a space, which acts as a START PULSE. The final bit, or STOP PULSE, is always a mark, and the line condition remains as a mark until another character is transmitted.

mark inversion See ALTERNATE MARK INVERSION.

marker A CONTROL device that determines the switching path required in an EXCHANGE for a particular CALL and that operates the appropriate CROSSPOINTS.

master clock A timing device that generates SIGNALS to control events and has control over other CLOCKS in the same equipment or the same NETWORK.

maximum frequency error The specified or recommended span of FREQUENCY ERROR allowed in a specific system in order to remain within operating tolerances. For example, in MULTIPLEXED CHANNELS for TELEPHONY, a maximum frequency error of ± 2 Hz in a CARRIER system is a CCITT recommendation.

maximum justification rate The maximum rate at which BITS can be inserted (or withdrawn) from a DIGITAL SIGNAL to make the rate of the signal conform to another desired rate. See also JUSTIFICATION.

maximum stuffing rate Same as MAXIMUM JUSTIFICATION RATE.

mean busy hour An uninterrupted period of 60 minutes in the daily operation of a system for which the total TRAFFIC is greater than for any other 60-minute period.

mean down time An expression used in assessing the reliability of a system, or system component, and referring to the average time for which a failure persists before it is corrected and the unit is operational once more. See also FAULT RATE.

mean holding time The average time for which CALLS occupy equipment in a given period. If, in a given period T, the system carries n calls and the durations of the calls are h_1, h_2, h_3 . . . h_n seconds, then the utilization of the system is:

$$\sum_{i=1}^{i=n} h_i$$

The mean holding time h is given as: MECHANICAL INTERFACE

$$h = \frac{\sum_{i=1}^{i=n} h_i}{n} \text{ seconds}$$

See also TRAFFIC VOLUME.

mean time between failure (MTBF) A measure of the time between consecutive failures of equipment under certain conditions.

mean time to repair (MTTR) The average time it takes to correct a failed system.

mechanical interface The physical construction of the linkage between two devices, e.g., the pin connections and sockets connecting two units in order to carry ELECTRICAL SIGNALS to control communication.

medium speed modem A device for connecting DATA TERMINAL EQUIPMENT to a communications line and capable of operating at speeds up to 2,400 BITS per second. See also MODEM.

memory unit A storage device that stores DIGITAL SIGNALS until they are required for further processing, e.g., in a TERMINAL, the memory unit is used to store DATA passing to or from the communications LINE.

menu A display of options from which a COMPUTER operator may choose.

mesh network A NETWORK in which NODES are connected to several other nodes; possibly every node is connected to every other. In this way there are a variety of paths for the transmission of MESSAGES. Contrast with RING NETWORK and see also NETWORK TOPOLOGIES.

mesochronous signals Two SIGNALS whose significant timing intervals coincide.

message See MESSAGE SIGNAL.

message feedback system A system in which the accuracy of DATA TRANSMISSION is checked by automatically feeding received SIGNALS back to the TRANSMITTING TERMINAL for comparison with the original MESSAGE. The transmitting terminal automatically retransmits ERRONEOUS BLOCKS. Same as INFORMATION FEEDBACK SYSTEM.

message information That part of any transmitted signal representing information to be conveyed from one end USER to another.

message queues In a STORE AND FORWARD SYSTEM the TRANSMISSION LINKS may be temporarily overloaded by TRAFFIC passing through them. MESSAGES within the NETWORK are then stored in COMPUTER-controlled EXCHANGES. Message queues are formed and messages released according to priorities when a suitable ROUTING is available.

message signal That part of a transmitted SIGNAL that contains INFORMATION intended for a USER at a remote location. It is sometimes used to distinguish the message from CONTROL INFORMATION required for the management of the message through the NETWORK.

message source The TERMINAL from which a particular MESSAGE is first transmitted, e.g., a particular TELEPHONE or TELEPRINTER.

message switched exchange Message switched exchanges are used in DATA NETWORKS. In a message switched exchange, it is not necessary for a point-to-point connection to be made between two TERMINALS. In practice, the exchange has the capacity to store MESSAGES that it receives until it is able to establish a path to the required destination. Unlike CIRCUIT SWITCHED SYSTEMS, the SIGNALING processes are not separated from the communication processes in a message switched system. In fact, the required destination of the message is stored as a HEADER to the information contained in the message.

Messages are associated by the DESTINATION ADDRESS with a particular exchange to which the DESTINATION TERMINAL is connected. Thus, a message switched exchange has to examine the address, determine whether the destination terminal is connected directly to the exchange and deliver the message to that terminal or to another exchange as soon as the appropriate CHANNEL is available. Messages are transmitted one after another down each LINK (but see also PACKET SWITCHING, in which messages may be interleaved), regardless of whether the destination terminal is free. When any particular NODE (or exchange) in the network is overloaded or when a particular terminal or link is unavailable, the messages are queued in store at one or more exchanges.

There is a ROUTER in each exchange that manages these queues, placing the messages into output BUFFERS when appropriate links are available.

A router, in this context, is usually realized as a SOFTWARE program operating at high speed in a general-purpose COMPUTER. The router has basically three functions: (a) collecting incoming messages, (b) determining message routing and (c) sending messages to required destinations.

message switched system A system in which point-to-point connections need not be available to successfully transmit a MESSAGE from sender to receiver. Instead, the TRANSMITTING STATION transmits the message to the NETWORK where it will be received and acknowledged by an EXCHANGE or NODE that will take responsibility for ROUTING the message to the destination. See also MESSAGE SWITCHED EXCHANGE.

message switching The techniques concerned with transmitting MESSAGES over a NETWORK which includes EXCHANGES (or NODES) that are able to store messages and forward them on when appropriate CIRCUITS are available. See also MESSAGE SWITCHED EXCHANGE, and contrast with CIRCUIT SWITCHED EXCHANGE.

message synchronization With synchronous DATA TRANSMISSIONS systems, the beginning and end of each MESSAGE is usually indicated by special CONTROL codes. These CODES are identified by the RECEIVING STATION, and it is thus possible to divide a stream of incoming BITS into messages, BLOCKS or FIELDS. Examples of such codes are given under the heading TRANSMISSION CONTROL CODES.

message transfer The activity associated with making a CALL on a SWITCHED CIRCUIT is usually considered in three phases. These are: CALL ESTABLISHMENT, MESSAGE TRANSFER and CALL CLEARING.

Once a TRANSMISSION PATH is established, the transfer of the MESSAGE SIGNAL takes place. This phase is referred to as message transfer (or DATA TRANSFER).

The concepts applied to these phases are the same for both DATA TRANSMISSION and VOICE TELEPHONY, but the detailed methods of transmission differ.

metropolitan area network (MAN) A NETWORK designed to provide data communications within the LATA. The IEEE 802.6 standard specifies a PROTOCOL for MANs called Distributed Queue Dual Bus (DQDB). Many of the 22 BELL OPERATING COMPANIES are building networks that comply with the MAN standard to serve the 50-kilometer range of most cities.

MF signaling See MULTIFREQUENCY TONE SIGNALING.

microcomputer A class of small DIGITAL COMPUTERS based upon the technology of MICRO-ELECTRONICS which began to appear in commercial applications in the late 1970s. The first microcomputers were based upon 8-bit MICROPROCESSOR central processing units mounted on a board with RANDOM ACCESS MEMORY (RAM) chips for program and DATA storage—the equivalent of MAIN MEMORY in a MAINFRAME or MINICOMPUTER. Also mounted on the board are READ-ONLY MEMORY (ROM) chips, which contain SOFTWARE providing programming and OPERATING SYSTEM instructions. Usually microcomputers are programmed in an ASSEMBLER language or a HIGH LEVEL LANGUAGE such as BASIC.

In the simplest form, input is via a KEYBOARD, and output is displayed on a TV-monitor driven from a UHF TV MODULATOR mounted on the board.

Typically, a low-level microcomputer has a minimum of 4K BYTES of RAM, capable of expansion in 4K byte modules up to, for example, 32K bytes and from 4K bytes to 16K bytes of ROM.

Additional data storage facilities are available via an INTERFACE to a standard audio cassette player or a FLOPPY DISK DRIVE.

In the early 1980s, the first 16-bit microprocessors were introduced and a wider range of PROGRAMMING LANGUAGES became available for microcomputers as well as 200 megabyte HARD DISK STORAGE systems; 32-bit microprocessors are now becoming popular, giving the microcomputer a strong engine.

First introduced as personal computers and educational tools, microcomputers are now being used as INTELLIGENT TERMINALS in business applications, as FRONT END PROCESSORS to interface minicomputers to NETWORKS, and to augment minicomputers by providing special arithmetic or GRAPHICS PROCESSING applications. Also called personal computer (PC). See also MAINFRAME and MINICOMPUTER.

micro-electronic technology The application of solid state technology in which semiconductors, constructed of silicon, can be arranged to provide complex logical functions within very small components, designed, manufactured and tested by automated methods. The devices produced by this technology create opportunities for integration of many components and logic functions into exceedingly small physical size. The concepts of LARGE SCALE INTEGRATION (LSI) and VERY LARGE SCALE INTEGRATION (VLSI) have been introduced through this technology.

These developments continue to have a large impact upon the communications industry; they mean that systems can be constructed with high inherent reliability, with small physical space and electrical power requirements and with economic benefits of automation in manufacture and testing.

microphone A TRANSDUCER that converts SOUND WAVES into ANALOG ELECTRICAL SIGNALS in the AUDIO FREQUENCY BAND.

microprocessor A small micro-electronic device providing a powerful central processing unit for a COMPUTER on a single chip with INTERFACES to enable it to be interfaced to various peripheral units for the input, storage and output of DATA. The central element of a MICROCOMPUTER.

micro-to-mainframe link The communications CHANNEL between a HOST PROCESSOR and a MICROCOMPUTER.

microwaves RADIO WAVES having very short WAVELENGTHS and occupying frequencies in the range above 1 gigahertz ($1 \text{ GHz} = 1 \times 10^9$ hertz). They are used to transmit SIGNALS along WAVEGUIDES and for point-to-point directional radio links.

minicomputer This term applies to a class of DIGITAL COMPUTER that began to be introduced in the late 1960s and gained rapid penetration among USERS who wished to develop dedicated APPLICATIONS for multiple users rather than establish large general-purpose COMPUTERS to control all the applications in an organization. Minicomputers have been applied across a wide variety of commercial and scientific applications and have been extensively used as COMMUNICATIONS CONTROLLERS in DATA TRANSMISSION and MESSAGE SWITCHING applications. The precise distinction between minicomputers and MAINFRAME computers is difficult to define since advancing technology is increasing the power and scope of minicomputers. Typically, a low-level mini would operate with a 16-bit central processing unit, have up to 32 communications PORTS, up to 64K bytes of MAIN MEMORY and up to 60 megabytes of BACKING STORAGE. Models with 32-bit central processing units typically have up to 200 communication ports, a minimum of 512K bytes of main memory and a minimum of 250 megabytes of backing storage.

Minicomputers usually support a wide range of PROGRAMMING LANGUAGES and are particularly suited to DISTRIBUTED DATA PROCESSING applications. See also MAINFRAME and MICROCOMPUTER.

minimum signal level Communications equipment is designed to respond to ELECTRICAL SIGNALS of a particular strength. Often the power of a signal is ATTENUATED over a TRANSMISSION CHANNEL, and REPEATERS are used to boost the signal to the correct strength. The minimum signal level is the level below which a signal will not be acceptable to a particular class of receiving equipment.

modem This term is a contraction of MODULATOR/DEMODULATOR. Modems are devices used to INTERFACE communications equipment (e.g., TERMINALS and NODES) to a TRANSMISSION LINE. There are a variety of modems, and the evolution of the modem has seen a number of new technologies absorbed into the design.

Modems are classified into speeds:

low speed—up to 1,200 BITS per second
medium speed—up to 2,400 bits per second
high speed—up to 9,600 bits per second and beyond.

Most modems are designed to connect DATA TERMINAL EQUIPMENT to PUBLIC NETWORKS, but there is an increasing demand for communications networks covering large IN-PLANT installations that do not use the public network. Modems for this purpose are known as SHORT-HAUL MODEMS, and they provide a means of interfacing TERMINALS in LOCAL MODE.

Early modems operated using ANALOG TECHNIQUES for transmission of data over TELEPHONE NETWORKS, but the increasing spread of digital technology allowing high-speed transmission with very low ERROR RATES has seen the development of modems that directly interface a DIGITAL TERMINAL to a digital TRANSMISSION CHANNEL. These devices are more strictly titled NETWORK INTERFACE UNITS but are called modems by popular convention. The term DATA CIRCUIT TERMINATING EQUIPMENT is the term preferred by the CCITT to denote a device that interfaces a data terminal to a network.

modem pool A collection of several MODEMS that may serve hundreds of USERS. A modem pool can be located at the CENTRAL OFFICE or the CPE.

modulated carrier wave A SIGNAL used to carry a MESSAGE SIGNAL that has been imprinted upon it for the purpose of transmission. See also FREQUENCY DIVISION MULTIPLEXING.

modulation LOW FREQUENCY signals (e.g., AUDIO FREQUENCY) cannot be effectively radiated through space. Thus, from the beginning of the history of RADIO TRANSMISSION, it became necessary to carry low frequency signals imprinted onto a HIGH FREQUENCY carrier wave. There are two principal methods for achieving this: (a) AMPLITUDE MODULATION and (b) FREQUENCY MODULATION.

In amplitude modulation (AM), the frequency of the CARRIER WAVE is retained constant, but the amplitude of the carrier wave signal is varied in exact proportion to the MESSAGE SIGNAL to be transmitted. The receiving equipment DEMODULATES the signal by comparing it with a generated CARRIER SIGNAL of constant amplitude.

In frequency modulation (FM), the frequency of the carrier wave is not retained constant but is allowed to vary about a reference point in proportion to the low frequency signal to be transmitted. The receiving equipment demodulates the signal by comparing it to a generated carrier signal of constant frequency.

Both forms of modulation are widely used. Frequency modulation is often used for SOUND radio broadcasts today because it is far less likely to be distributed by interference or NOISE. Modulation has become widespread in other fields of TELECOMMUNICATIONS. For example, in TELEPHONY, a single TRANSMISSION PATH can be used to carry hundreds or thousands of separate CALLS using the technique known as MULTIPLEXING. A different carrier wave is modulated by each call so that resulting signals are separated from one another by a frequency displacement that ensures that there is no mutual interference as they are transmitted along the same path.

Amplitude modulation is often used in DATA COMMUNICATIONS in preference to frequency modulation because it is more efficient in the use of BANDWIDTH, but a special variant of frequency modulation is also used to transmit DIGITAL INFORMATION. This is described under the heading FREQUENCY SHIFT KEYING (FSK).

A third form of modulation is known as PHASE MODULATION. This is a system whereby binary values such as 0 and 1 are indicated by an alteration of the PHASE of an ALTERNATING CURRENT (AC) carrier signal. Thus, without changing amplitude or frequency, information is carried and the message signal is detected by comparing the carrier with a REFERENCE WAVE to determine the angle of phase lag.

There are many variations of these basic modulation techniques; an example occurs in television BROADCASTING. The objective of such a mass system of communication is to have a cheap and simple TV RECEIVER without appreciable DISTORTION arising in the DEMODULATION process. At the same time, it is necessary to economize in the bandwidth and power required in transmission. A form of amplitude modulation known as VESTIGIAL SIDEBAND MODULATION is used.

The normal process of amplitude modulation produces a SPECTRUM ENVELOPE that contains two identical sidebands: one below the carrier wave and one above the carrier wave. The message signal is repeated in both sidebands. A great saving in power and bandwidth is possible by suppressing the carrier wave and one of the sidebands, using a technique known as SINGLE SIDEBAND MODULATION (SSB).

This SSB technique is used extensively in communications, but it requires greater complexity at the RECEIVING STATION to demodulate an SSB signal. In the case of television broadcasting, the UPPER SIDEBAND is transmitted along with part of the LOWER SIDEBAND, known as the VESTIGIAL SIDEBAND (VSB). This simplifies the circuitry required in the TV receiver. See also MULTI-LEVEL AMPLITUDE MODULATION, VARIABLE AMPLITUDE MODULATION and DETECTION.

modulation rate A term used to express the performance of a CIRCUIT, indicating the rate at which pulse changes occur. For example, if a SIGNAL consists of pulses of 20 milliseconds' duration, the modulation rate is $1 \div 0.02 = 50$ per second. This is also known as the BAUD RATE but does not necessarily refer to the rate at which information is transmitted. See also DATA SIGNALING RATE and DATA TRANSFER RATE.

modulator A device that converts a MESSAGE SIGNAL into another form suitable for transmission as a RADIO SIGNAL or a signal to be combined with other message signals in a MULTIPLEXED transmission system. See also MODULATION.

monochrome display A television, or a VISUAL DISPLAY device, based on the principles of the CATHODE RAY TUBE, which is able to display information in one basic color such as black and white, i.e., not a full color display.

monochrome receiver See MONOCHROME DISPLAY.

Morse code A CODE developed for the ELECTRICAL TELEGRAPH by Samuel Morse, an early pioneer of electrical TELEGRAPHY. The code enabled CHARACTERS to be represented as a series of electrical pulses of short and long duration that were generated by a manually operated key used to interrupt a CIRCUIT. These pulses were detected as sounds by a person wearing earphones at the RECEIVING STATION. In 1838, Morse succeeded in transmitting a MESSAGE over 5 kilometers. In 1844 the Morse code was used for the first public telegraph between Washington and Baltimore. Some years later, the Morse telegraph was recognized by the INTERNATIONAL TELEGRAPH CONVENTION as an international standard.

mosaic graphics set A set of CHARACTERS, and the CODES representing those characters, that are used in creating images for display in any VIDEOTEX SYSTEM using ALPHAMOSAIC CODING. The characters can be combined to form images of relatively LOW RESOLUTION, but, for example, cannot be used to draw fine lines and arcs.

most significant bit In any BINARY NUMBER or unit of BINARY CODED INFORMATION, the highest order BINARY DIGIT. In a communications system, this may not necessarily be the first BIT transmitted.

motherboard The main board to which circuit boards are attached to construct a COMPUTER system.

MSB See MOST SIGNIFICANT BIT.

MTBF See MEAN TIME BETWEEN FAILURE.

MTTR See MEAN TIME TO REPAIR.

muldex Short form of MULTIPLEXER/DEMULTIPLEXER. See also DEMUX.

multiaddress calling A system in which DATA can be BROADCAST to many USERS in a NETWORK by nominating individual ADDRESSES or by use of a special

CODE that identifies a predetermined group of addresses.

multi-block In SIGNALING SYSTEM NO. 6, a group of 96 SIGNAL UNITS transmitted as a BLOCK on the signaling CHANNEL.

multi-block synchronization unit A SIGNAL UNIT carrying information to synchronize a number of units of signal information transmitted as a MULTI-BLOCK on a signaling CHANNEL.

multi-cast address A DESTINATION ADDRESS that relates to a specified group of logically related STATIONS (e.g., a CLOSED USER GROUP) or a set composed of all the stations on the NETWORK.

multidrop line A COMMUNICATION CHANNEL that services three or more DATA TERMINALS at different geographical locations and in which a COMPUTER (NODE) controls utilization of the channel by POLLING techniques.

multidrop network A NETWORK in which the various NODES or TERMINALS are positioned along a single TRANSMISSION LINK, so that transmission must proceed between any two nodes via any intermediate nodes, with the controlling node positioned at one end of the LINK. See also NETWORK TOPOLOGIES.

multi-exchange call A CALL that passes through more than one EXCHANGE, i.e., not an OWN EXCHANGE CALL.

multi-exchange connection Same as MULTI-EXCHANGE CALL.

multiframe A group of FRAMES considered as an entity in a system. The position of each frame is detected by reference to a multiframe alignment SIGNAL.

multifrequency tone signaling The traditional method of sending SIGNALS to a telephone LINE is by creating pulses by interruption of a CIRCUIT. A TELEPHONE dial or push-button panel can be used to cause this interruption, which is known as LOOP-DISCONNECT SIGNALING.

Multifrequency tone signaling is a more modern method of SIGNALING in which each DIGIT is represented by two tones of different frequency sent to the line. Each button of the telephone is connected to two OSCILLATORS that are activated when the button is pressed. The oscillators are situated on the telephone and draw DC power from the LOCAL LINE. This method of signaling allows the CALLING SIGNALS to be generated more quickly than with a telephone, which uses loop-disconnect signaling. However, only certain types of exchanges can respond to multifrequency tone signaling.

multi-level amplitude modulation A form of AMPLITUDE MODULATION in which the AMPLITUDE of a CARRIER WAVE is varied to represent digital information and in which certain predetermined levels of amplitude are used to represent a BINARY NUMBER, e.g., a separate level exists for 00, 01, 10 and 11. See also MODULATION.

multi-level signaling Any method of transmitting BINARY CODED INFORMATION in which groups of BINARY DIGITS (e.g., 00, 01, 10, 11) are represented by different signal status. For example, in FREQUENCY SHIFT KEYING, a number of frequency levels can be used to represent such conditions.

multi-link calls A CALL in which a TRANSMITTING TERMINAL is able to transmit information to more than one RECEIVING STATION at the same time.

multi-party connection A facility provided, particularly in DIGITAL EXCHANGES, to allow three or more parties to participate in a single telephone CONVERSATION.

multi-phase modulation A method of PHASE MODULATION in which more than two variations of PHASE angles are used. Thus, more than two values can be represented. For example, in a four-phase systems: $0° = 01$, $90° = 00$, $180° = 10$,

270° = 11. In an eight-phase system, sufficient combinations are available to represent values for 3 BITS per phase.

multiplex aggregate bit rate In a TIME DIVISION MULTIPLEXING system, the sum of the BIT RATES of the individual INPUT CHANNELS plus the overhead bits required by the MULTIPLEXING process.

multiplexed Pertaining to any CIRCUIT or TRANSMISSION PATH in which a number of CHANNELS are combined onto one physical path using the techniques of FREQUENCY DIVISION MULTIPLEXING (FDM) or TIME DIVISION MULTIPLEXING (TDM).

multiplexed channel A CHANNEL used to carry simultaneously a number of MESSAGE SIGNALS, which have been combined by MULTIPLEXING them onto a CARRIER SIGNAL. For example, a TELEPHONE message signal occupies a BANDWIDTH of 3 kHz, but several TELEPHONE CHANNELS can be obtained for simultaneous transmissions over a single BROADBAND CHANNEL. Thus, a channel having a bandwidth of 1 MHz would support up to 250 channels, each of 4 kHz using FREQUENCY DIVISION MULTIPLEXING. In such cases, telephone channels are each allowed 4 kHz in order to reduce the need for sharp cutoff FILTERS when DEMULTIPLEXING.

multiplexed traffic Relating to MESSAGE SIGNALS that have been converted into a form and combined in such a way so that hundreds or thousands of signals may be transmitted down the same TRANSMISSION PATH at the same time. See also FREQUENCY DIVISION MULTIPLEXING and TIME DIVISION MULTIPLEXING.

multiplexer A device that enables a number of MESSAGE SIGNALS to share the same physical TRANSMISSION CHANNEL by using the techniques of FREQUENCY DIVISION MULTIPLEXING (FDM) or TIME DIVISION MULTIPLEXING (TDM). Such devices are used to improve the utilization of communication NETWORKS. A TRANSMISSION PATH that is used in this way is known as a MULTIPLEXED CHANNEL.

multiplexing A technique used to carry several hundreds, or thousands, of MESSAGE SIGNALS on a single TRANSMISSION CHANNEL. Two main techniques are used. See also FREQUENCY DIVISION MULTIPLEXING (FDM) for ANALOG SIGNALS. See TIME DIVISION MULTIPLEXING (TDM) for DIGITAL SIGNALS.

multipoint line See MULTIDROP LINE. Contrast with POINT-TO-POINT LINE.

multi-state signaling A system for handling DIGITAL SIGNALS in which several values can be encoded in a signal element. In most digital systems, information is transferred as a series of pulses representing the BINARY DIGITS 0 or 1 according to the pulse polarity—all the pulses being of constant duration. In some systems, pulses may take on different values according to the AMPLITUDE of each pulse, the duration of pulses remaining identical in each case. As an example, a system in which pairs of binary digits, 00, 01, 10 and 11, are represented by different amplitudes provides for four possible states for any pulse and gives a higher DATA SIGNALING RATE than the more familiar TWO-STATE SIGNALING method.

multistation DLC A DATE LINK CONTROL that performs error checking facilities on a number of MULTIPLEXED streams of DATA, interleaved upon the same LINE by TIME DIVISION MULTIPLEXING techniques. Used where a number of NODES use the same LEASED LINE and the DLC includes link address fields and CONTROL INFORMATION, which assist the DLC to avoid conflict on the line.

music circuit A high-quality CIRCUIT having a BANDWIDTH capable of handling a range of frequencies sufficient to carry SIGNALS over the whole AUDIO FREQUENCY BAND.

mutually synchronized network A NETWORK in which all the CLOCKS exert some degree of control on one another and no single clock is dominant. Also known as DEMOCRATIC NETWORK and contrasted with DESPOTIC NETWORK.

MUX Abbreviation of MULTIPLEXER.

N

NAK See NEGATIVE ACKNOWLEDGMENT.

nanosecond One billionth of a second.

narrow bandwidth Relating to a CHANNEL that can carry SIGNALS of only LOW FREQUENCY (e.g., VOICE FREQUENCY SIGNALS). See also BANDWIDTH.

National Telecommunications and Information Administration (NTIA) A division of the U.S. Department of Commerce that advises the government on TELECOMMUNICATIONS and related issues, for example, telecommunications spending and policy planning.

National Television Systems Committee (NTSC) A committee appointed to develop the standards and principles of the television broadcast system used in the United States, also adopted in Mexico, Canada and Japan. The system uses 525 picture lines and a 60 Hz FIELD FREQUENCY. See also SECAM and PAL.

nature-of-circuit indicator Information included in the CALL ESTABLISHMENT process and transmitted on a FORWARD CHANNEL to instruct an EXCHANGE of the type of CIRCUIT already used for the connection. This assists in the selection of an appropriate circuit for ongoing connection.

NCTE See NETWORK CHANNEL TERMINATING EQUIPMENT.

negative acknowledgment (NAK) An international TRANSMISSION CONTROL CODE returned by a RECEIVING TERMINAL to signify that a FRAME of INFORMATION has been received but is incorrect. Contrast with ACKNOWLEDGE (ACK).

negative bit stuffing Same as NEGATIVE JUSTIFICATION.

negative justification The deletion of DIGIT PULSES from a DIGITAL SIGNAL to reduce the BIT RATE to a rate required. See also JUSTIFICATION.

network The basic objective of any network is to provide ACCESS PATHS between USERS at different geographical locations. A great variety of terminal types may exist in the network, and a large number of NODES may be present. The network may have a number of possible ROUTINGS for a CALL, depending upon the geographical distribution of the nodes (or EXCHANGES) and the CIRCUITS linking these nodes. The network makes it possible for end users to be connected and to communicate intelligibly in spite of errors, difference in speed of operation, PROTOCOL and format.

network architecture A precise definition of the PROTOCOL, functions and logical components of a NETWORK and how they should perform. Such architectures embrace the interaction of different levels of CONTROL that must be implemented at TRANSMITTING and RECEIVING STATIONS to maintain a coherent system of communication. An example is described under the entry OPEN SYSTEMS INTERCONNECTION.

network attachment It is usual for authorities who operate PUBLIC TELEPHONE or DATA NETWORKS to have control over the approval of TERMINALS or other devices that may be connected to the network by SUBSCRIBERS. The object of this is to ensure that the electrical and functional characteristics of devices attached to the network do not impair the reliability of the network or impair the quality of service enjoyed by other subscribers.

network channel terminating equipment (NCTE) Classified as a type of CUSTOMER PREMISES EQUIPMENT by the FCC in COMPUTER INQUIRY II, NCTE includes units that convert SIGNALS coming from the USER'S equipment into those expected by the NETWORK and vice versa. Interfaces between NCTE and TELECOMMUNICATIONS service providers must meet industry standards.

network control A NETWORK may consist of a number of diverse STATIONS operating according to different PROTOCOLS and with a wide geographic distribution. A most important element in any network is the set of functions that control the activation and deactivation of ACCESS PATHS between TRANSMITTING and RECEIVING STATIONS. These functions include certain aspects concerned with the operation of the network, including the management of recovery procedures in the event of failure of a NODE or TRANSMISSION LINK.

Network control is sometimes centralized (i.e., resides in a single node) or decentralized (no single node dominant).

In a typical network, using PACKET SWITCHING technology, the following network control functions must exist:

1. Establishing the TRANSMISSION PATH between nodes (e.g., providing onward dial-up information).
2. Maintaining ROUTING tables to allow each node to select outgoing links for onward transmission.
3. Assigning authority for activation of DATA LINK CONTROL functions to appropriate stations.
4. Maintaining directories of all USERS in the system.
5. Setting up and deactivating the pattern of DIALOGUE MANAGEMENT requested by a user for a particular CALL.
6. Managing queues of requests and responses within a SESSION.
7. Communicating network status to the operational staff and conducting tests and measurements of activity.

Network control is a vital consideration in any data network but is particularly emphasized where combinations of protocols involving private and public facilities are to be utilized.

network control layer In a layered NETWORK ARCHITECTURE, this term defines the layer of logic that provides for NETWORK CONTROL between adjacent network NODES; e.g., the standard that allows for PACKET formatting and VIRTUAL CIRCUITS in an X.25 implementation. Also called network layer. See also OPEN SYSTEMS INTERCONNECTION.

network control phase During a CALL in a DATA NETWORK, any period during which a DATA TERMINAL exchanges information with the network to manage the setup, progression or disconnection of a CALL.

network diagnostic controller A device that is connected to a DATA COMMUNICATIONS network to monitor and automatically test the quality of LINES, MODEMS or other equipment forming part of a NETWORK. It will help to detect and isolate network problems, and, in the event of failure or poor performance in some aspect of the network, it will provide for reconfiguration of the network from a central location without manual intervention at remote sites.

In some cases, monitoring can be carried out on secondary low-speed lines independent of the PRIMARY CHANNELS so that monitoring does not interfere with the main data paths.

Diagnostic information is usually presented on a CATHODE RAY TUBE (CRT) display, and often a HARD COPY PRINTER is provided to give a permanent record of all tests.

Automatic alarm systems can be included in such systems to give visible and audible warning of major faults that have interrupted, or are likely to interrupt, key services.

network facilities In any NETWORK there may be a range of facilities available to a USER making a CALL REQUEST. The selection of the facilities required for a CALL are defined when the call is established. In many DATA NETWORKS this is defined as part of a FACILITY REQUEST, which is a sequence of CHARACTERS transmitted as part of a MESSAGE SIGNAL.

network implementation The particular realization of a NETWORK ARCHITECTURE in HARDWARE and SOFTWARE, i.e., the way in which the system builders have built a system to conform with the logical and PROTOCOL requirements of the architecture.

network interface unit A device used to connect a DIGITAL TERMINAL to a DIGITAL CHANNEL for sending or receiving MESSAGE SIGNALS representing DATA. The input and output signals are in digital form, and the essential function is to balance the signals produced in the terminal with the standards expected on the TRANSMISSION CHANNEL. See also DIGITAL DATA TRANSMISSION.

network layer See NETWORK CONTROL LAYER.

network maintainability A quality desired in a NETWORK that allows for operation of the network under various conditions including scheduled and unscheduled maintenance. It also allows for planned extension of the network and its TRAFFIC capacity to be carried out without disruption of service to users.

network maintenance signals A special class of SIGNAL used to assist in the management and operational maintenance of a NETWORK See also SIGNALING.

network management Relates to the set of functions that perform control over the operation of a communications network, e.g., the selection and release of the various paths through the NETWORK to service a particular CALL, the management of all RECOVERY PROCEDURES to ensure continuous operation of the network and protection for SUBSCRIBERS' messages during failure. In private networks, examples of products that perform these functions are Netview, from IBM, and Unified Network Management Architecture, from AT&T. Standards for network management are emerging, and the Internet Engineering Task Force, a standards body for TCP/IP, has formulated a set of standards called Netman to help provide a migration to the OSI model.

The network management also includes maintaining a directory of all subscribers to the network and providing conversion from subscriber name to the ADDRESS required. Another important function is the management of queues of requests and responses within the system and, not least, the interaction with the human NETWORK MANAGER.

In large PUBLIC NETWORKS there are also specific tasks performed in a NETWORK MANAGEMENT CENTER, including TRAFFIC ANALYSIS, NETWORK PERFORMANCE, BILLING and ACCOUNTING, CONFIGURATION CONTROL and FAULT DETECTION. Also known as NETWORK CONTROL.

network management center (NMC) An overall center for control of a NETWORK, including: recording for BILLING and ACCOUNTING; TRAFFIC ANALYSIS and NETWORK PERFORMANCE; SOFTWARE loading and maintenance of NODES; CONFIGURATION CONTROL; and FAULT DETECTION and diagnosis.

network management point A location in a NETWORK at which information regarding the loading, utilization and maintenance of the network is concentrated and analyzed. Such a location may have human operators who are responsible for NETWORK MANAGEMENT and who use the information presented to ensure the maximum utilization of the network under various operating conditions.

network management signals Special SIGNALS transferred to and from NETWORK MANAGEMENT POINTS to notify conditions related to the CIRCUITS and transmission and SWITCHING EQUIPMENT. Concerned with NETWORK MANAGEMENT rather than the progress of the individual CALLS and intended to improve utilization and FLOW CONTROL.

network manager A person who has responsibility for the maintenance of a NETWORK and for the level of service experienced by SUBSCRIBERS. See also NETWORK MANAGEMENT.

network operating system (NOS) Software that manages shared resources on a LAN. It provides access to FILES and PRINTERS plus various levels of security to control the access by multiple USERS.

network operator An organization responsible for the operation of a NETWORK, e.g., a COMMON CARRIER providing a service to business USERS by providing CIRCUITS and SWITCHING EQUIPMENT to carry DATA over a PUBLIC DATA NETWORK.

network performance The performance of a NETWORK is measured in a number of ways. First, a network should allow a SUBSCRIBER to gain access to the network with a high probability of obtaining connection to the LOCAL EXCHANGE or NODE and with a high probability of obtaining an ACCESS PATH to a particular CALLED LOCATION. This aspect of service is referred to as AVAILABILITY OF SERVICE. The quality and reliability of the service are also important considerations and affect both availability and the delay across a network. Poor-quality CIRCUITS will result in noticeable delays or poor reception in SPEECH CIRCUITS. Studies of TRAFFIC patterns are necessary to maintain a network capable of handling a PEAK LOAD of MESSAGE SIGNALS. Performance is one of the aspects of NETWORK MANAGEMENT.

network terminating unit A device that INTERFACES one or more TERMINALS to a NETWORK and converts SIGNALS to or from the form expected by the network.

network termination type 1 (NT1) In networks conforming to the INTEGRATED SERVICES DIGITAL NETWORK standard, equipment that performs the functions of OSI layer one (the physical link layer); NT1 devices separate the USER'S equipment from that of the service provider.

network termination type 2 (NT2) In networks conforming to the INTEGRATED SERVICES DIGITAL NETWORK STANDARD, NT2 equipment is a device that can perform the functions of OSI layer two (the DATA LINK LAYER) as well as layer three (the NETWORK LAYER); NT2 includes DIGITAL PBXS, for example.

network topologies The purpose of any NETWORK is to provide ACCESS PATHS for end USERS to communicate. In networks that involve computer DATABASES, the purpose of such communication may be to obtain answers to inquiries addressed to the database, to update RECORDS in the database, to send MESSAGES between one user TERMINAL and another or to transfer sections of the database from one location to another.

The physical arrangement of the NODES and the interconnecting communication LINKS in the network are dependent upon the requirements of the APPLICATION and the geographical distribution of the users. Certain distinctive patterns can be discussed; these patterns are referred to as network topologies. Five such topologies are referred to below and are illustrated in Appendix 11:

1. STAR NETWORK: This type of network is characterized by having a central node at which a controlling COMPUTER handles all functions involved in communication. The users all communicate to this center directly along individual communication links. There may be intelligent concentrators at certain locations, but in principle, all inter-

communication between users takes place to and from, or via, the center.

2. LOOP (OR RING) NETWORK: In such a network there is no central controlling computer but instead an agreed upon PROTOCOL by which each node in the network communicates with others. One node may have certain overall administrative functions (such as collection and generation of performance statistics), but in principle, each node directly communicates with adjacent nodes only, and transactions may be routed around the ring in any direction.
3. MULTIDROP NETWORK: This is one of the simplest networks in which nodes are positioned along a single communication link. Such patterns are common where the cost of a LEASED LINE is a predominant expense in the construction of the network and it is desired to utilize the link fully rather than invest in additional lines. The controlling node occurs at one end of the link.
4. TREE NETWORK: A tree network involves a hierarchy of CONTROL, which can be represented as a pyramid of nodes, in which the controlling node appears to be the apex of the pyramid. The lower levels of the pyramid act as CONCENTRATORS or distribution nodes for all communication to and from the controlling node.
5. MESH NETWORK: A network in which there are many interconnections between nodes and many choices of possible ROUTING for a message or transaction. Taken to extremes, every node would be connected to every other, but this tends to be expensive in terms of communication links, unless of course a dial-up service is available to connect nodes over a public network.

In practice, most networks are formed of some combinations of the topologies described above and, in fact, examination of the exact topology of the network is not necessarily the best way to understand its nature. It is more important to examine what the network has to do to meet the functions and volumes required by users and the method of control. However, the topology does suggest where problems of control may be found.

network user address (NUA) An identify number given to a SUBSCRIBER to a NETWORK service to identify the ADDRESS of a location from which the subscriber operates or the address to which bills and utilization information are provided in respect of a given group of USERS; the exact use is dependent upon the service concerned. See also NETWORK USER IDENTITY and SUB-ADDRESS.

network user identity (NUI) An identity number given to a SUBSCRIBER to a NETWORK service once the person has been registered as an authorized USER. Very often an NUI relates to a specific terminal ADDRESS, but in retrieval systems it can relate to a specific person who may gain access to the service from several TERMINAL locations. On gaining entry to the service, a user may have to provide the NUI in order for the network to validate the use to be made of the service. It is also common for NUIs to be allocated under the umbrella of a NETWORK USER ADDRESS (NUA), which is the registered point at which a subscriber will accept bills for utilization of the services by associated NUIs.

networking The techniques and principles concerned with maintaining a system of communication in which USERS in different locations are able to communicate with one another (for the duration required for a particular CALL) by establishing TRANSMISSION PATHS through a series of EXCHANGES (or NODES). See also NETWORK ARCHITECTURE, NETWORK CONTROL and NETWORK IMPLEMENTATION.

1992 This is the year targeted for the unification of the European community. Emerging policies regarding, for example the protection of intellectual property rights, technical standards and competition among vendors are expected to affect the trade between the United States and the European Community. State-run telecommunications operators, such as France Telecom, may become privately held companies, and basic telecommunications services may be deregulated.

NIST Abbreviation for National Institute of Standards and Technology.

NMC See NETWORK MANAGEMENT CENTER.

no charge answer signal See ANSWER SIGNAL, NO CHARGE.

node A point in a communications network in which a number of COMMUNICATION CHANNELS may converge and wherein some switching or CONTROL functions take place. The term is commonly used in describing DATA NETWORKS.

Nodes are generally computer controlled and may have a variety of functions according to the ARCHITECTURE and purpose of the NETWORK in which they exist. For example, a TELEPHONE EXCHANGE is a node; a PACKET SWITCHING EXCHANGE is also a node. Some nodes may be simple CONCENTRATORS or MULTIPLEXERS, whereas other nodes will have important NETWORK CONTROL functions. They may contain structures for receiving MESSAGES, CONTROLLING ROUTING and scheduling the transmission of messages via the TRANSMISSION LINKS to other nodes. They may also store messages and control the maintenance of MESSAGE QUEUES.

node-to-network protocol A PROTOCOL that regulates the INTERFACE of a NODE to the next adjacent node in the NETWORK, to be contrasted with an END-TO-END PROTOCOL, which regulates transmission from one end user to another. For example, in the X.25 architectures, an end-to-end protocol exists to set up VIRTUAL CIRCUITS, but thereafter the ADDRESSING is between each end user node and the network.

noise Any interference to a SIGNAL picked up along a cable and caused by the operation of electrical equipment, or, for example, in RADIO TRANSMISSION, by a competing transmitter operating at, or near, the same point in the FREQUENCY SPECTRUM.

Other examples include noise from the AMPLIFICATION of signals arising from electron agitation in CONDUCTORS or resistors. This phenomenon varies with temperature. This is known also as circuit noise, thermal agitation, WHITE NOISE, GAUSSION NOISE and RANDOM NOISE.

CROSSTALK and QUANTIZATION noise are also forms of noise arising in communication links. See also SIGNAL-TO-NOISE RATIO.

nominal overall loss ELECTRICAL SIGNALS transmitted over CIRCUITS are attenuated (or weakened) by resistance in the TRANSMISSION MEDIUM. This is known as LOSS. Losses can be attributed to the various components that make up the overall TRANSMISSION PATH, and the losses are cumulative. Thus, an overall loss, or INSERTION LOSS as it is also known, can be determined. The loss varies with frequency, and it is usual to use a test frequency of 800 Hz in specifying and measuring losses. The nominal overall loss is the loss expected in a circuit of defined quality and length. Also known as NOMINAL TOTAL ATTENUATION.

nominal total attenuation In all communication NETWORKS there is a tendency for MESSAGE SIGNALS to become impaired by loss of signal strength over distance—this is known as ATTENUATION. In planning the implementation of a network or TRANSMISSION SYSTEM, a nominal value for attenuation is considered. For a given CALL, this nominal total attenuation is the accumulation of the nominal values arising in each TRUNK or LOCAL CIRCUIT used for the call.

Attenuation can be dealt with by use of AMPLIFIERS and FOUR-WIRE CIRCUITS, and this must be done to ensure that individual trunks do not introduce an unwarranted level of attenuation. These matters are considered when planning transmission systems. Also known as NOMINAL OVERALL LOSS.

nonassociated signaling Relating to a system in which SIGNALING information is transmitted on one or more CHANNELS specifically designated to handle SIGNALS for a group of CIRCUITS. Contrast with CHANNEL ASSOCIATED SIGNALING, wherein signals are carried on (or associated with) each individual TRANSMISSION PATH.

nondirectional antenna A transmitting ANTENNA used to BROADCAST information more or less evenly in any direction, or a receiving antenna sensitive to RADIO WAVES arising from any direction.

nondirector exchange See DIRECTOR EXCHANGE.

nonlinearity An effect experienced in processing ELECTROMAGNETIC WAVES in which various components of an input SIGNAL may be treated differently, causing DISTORTION of output. For example, the GAIN or LOSS produced in a system may vary significantly across different frequencies in the AUDIO FREQUENCY BAND. If steps are not taken to compensate, serious audible distortion may arise on output of the system USERS. These problems arise in RADIO FREQUENCIES also and have to be considered in the designs for all kinds of transmission and receiving equipment. See also DISTORTION.

nonlinearity distortion A form of distortion that arises in processing ELECTROMAGNETIC WAVES in which the AMPLITUDE of output produced is not proportional to the input across the BAND of frequencies being processed. See also NONLINEARITY.

nonrevertive error checking A system of ERROR CHECKING in which a separate CHANNEL is used to report on errors detected at a RECEIVING TERMINAL, the main channel being used continually for MESSAGE transmission. Contrast with REVERTIVE ERROR CHECKING.

nonspectral colors Colors produced by combination of ELECTROMAGNETIC WAVES from sources that simultaneously radiate energy from different BANDS of the visible light spectrum. Contrast with SPECTRAL COLORS.

nonsynchronous network A NETWORK in which the CLOCKS are not synchronized.

nonuniform quantization A QUANTIZATION method in which the intervals of quantization are not equal.

NSFnet National Science Foundation network, funded by the U.S. government and participating as a test bed for gigabit technology.

NT1 See NETWORK TERMINATION TYPE 1.

NT2 See NETWORK TERMINATION TYPE 2.

NTSC Abbreviation of NATIONAL TELEVISION SYSTEMS COMMITTEE of the United States.

NUA See NETWORK USER ADDRESS.

NUI See NETWORK USER IDENTITY.

nul See NULL CHARACTER.

null character An ASCII CHARACTER that is used to fill a sequence of characters without affecting the meaning of that sequence. Its presence, however, can affect CONTROL of equipment that may encounter the null character during DATA TRANSMISSION.

number A CODE used to denote the ADDRESS of a SUBSCRIBER, e.g., a LOCAL NUMBER in a TELEPHONE NETWORK or an INTERNATIONAL NUMBER.

No. 6 exchange An EXCHANGE equipped with STORED PROGRAM CONTROL and able to operate in accordance with the specification of SIGNALING SYSTEM NO. 6.

Nynex See REGIONAL BELL HOLDING COMPANY.

nyquist flank A region forming part of the SPECTRUM ENVELOPE for a transmitted television SIGNAL using VESTIGIAL SIDEBAND MODULATION. This region is shaped on either side of the VISION CARRIER and has the purpose of keeping DISTORTION within acceptable limits.

Nyquist theorem This theorem states the minimum theoretical SAMPLING rate necessary for recovering a transmission signal at a point distant from the transmitter. It is named after H. Nyquist, whose discussions of the theorem were first published in academic journals in the 1920s.

O

OCR See OPTICAL CHARACTER RECOGNITION.

octet A unit of data consisting of 8 BITS (BINARY DIGITS). For example, PACKETS in a PACKET SWITCHING SYSTEM are usually transmitted in multiples of 8 bits, e.g., the packet size may be expressed as 1,024 octets, meaning 8,192 bits.

octet timing signal A SIGNAL in a PACKET NETWORK that is used to identify the first BIT of an 8-bit sequence (or OCTET) occurring in a continuous sequence of octets.

odd parity check A check performed upon a unit of DATA where parity BITS have been added to the data for ERROR CONTROL purposes and where the error control scheme is constructed to create odd parity in the rows or columns of bits that make up each BLOCK or CHARACTER. See also EVEN PARITY CHECK.

OEM See ORIGINAL EQUIPMENT MANUFACTURER.

offered traffic The volume of TRAFFIC that would arise if all CALLS required by USERS would be accepted by the system. Contrast with CARRIED TRAFFIC.

office In TELECOMMUNICATIONS, the term "office" refers to an element in a telecommunications system that controls the TRAFFIC between different points. The office generally houses a COMMON CARRIER'S SWITCHING EQUIPMENT and allows any SUBSCRIBER of a common carrier's service to communicate with any other within a prescribed area.

The most modern offices are capable of carrying VOICE, DATA, and TELEX TRAFFIC, but many of the offices in use today are still designed specifically for one kind of traffic, such as, voice traffic over a PUBLIC SWITCHED TELEPHONE NETWORK or data over an international telex network. The term is often synonymous with EXCHANGE. For the five categories of offices, see OFFICE CLASS. See also EXCHANGE, EXCHANGE HIERARCHY.

office class Categories of switching points within a COMMON CARRIER'S NETWORK. Class 1 is the REGIONAL CENTER; class 2, SECTIONAL CENTER; class 3, PRIMARY CENTER; class 4, TOLL OFFICE; and class 5, END OFFICE. Also known as class of EXCHANGE.

off-line When DATA COMMUNICATIONS equipment is not being directly controlled by a HOST PROCESSOR or is not linked to a TRANSMISSION LINE, it is said to be off-line.

off-resistance The electrical resistance presented by any switch or relay in the off position.

oligarchic network A NETWORK in which most of the CLOCKS that establish timing for events are under the control of a few of the clocks. It is an example of a SYNCHRONIZED NETWORK.

ONA See OPEN NETWORK ARCHITECTURE.

one-to-many calls A CALL in which a single TERMINAL is connected by a CIRCUIT to a number of user terminals at distant locations. Thus, it is possible to have several USERS involved in a CONVERSATION. Contrast with ONE-TO-ONE CALL.

one-to-one call A CALL in which two TERMINALS are connected for MESSAGE transmission but only one USER terminal is connected at each end of the TRANSMISSION CHANNEL. Contrast with ONE-TO-MANY CALL or MANY-TO-MANY CALL.

one-unit message A complete MESSAGE that is transmitted within a single unit of DATA, e.g., a CONTROL signal.

on-line processing A term used in DATA PROCESSING to denote any system in which the end USERS are directly connected by CIRCUITS to a COMPUTER running an APPLICATION. The users are able to interact with the system at any time when they wish to process a transaction. Contrast with BATCH PROCESSING.

on-line program development A method used for the development of computer programs in which programmers are on-line to a COMPUTER, which contains COMPILERS, editors, and testing aids and which enables the programmer to write, check, test, correct and update programs.

on-line system A DATA PROCESSING SYSTEM in which all functions are performed under control of a computer processor, including the preparation and entry of input DATA and the transmission and distribution of output results. Transactions are often dealt with as they arise in the normal course of business with minimal delay rather than being batched for processing at a convenient time. See also REAL-TIME SYSTEM.

Open Network Architecture (ONA) An FCC mandate issued as part of COMPUTER INQUIRY III, Open Network Architecture is concerned with TELECOMMUNICATIONS and information NETWORKS. A detailed definition of ONA is emerging, but it is still largely a concept that reinforces the goal of equal access.

open systems architecture A design for a DATA NETWORK that fulfills the objective of allowing any USER to communicate with any other user, regardless of the types of COMPUTER systems and TERMINALS in use. Such a system is a theoretical concept which is being sought by international standards organizations and which will require the cooperation of equipment vendors, communications authorities and corporate users.

Such a system would require standard conventions to be used throughout the world, including the communications aspects and the processing aspects which take place in computer APPLICATIONS. An open system concept does not imply that a particular COMPUTER will automatically be obliged to receive CALLS from other such systems; it refers to the potential for such systems to communicate with one another if they agree to do so.

The article headed OPEN SYSTEMS INTERCONNECTION explains in more detail the nature and structure of such systems.

Open Systems Interconnection (OSI) A model for the logical structure of networked DATA COMMUNICATIONS EQUIPMENT. It was developed by the INTERNATIONAL ORGANIZATION FOR STANDARDIZATION and first published in November 1978. It was intended to provide a basis for open systems interconnection, i.e., a network in which there is no single central control point; CONTROL resides in the various NODES of the network operating to common standards. These standards are expressed in an ARCHITECTURE that provides seven control levels.

Each control level provides a clear definition of the PROTOCOLS and formats and allows a PEER INTERACTION between USERS who have implemented the architecture, i.e., the control levels of one user communicate with the equivalent level of another user. Thus, two users who have correctly implemented at least the first two levels of control are able to exchange INFORMATION over a network.

The control levels are as follows:

Level 1—this is called the PHYSICAL CONTROL LAYER and defines the PHYSICAL INTERFACE between DATA TERMINAL EQUIPMENT (DTE) and DATA CIRCUIT TERMINATING EQUIPMENT (DCE); it presents the electrical characteristics and SIGNALING needed to establish, maintain, and clear the physical connection between line terminating equipment.

Level 2—this is known as the LINK CONTROL and equates with the HIGH LEVEL DATA LINK CONTROL (HDLC). It provides the protocol for checking that information transmitted in small units known as FRAMES has been correctly exchanged across the network between two TERMINALS.

Level 3—this is called the NETWORK CONTROL LAYER and provides control between two adjacent network nodes and between DTE and the network, e.g., the X.25 PACKET NETWORK standard, which allows packet formatting and VIRTUAL CIRCUITS.

Level 4—known as the TRANSPORT LAYER. Sometimes called the END-TO-END LAYER. This provides control from USER NODE to user node including ADDRESSING, DATA ASSURANCE and FLOW CONTROL.

Level 5—known as the SESSION CONTROL LAYER, it provides for establishing, maintaining and releasing logical connections for DATA TRANSFER.

Level 6—known as the PRESENTATION CONTROL layer, it provides for data-formats and transformations, e.g., those required for VISUAL DISPLAY screens or printers.

Level 7—this is the APPLICATION LAYER.

In publishing this model, ISO aims to achieve progress toward a complete family of standards for operating on PUBLIC DATA NETWORKS. Implementations of the standard have been achieved; for example, the X.25 standard defines a three-level protocol corresponding to the first three levels of the ISO model. It is expected that convergence toward a single standard covering all layers of the ISO model will take several years, but the goal of any terminal being able to access any application is closer to being realized.

open systems interface A specification of a standard method of NETWORK interconnection that allows any USER to communicate with any other, regardless of the manufacturer of the equipment and SOFTWARE involved. See also OPEN SYSTEMS ARCHITECTURE and OPEN SYSTEMS INTERCONNECTION.

operating system A special program permanently resident in a COMPUTER or a COMMUNICATIONS CONTROLLER to control the HARDWARE and SOFTWARE resources and to supervise the running of other programs, including USER APPLICATIONS.

optical amplifier A device made of erbium-doped OPTICAL FIBER plus a diode LASER. It helps overcome the signal loss in data transmission via fiber optic cable. Many industry observers think it will revolutionize telecommunications.

optical character recognition (OCR) The conversion of printed or written CHARACTERS into DIGITAL CODE via a light-sensitive scanning device.

optical disk A disk on which data is recorded by LASERS. It has more storage capacity than a magnetic disk.

optical fibers Optical fibers provide a BOUNDED TRANSMISSION MEDIUM along which information is carried as pulses of light. The main application of this technology is to transmit DIGITAL SIGNALS for DATA or telegraphic communication. The medium provides a BROADBAND TRANSMISSION CHANNEL, and the signals can be carried over significant distances without DISTORTION. In this respect, optical fiber channels have advantages over COAXIAL CABLES.

An optical fiber is usually about one-tenth of a millimeter in diameter and consists of a central core of glass (silica) surrounded by a sheath of similar material but with a lower refractive index than the central core. Light energy transmitted along the fiber is gradually lost but, with fibers in use today, 10% of the energy transmitted can be delivered over a distance of 3 to 4 kilometers, and there are expectations that this distance can be extended to 50 kilometers without the need for REPEATERS to regenerate the signal. See also OPTICAL AMPLIFIER.

Information to be transmitted must first be generated as electrical DIGITAL PULSES representing a series of ones or zeros. This signal is used to activate a laser light source, which generates the pulses of light that travel along the optical fiber. The light is detected at the far end and converted back to electrical forms.

The great advantage of today's optical fibers is that they provide an almost distortionless medium over 10 kilometers with DATA RATES of up to 8 million BITS per second on a single fiber.

A great deal of development is being undertaken on the composition of fibers, which presently allow transmission of light in the infrared region. It seems likely that very large BANDWIDTH systems will be operated, in future, for applications in both residential and business communications—the impact would be truly revolutionary.

Most offices and private homes are today connected to national communications networks by a simple wire transmission channel affording a bandwidth of only 3 to 4 kHz. Optical fibers provide an enormous increase in the bandwidth and would allow a great range of services involving the transmission of wideband VIDEO and digital signals directly into every home and office.

In many areas, optical fibers are used in the replacement of coaxial cable routes between exchanges in city areas for intercity routes. Coaxial systems require repeaters every 2 to 3 kilometers. Optical fiber systems afford significant savings in the size and cost of equipment and improve the utilization of underground ducts and cableways.

Optical fibers represent one of the most significant technological improvements in the field of telecommunications. See also PLASTIC FIBER.

optical waveguides A WAVEGUIDE that carries MESSAGE SIGNALS as light signals along a BOUNDED MEDIUM constructed of glass fibers. Present developments using INFRARED LIGHT indicate that vast BANDWIDTHS are available, e.g., up to 100 THz. See also OPTICAL FIBERS.

original equipment manufacturer (OEM) A manufacturer that sells the equipment it makes to vendors that resell it under another name.

originating traffic This term defines the use made of a particular TERMINAL to generate OUTGOING CALLS in contrast to INCOMING CALLS (referred to as TERMINATING TRAFFIC). See also TRAFFIC, INSTANTANEOUS TRAFFIC, TRAFFIC VOLUME and CALLING RATE.

oscillator A device containing electrical CIRCUITS that can create ALTERNATING CURRENT signals at a prespecified frequency or at a selected frequency. Used, for example, to generate CARRIER WAVES in a TRANSMISSION SYSTEM.

OSI See OPEN SYSTEMS INTERCONNECTION.

out-of-band signaling A system of SIGNALING in which SIGNALS are conveyed outside the BAND of frequencies normally used for MESSAGE transmission but instead are carried on (or associated with) the TRANSMISSION CHANNEL.

outgoing call Any CALL that is routed to a distant ADDRESS, e.g., from an originating DATA TERMINAL or from a SWITCHED TELEPHONE EXCHANGE.

outgoing lines The CIRCUITS that are used to output MESSAGE SIGNALS from SWITCHING EQUIPMENT to a distant ADDRESS.

outgoing trunks The TRUNK LINES connected to a central office or switching center for the purpose of carrying outgoing TRAFFIC.

out-of-band components Elements that arise as stray signal currents arising from MESSAGE SIGNALS but are transferred onto to TRANSMISSION CHANNELS outside of the FREQUENCY BAND normally used for message transmission. Although they may not interfere directly with messages, they may be designated as harmful if they have any interference with other frequencies used in the monitoring or maintenance of transmission facilities.

out-of-order signal A SIGNAL sent on a BACKWARD CHANNEL to indicate that the TERMINAL of a CALLED SUBSCRIBER is faulty.

out-slot signaling SIGNALING information associated with a DIGITAL CHANNEL but transmitted in TIME SLOTS not within the slots used for message BITS within the channel time.

overall loss The sum of all the LOSSES that arise end-to-end in a CIRCUIT; usually measured in BELS or DECIBELS. Also known as INSERTION LOSS.

overflow A condition that occurs when a CALL cannot be connected via a particular group of CIRCUITS and an automatic ROUTING is arranged through another group in which a free circuit exists.

overflow bid An attempt to ROUTE a CALL through a particular CIRCUIT GROUP in which the attempt has to be satisfied by a route through an available circuit on another circuit group, the first circuit group being fully loaded and unable to accept the bid.

overhead bits Signal elements that are added to INFORMATION BITS as part of the management of a communications process and not intended for transmission to the end USER.

overlap 1. An erroneous condition in FACSIMILE TRANSMISSION in which the scanning process causes elements of the picture to be overlapped.

2. An overlap operation occurs in certain SIGNALING SYSTEMS in which ADDRESS INFORMATION is transmitted before a CALLING SUBSCRIBER has finished dialing the address.

own exchange call A CALL between two SUBSCRIBERS connected to the same LOCAL EXCHANGE. Contrast with MULTI-EXCHANGE CALL.

P

PABX See PRIVATE AUTOMATIC BRANCH EXCHANGE.

Pacific Telesis See REGIONAL BELL HOLDING COMPANY.

packet A relatively small unit of DATA (up to about 8,000 BITS), transmitted over a PACKET SWITCHING NETWORK as part of a MESSAGE to be transferred from one USER to another. Each packet includes information as a HEADER that identifies the DESTINATION ADDRESS and the sequence of the packet within the overall message. Packets travel independently of one another, and perhaps by different routes, but are reassembled as a coherent MESSAGE at the RECEIVING STATION.

There are different types of packets; some carry user information (e.g., data packets) but others (e.g., CALL REQUEST PACKETS) are used to request the NETWORK CONTROL to perform operations to establish or clear CALLS. See also PACKET SWITCHING NETWORK.

packet assembler/disassembler A SOFTWARE routine or a system element that deals with PACKET ASSEMBLY and DISASSEMBLY in a PACKET SWITCHING SYSTEM, i.e., it assembles the USER DATA into PACKETS complete with HEADER and identifying information used to control the correct ROUTING and sequencing of packets during the transmission process.

packet assembly The process involved in converting a MESSAGE SIGNAL into PACKETS. See also PACKET SWITCHING NETWORK and PACKET ASSEMBLER/DISASSEMBLER.

packet buffer Part of a SWITCH or PROCESSOR where PACKETS are temporarily stored.

packet delay A measure of the performance of a PACKET SWITCHING NETWORK is the time taken to transfer PACKETS from the transmitting to the receiving location. If the network is congested, the packets are stored temporarily until a VIRTUAL CIRCUIT is available. In interactive systems, the delay may be noticeable to the USERS and affect the quality of service. Generally speaking, the average delay should be on the order of no more than 200 milliseconds for interactive data users and 600 milliseconds for bulk DATA TRANSFER.

packet disassembly The process involved in reassembling a MESSAGE SIGNAL from PACKETS received over a PACKET SWITCHING NETWORK.

packet level protocols Formal rules that define the structure of commands, responses and BIT PATTERNS concerned with the handling of PACKETS of INFORMATION in a PACKET SWITCHING NETWORK.

packet mode terminal A DATA TERMINAL that has the necessary logical structures built into the HARDWARE and SOFTWARE to enable the terminal to format and transmit/receive PACKETS to and from a packet switching network.

packet network See PACKET SWITCHING NETWORK.

packet sequence In a PACKET SWITCHING NETWORK each MESSAGE SIGNAL is broken into a number of smaller elements for the convenience of transmission across the NETWORK. These elements, known as PACKETS, may not be transmitted in strict sequence, but each packet contains identifying and sequence information to enable the message to be reconstructed.

packet switching exchange (PSE) A NODE in a PACKET SWITCHING NETWORK capable of carrying out the full range of packet switching operations, including managing TRANSMISSION LINES, switching PACKETS and performing PACKET ASSEMBLY and PACKET DISASSEMBLY functions as well as all command functions to set up and clear CALLS.

In such a network there may be other nodes that simply provide access to the network for remote SUBSCRIBERS by concentrating USERS onto a transmission line having access to a PSE. These are known as REMOTE ACCESS POINTS (RAP).

packet switching network In a CIRCUIT SWITCHED SYSTEM, a physical CIRCUIT is made between two TERMINALS for the duration of a CALL. With high-speed circuits carrying DIGITAL DATA, a much greater resource utilization can be achieved by sharing paths through the NETWORK. Packet switching systems achieve such improvements in use of transmission resources.

To allow such path sharing, data is transferred through the network in PACKETS, which include, apart from the data itself, ADDRESSING and sequence information to control the progress of the packet in the network.

If at any time the arrival rate of packets exceeds the capacity of any NODE in the network, the packets are queued in COMPUTER stores and forwarded when transmission time is available.

Packet networks provide a VIRTUAL CIRCUIT, which appears to the USERS as a permanent connection between two terminals but which, in fact, is shared with other users.

The logical structure of the packets is determined by the PROTOCOL of the system and has no relevance to the structure of the message to be transmitted. The TRANSMITTING and RECEIVING STATIONS have to be designed to INTERFACE with this protocol and may be responsible for PACKETIZING and DEPACKETIZING the USER DATA. This operation may also be performed in PACKET SWITCHING EXCHANGES to which SUBSCRIBERS are connected.

A packet switching system is an example of a STORE-AND-FORWARD SYSTEM, and, as such, it can be adapted to provide speed, CODE or PROTOCOL CONVERSIONS, enabling a number of dissimilar terminals to operate within the same network.

Originally, packet switching was designed to provide a more efficient method of transferring data over networks, but it is also possible to transfer digitized VOICE provided the end-to-end PACKET DELAY is not more than 200 milliseconds. See also FAST PACKET SWITCHING, VOICE PACKET SWITCHING, X.25.

packet switching service A service provided by a service operator to make available the facilities of a PACKET SWITCHING NETWORK to registered SUBSCRIBERS.

packet switching system See PACKET SWITCHING NETWORK.

packetized voice The DIGITAL representation of VOICE signals.

packetizing The process by which a MESSAGE is broken up into smaller segments or PACKETS for transmission to the LINE in a PACKET SWITCHING NETWORK. Each packet contains ADDRESSING information to identify the USER to whom it is intended, the transmitting user and the packet sequence.

PAD See PACKET ASSEMBLER/DISASSEMBLER.

page A unit of information to be printed or displayed for a USER of an information service. For example, a page retrieved using a VIDEOTEX SYSTEM. Also referred to as a FRAME, but in the British system known as PRESTEL, each page can consist of up to 26 frames, each of 960 CHARACTERS.

page charge The TARIFF charged to a USER of a VIDEOTEX SYSTEM by an INFORMATION PROVIDER for access to a PAGE of INFORMATION.

page store A MEMORY UNIT capable of storing a display of INFORMATION for a PAGE of TEXT/GRAPHICS. For example, the memory unit in a VIDEOTEX TERMINAL. Also known as FRAME STORE.

paired-disparity code A CODE in which BITS or CHARACTERS may be represented under a given set of rules by two different conditions. An example is given under ALTERNATE MARK INVERSION. Also known as an ALTERNATING CODE.

PAL See PHASE ALTERNATION BY LINE.

PAM See PULSE AMPLITUDE MODULATION.

paper tape See PUNCHED PAPER TAPE.

paper tape punch A device for recording DATA as holes in PUNCHED PAPER TAPE. It may be designed for off-line preparation of MESSAGES or to record messages received over a COMMUNICATION CHANNEL.

P/AR See PEAK TO AVERAGE RATIO.

parallel attribute coding A system for coding in which the attributes of a CHARACTER to be displayed (e.g., its color, height or flashing/steady indicator) are stored as CODES but not serially in the PAGE STORE. Thus, the attribute characters do not result in a compulsory space in the TEXT as is the case with SERIAL ATTRIBUTE CODING.

The parallel attribute system is more flexible and allows more information per PAGE, but the terminal logic is more complex than that required for serial coding, and serial attribute coding can cope with most practical situations.

parallel data transmission A method of transmission in which the BITS that make up a CHARACTER or BYTE pass simultaneously along separate paths rather than in BIT SERIAL mode.

parallel mode Pertaining to the transfer or transmission of all the SIGNAL elements of a CHARACTER or BYTE at the same time along independent paths. Compare with SERIAL MODE.

parallel transmission All forms of DATA TRANSMISSION are serial in nature, i.e., BITS, CHARACTERS or FRAMES are sent one after another along the TRANSMISSION PATH. However, over very short distances, or within an electronic device, it is sometimes arranged that a separate signal path is available for each each constituent bit of a character. This is known as BIT PARALLEL TRANSMISSION.

parallel-to-serial converter A device that receives CHARACTERS (or some similar unit of DATA) as a set of simultaneous signal elements along separate paths and then presents these elements in serial form to an outgoing path. It may automatically generate START BITS and STOP BITS for each character.

parity check A check made upon the rows or columns of BITS forming a CHARACTER, BLOCK or FRAME of DATA. This is made as part of an ERROR CONTROL procedure in which parity bits are appended to data prior to transmission deliberately to create an EVEN (or, in some systems, ODD) parity.

partial transmission A technique for entering DATA over a NETWORK in which an operator enters variable data onto a predetermined form format displayed on a VISUAL DISPLAY unit. When the operator transmits the form, only the variable data is sent to the LINE. Also known as SPLIT SCREEN TRANSMISSION.

partitioned database In a system in which a geographically distributed population of USERS requires access to update or retrieve information from computer FILES, there are certain choices in deciding where to locate the DATABASE. These choices include: (a) a single central location in which all updating and inquiry takes place, (b) a central update center, but with remote replicated versions of the database for local inquiry or (c) a database in which information relevant to certain regions is updated, maintained and stored in each region.

The latter is referred to as a partitioned database and would be chosen where there is a need for an accurate and up-to-date version of the files in each region and where an economic analysis of TRAFFIC flows within the total system and within regions supports the argument for such partitioning across network NODES. See also SHARED DATABASE.

passive broadcast medium A physical medium, such as a COAXIAL CABLE LOOP, that allows FRAMES of INFORMATION to be propagated for reception by any of the STATIONS connected to it. No attempt is made to ROUTE frames to specific ADDRESSES, but each station includes a FRAME GRABBER.

path The complete set of resources that provides a connection between two points for the purpose of transmitting and receiving a MESSAGE SIGNAL. Paths may be linked by switches (EXCHANGES) to form a SWITCHED CONNECTION. Where the method of transmission includes a separate CHANNEL for GO and RETURN directions, these are considered to form a single path.

path control An element in a NODE of a PACKET SWITCHING SYSTEM. It is responsible for ROUTING packets to the correct DATA LINK CONTROL for transmission to another node or to the correct STATION attached to the node itself. It is also responsible for PACKETIZING or DE-PACKETIZING.

path independent protocol (PIP) A method used to transmit INFORMATION over a PACKET SWITCHING NETWORK in which no specific path is established and each PACKET may, therefore, be ROUTED independently of other packets in the same CONVERSATION. Contrast with FIXED PATH PROTOCOL.

pattern of intermittency A term used to describe the nature of transmission between two USERS in a DATA NETWORK. For example, a pattern that entails transmission of a single information PACKET from one user to the other is known as a DATAGRAM. A DIALOGUE that entails transmission in both directions to complete a series of connected functions is known as a TRANSACTION, and a dialogue in which a number of transactions are progressed is known as a SESSION.

PBT See PUSH-BUTTON TELEPHONE.

PBX See PRIVATE BRANCH EXCHANGE.

PC See MICROCOMPUTER.

PCM See PULSE CODE MODULATION.

PDI See PICTURE DESCRIPTION INSTRUCTIONS.

PDN See PUBLIC DATA NETWORKS.

peak load The maximum TRAFFIC experienced by a NETWORK or planned for in the operation of a network. In PUBLIC NETWORKS, the peak load occurs at the BUSY HOUR. In PRIVATE NETWORKS, such as in DATA PROCESSING applications, the peak load may occur after a system failure, when the traffic that has been suspended or delayed is restarted.

peak volume Relating to TRAFFIC studies in communications NETWORKS and defining the number of simultaneous CALLS being conducted at the busiest period in the operation of a system.

peer interaction A concept that derives from considering the related functions performed at each end of a DATA TRANSMISSION channel, in which components of the system act in pairs. For example, the MODEMS at each end communicate with one another, regardless of information about the TEXT or information for controlling the LINK. The DATE LINK CONTROL elements at each end manage the transmission and ERROR CHECKING without regard to MODULATION and DEMODULATION performed by the modems. The APPLICATION PROGRAMS are concerned only with the text transmitted.

There is an implication that in a NETWORK with a totally peer style of interaction, no one COMPUTER has total responsibility for NETWORK MANAGEMENT.

peer-to-peer network When NODES on a NETWORK can communicate without transmitting DATA through a HOST PROCESSOR, they are performing peer-to-peer networking. CCITT X.400 describes a peer-to-peer application, for example.

penetration of service A measure of the degree to which a particular service is accepted by the TARGET USER POPULATION. It is measured by the number of USERS from the target population who have installed a TERMINAL. For example, the penetration of the TELEPHONE service into the residential market can be expressed as the average number of telephones per home.

per setup unit A type of CONTROL device associated with a CALL during the period of CALL ESTABLISHMENT.

per-call unit A class of CONTROL device that is associated with a particular CALL while that call is in progress, e.g., a device to monitor a CALL ANSWERED SIGNAL.

percentage overflow Derived from the ratio of CALLS that are required for

OVERFLOW (known as OVERFLOW BIDS) to the total number of calls bidding for a particular CIRCUIT GROUP.

perception data Information collected directly from the human USERS of a communication system as a result of tests conducted to find factors that make the service attractive and satisfactory to users.

peripheral equipment Any device (such as DATA PRINTER, FLOPPY DISK, or PAPER TAPE PUNCH) that can be connected to a DATA TERMINAL to provide additional methods of inputting, storing or outputting DATA.

per-line unit A class of CONTROL device that is permanently associated with a particular LINE and cannot be shared, e.g., a device attached to a line to recognize CALL REQUEST SIGNALS.

permanent copy A MESSAGE produced on a physical medium, e.g., a printed message. See also HARD COPY. Contrast with TRANSIENT COPY or SOFT COPY.

permanent virtual circuit A VIRTUAL CIRCUIT is one that appears to be a point-to-point connection between two TERMINALS in a PACKET SWITCHING NETWORK. In fact, part of the path between the two terminals is shared by many other terminals using TIME DIVISION MULTIPLEXING techniques. A permanent virtual circuit occurs where terminals are permanently associated via a virtual circuit. In concept, this is equivalent to a LEASED CIRCUIT providing permanent point-to-point connection between two terminals, i.e., no CALL SETUP or CLEARING procedures are needed. See also PACKET SWITCHING and PUBLIC DATA NETWORKS.

personal computer (PC) See MICROCOMPUTER.

person/machine interface The PROTOCOL that a human USER must understand and operate in order to use a particular device for its defined purpose. This protocol should be as easy and natural to the USER as is possible.

phase Any SIGNAL based upon ALTERNATING CURRENT can be represented by a time graph that shows the variation in the voltage of the signal over time. Two signals of identical frequency and identical voltage AMPLITUDE can still differ from one another in that they may be out of phase, i.e., one signal voltage lags behind the other. In PHASE MODULATION, signals that are 180° out of phase are used to represent opposite conditions (e.g., the two conditions 0 and 1 in a system of BINARY NOTATION). In theory, there are infinite variations of possible phase, but, in practice, it is expensive to detect many variations economically. Phase modulation systems involving more than two phase angles are, however, used in TELECOMMUNICATIONS to represent different signal values. See also MULTI-PHASE MODULATION.

phase alternation by line (PAL) A color television broadcasting system developed in the United Kingdom and West Germany that uses 625 pictures lines and a 50 Hz FIELD FREQUENCY. See also SECAM and NTSC.

phase inversion A technique used in PHASE MODULATION in which the binary values 0 and 1 are represented by UNIT SIGNAL ELEMENTS commencing with a change of signal phase in a specific direction. See also PHASE.

phase jitter The length of SIGNALS can be randomly distorted when the frequency of the TRANSMISSION changes. This DISTORTION is called phase jitter, and it can create misinterpretation of transmitted DATA.

phase modulation A method of MODULATION used to represent BINARY INFORMATION in which the PHASE of the CARRIER SIGNAL is continually inverted to indicate the BINARY DIGITS 0 and 1.

Two methods of phase modulation are: (a) DIFFERENTIAL PHASE MODULATION and (b) FIXED REFERENCE PHASE MODULATION.

In case (a), a change in phase simply indicates a change from 0 to 1 or 1 to 0. No REFERENCE WAVE is required to detect the signal.

In case (b), the process is as follows: A 0 DIGIT is indicated by a group of contiguous cycles beginning from a PHASE INVERSION in one direction and the 1 digit by a group of contiguous cycles beginning from an opposite phase inversion. The DEMODULATION of the original signal involves the DETECTION of different phase relationships.

phase-shift keying (PSK) One way to modify the CARRIER SIGNAL so that it transmits digital DATA, phase-shift keying causes the data to be represented as varying PHASES of the carrier signal.

phasing In FACSIMILE systems, a process that takes place at the RECEIVING TERMINAL to ensure that a transmitted picture is correctly positioned on the recording medium. The process entails achieving coincidence between the significant points of the scanning field at each end of the TRANSMISSION LINE.

phosphorescence A form of light radiation that continues after external excitation has ceased; the afterglow effect that is produced by the properties of phosphor materials after they have been excited by the action of an ELECTRON BEAM. For example, the light from a TV tube is created first by FLUORESCENCE, which arises when the beam strikes phosphor materials on the tube surface; this light fades slowly due to the properties of the phosphor, e.g., it takes 4 milliseconds to fade to 5% of its original value.

photograph facsimile telegraphy A form of TELEGRAPHY in which SIGNALS containing information relating to continuous tonal densities are transmitted to permit a faithful reproduction of any photographic image over a communications CIRCUIT. Compare with DOCUMENT FACSIMILE TELEGRAPHY and ALPHABETIC TELEGRAPHY.

photometric power The electromagnetic energy per second flowing from a light source measured to account for the human perception of such energy, which varies by sensitivity to different WAVELENGTHS. See also VISIBILITY FUNCTION.

photometry The science concerned with the human perception of light energy radiated from a source. This would include light emitted directly by sources as well as light emitted as reflection and incident light. Compare with RADIOMETRY.

photopic response The average response curve obtained by observing human visual perception of ELECTROMAGNETIC WAVES. See also VISIBILITY FUNCTION.

physical address A unique identification associated with a particular STATION on a NETWORK.

physical channel The physical medium (e.g., COAXIAL or FIBER OPTIC CABLE) used to convey SIGNALS and having particular physical and electrical properties to meet the specified PHYSICAL LINK LAYER of a defined NETWORK ARCHITECTURE.

physical control layer See PHYSICAL LINK LAYER.

physical interface The specification of the ELECTRICAL SIGNALS needed to establish, maintain and clear the connection between a TERMINAL and DATA CIRCUIT TERMINATING EQUIPMENT (DCE). Compare with MECHANICAL INTERFACE and LOGICAL INTERFACE.

physical level interface In a layered NETWORK ARCHITECTURE, the lowest level of CONTROL responsible for actuating, maintaining and deactivating the LINKS between a TERMINAL and a NETWORK is called the PHYSICAL LINK LAYER. The specification of the electrical and physical connections at this level is known as the physical level interface.

physical link layer In a NETWORK ARCHITECTURE, this level of CONTROL represents the lowest level in the ISO REFERENCE MODEL FOR OPEN SYSTEMS. This layer is dependent upon the physical medium for the TRANSMISSION CHANNEL. It includes physical and electrical INTERFACES to the channel, including DATA ENCODING, timing interconnection and voltage levels. Compare with DATA LINK LAYER.

picture description instruction (PDI) A CODE that has been formed by compressing a HIGH RESOLUTION picture definition to enable detailed and complex graphic images to be transmitted efficiently over a narrow band channel. The PDI is able to regenerate the original picture. See also ALPHAGEOMETRIC CODING.

picture element In a television system, or in any VISUAL DISPLAY system used to display TEXT and/or GRAPHICS, a picture element is the smallest discrete element at which a component of an image can be resolved. The number of horizontal lines determines the VERTICAL RESOLUTION of the image, and in television systems 625 lines are recommended by CCIR.

In a visual display unit used for DATA PROCESSING, information to be displayed is created in a MEMORY UNIT as a matrix of BITS corresponding to the resolution possible by the properties of the screen. Individual CHARACTERS to be displayed are composed of groups of picture elements, say 12 to a character. Fewer elements may be used, but this will reduce the quality of the character display. Three or four lines may be used for each character row.

The arrangement of phosphor dots on the screen also imparts the resolution possible. The higher the resolution desired, the more dots are required.

The term pixel (a contraction of *picture element*) is often used.

picture frequency The frequency with which a complete set of LINES representing a picture is displayed in a television system. Measured in cycles per second (Hz), the picture frequency is normally exactly half the FIELD FREQUENCY. Typical picture frequencies are United States: 30 Hz; CCIR 625-line system: 25 Hz. See also INTERLACED SCANNING and VIDEO SIGNAL.

Picture Prestel The name given by BRITISH TELECOM to a VIDEOTEX SYSTEM first exhibited in March 1980 and demonstrating the storage and display of photographic images as part of a videotex picture. This concept is an extension of PRESTEL (which basically uses ALPHAMOSAIC GRAPHICS).

PIP See PATH INDEPENDENT PROTOCOL.

pipe Conceptual way to think of the transmission medium carrying BITS of INFORMATION.

pixel See PICTURE ELEMENT.

plain language transmission A form of telegraph transmission in which SIGNALS are transmitted in accordance with the international standard alphabet and are in the form of WORDS that have conventional meanings of the particular language, e.g., English, French.

plain old telephone service (POTS) A COMMON CARRIER's service for TELEPHONE CONVERSATIONS between humans, excluding the additional facilities needed for human-to-COMPUTER communications. POTS may be replaced by the BASIC ACCESS offering of INTEGRATED SERVICES DIGITAL NETWORK.

plastic fiber An OPTICAL FIBER, the core of which is made of thin plastic, rather than glass, strands. Plastic fiber is cheaper than glass, but it has a higher rate of light loss.

plesiochronous signals Two or more signals are said to be plesiochronous if their corresponding significant instants occur at the same rate but not in the same PHASE.

point of presence (POP) A term introduced after DIVESTITURE to indicate the physical access point in a LATA where the long-distance COMMON CARRIER terminates a SUBSCRIBER'S INTEROFFICE CIRCUITS.

point-of-sale terminal (POS) A device situated at a place where commercial transactions take place resulting in cash or credit payments. Such machines are located in shops, garages and stores where contact takes place between staff and customers. They are used to capture details of the transaction and to issue receipts to customers. They may be connected on-line to a credit checking center, but often they contain a storage device to record transactions throughout the day. They may be polled at close of business by a central COMPUTER to capture details of the day's business.

point-to-multipoint line See MULTIDROP LINE.

point-to-point line When the CIRCUIT links the locations directly without intervening processing NODES it is called a point-to-point line. Intermediary SWITCHING equipment can be included in the TRANSMISSION.

point-to-point network A NETWORK in which all connections between TERMINALS and NODES are by permanent direct communication over LEASED LINES. Such systems are less complex than SWITCHED SYSTEMS, and speed of response is very high, but they are usually inefficient in line utilization.

polling A technique used in the operation of a MULTIDROP NETWORK in which several TERMINALS are connected to only one LINE and to one computer interface PORT. Each terminal can transmit or receive information to and from the INTERFACE port, but the COMPUTER decides which terminal is active at any instant. The selection of specific terminals is achieved by SOFTWARE, and the process is known as polling.

POP See POINT OF PRESENCE.

port A point of entry to a service or NETWORK and, generally speaking, representing a single CHANNEL to which a USER can connect at a specified SIGNALING RATE.

POS terminal See POINT-OF-SALE TERMINAL.

positive justification In TIME DIVISION MULTIPLEXING, the insertion of JUSTIFYING DIGITS into a stream of INFORMATION BITS in order to create coincidence with a required series of TIME SLOTS. See also JUSTIFICATION.

possible crosstalk CROSSTALK components that exist but do not intrude on the USER at the point at which they have been measured but may intrude at another point.

possible crosstalk components Unwanted SIGNALS that arise from SPEECH SIGNALS and are not of sufficient AMPLITUDE to interfere with desired signals at the point at which they have been measured but may interfere elsewhere. See also CROSSTALK.

Postal, Telegraph and Telephone agency (PTT) In countries where the national government has a monopoly over communications, a governmental department called the Postal, Telegraph, and Telephone agency operates the COMMON CARRIERS. It is the legal entity responsible for the regulation and operation of all public communication services in a country. A PTT may license others to operate services on its behalf and the powers of a PTT may vary from country to country, but, in practice, they have extensive regulating powers and often act as communication carriers.

POTS See PLAIN OLD TELEPHONE SERVICE.

preamble sequence A series of BITS transmitted by a STATION to a CHANNEL to precede each FRAME in order to establish SYNCHRONIZATION with other stations using the channel. This technique is used in LOCAL AREA NETWORKS.

prefix Any set of coded information that qualifies information that follows; e.g., an INTERNATIONAL DIALING PREFIX that specifies the country for location of the SUBSCRIBER referenced by an ensuing set of ADDRESS DIGITS.

preparatory period A period of time allocated to maintenance operations prior to transmission of a television broadcast signal over a CIRCUIT. During this interval, engineers carry out tests and adjustments.

presentation control Those elements of a system, designed in accordance with the principles of OPEN SYSTEMS INTERCONNECTION, that deal with the DATA formats and transformations required by end USERS.

presentation layer Layer six of the OSI model, the presentation layer handles the way DATA is represented during TRANSMISSION so that the meaning is not altered. For example, data that is converted from ASCII to EBCDIC, encrypted or compressed requires coding that is done by the presentation layer before it becomes a BIT STREAM that can be transmitted.

Prestel The trademark and name given by British Telecom to the PUBLIC VIDEOTEX service in the UK.

preventive maintenance Work carried out to identify and clear faults before they can affect the quality of service offered by a system.

primary access See PRIMARY RATE INTERFACE.

primary center Categorized as a class 3 OFFICE, the primary center is a TELECOMMUNICATION provider's CONTROL center that links TOLL CENTERS together. It can also serve as a toll center for local END OFFICES.

primary channel A CHANNEL attached to a device, such as a MODEM as the main path for communication, as distinct from a SECONDARY CHANNEL used for diagnostic purposes.

primary colors The three primary colors of the VISIBLE COLOR SPECTRUM are red, green and blue, which can be combined to create other colors. They are, therefore, used in television systems to create a full range of colors for the images to be displayed.

Primary Rate Interface (PRI) A configuration of CHANNELS used to transfer DATA and SIGNALING information when accessing a network conforming to the INTEGRATED SERVICES DIGITAL NETWORK standard. The PRI has the same BIT RATE as that of T1. In North America and Japan, the PRI is 1.544 Mbps, and it uses 23 B CHANNELS at 64 kbps each for information and one 64-kbps D CHANNEL for SIGNALING DATA. In Europe, the PRI is 2.048 Mbps, and it uses 30 B channels plus one D channel. See also BASIC RATE INTERFACE.

primary routes CIRCUITS normally used for a given purpose in a NETWORK; but ALTERNATIVE PATHS (or SECONDARY ROUTES) may exist.

print mechanism A mechanical device used for printing INFORMATION from a COMPUTER or a DATA TERMINAL.

priority facility A feature of a communications system enables certain USERS, or classes of TRAFFIC, to be given preference over others.

private automatic branch exchange (PABX) An automatic PRIVATE BRANCH EXCHANGE.

private branch exchange (PBX) A manual or automatic TELEPHONE SWITCHED SYSTEM that usually serves one commercial entity and is located on that company's premises. It provides service within the premises and accesses the public network. The PBX is designed primarily for establishing voice-grade CIRCUITS.

private circuit connection A connection made to a NETWORK using a LOCAL CIRCUIT or LEASED LINE exclusively allocated to a particular SUBSCRIBER.

private leased circuit A CIRCUIT reserved for the use of a particular organization to provide communication between two points for VOICE and/or DATA TRAFFIC; the circuit being hired from a COMMON CARRIER or PTT.

private line A COMMUNICATIONS CIRCUIT intended exclusively for the use of a particular person or organization and not available for use by others. The connections to the circuit terminate at private locations, and access cannot be obtained ordinarily from a PUBLIC NETWORK.

private network Any NETWORK designed and operated for the exclusive use of a particular organization or group of USERS. It may use some public CIRCUITS but, in principle, circuits are leased and reserved for exclusive use, and NETWORK MANAGEMENT and CONTROL functions are operated by, or on behalf of, the organization.

private videotex system A VIDEOTEX SYSTEM set up by a corporation for internal communication purposes to collect and distribute information over the PUBLIC TELEPHONE NETWORK. Intended as a means of communication between staff in the organization, it may also communicate with people who are agents of the corporation or with whom the corporation normally does business.

private viewdata system See PRIVATE VIEDEOTEX SYSTEM.

probability of call blocking In a CIRCUIT SWITCHED SYSTEM, the probability that a requested connection may not be made at all. See also CALL BLOCKING and AVAILABILITY OF SERVICE.

probability of excessive delay In a CIRCUIT SWITCHED SYSTEM, the probability that a USER will not: (a) receive a DIAL TONE within a certain time of requesting A CALL or (b) receive a connection within a certain time of dialing.

probability of failure A measure of the reliability of equipment. It is expressed as the probability of the equipment failing over a given period of time, e.g., a failure once every 10,000 operational hours.

procedural model A definition of the functions to be provided in a particular system and specifying the required behavior of elements in the system.

proceed-to-select An event in the operation of a CALL over a DATA NETWORK in which a TERMINAL is advised that its CALL REQUEST signal is recognized and DIGITS representing the ADDRESS to be selected may now be transmitted.

proceed-to-send signal A SIGNAL generated by a NETWORK (e.g., a DIALING TONE signal) when it is ready to receive CALLING SIGNALS from a TERMINAL.

processing logic The rules designed for operation of a particular APPLICATION or system function and realized either by HARDWARE or SOFTWARE or by a combination of both.

program development The preparation of COMPUTER programs to carry out APPLICATIONS entailing: specifying the procedures required, writing the program of instructions, preparing test data, compiling and generating object code and performing tests to isolate and correct errors.

programming language A language designed to be understood by humans and used to provide instructions to COMPUTERS and computer-controlled devices. Some languages, known as HIGH LEVEL LANGUAGES, have the appearance of mathematical notation or look like conventional language-forms, such as English. Some languages, however, have forms that are convenient to use inside the machine but are not easily learned by humans. These are known as LOW LEVEL LANGUAGES.

propagation delay The time required for a SIGNAL to travel from one end of a NETWORK to the other. The ROUND-TRIP PROPAGATION DELAY also includes the time to propagate back to the TRANSMITTING STATION to detect errors or CONTENTION for network resources.

protocol A set of rules defining the way INFORMATION can flow in a system. In all forms of communication, a protocol has to be observed to ensure that correct interaction takes place between TRANSMITTING and RECEIVING STATIONS. In DATA NETWORKS, such protocols are formal and often elaborate. They involve a set of agreements (sometimes based upon international standards) which cover:

syntax—the structure of commands and responses in BIT PATTERNS and FIELD formats
semantics—the sets of requests, responses and actions which can be performed by each USER
timing—the definition of the sequence or ordering of events

Within many modern protocols the concept of PEER INTERACTION is observed, whereby elements of the system performing a given set of functions at each end are related by a protocol. For example, ADDRESSING and ROUTING functions have a related protocol; and DATA LINK CONTROL elements interact to an agreed protocol to ensure ERROR DETECTION and ERROR CORRECTION.

These protocols effectively define INTERFACES to communication facilities and are exemplified in a series of CCITT recommendations (see V SERIES and X SERIES recommendations) which define electrical and logical connections for LINK CONTROL and DATA TRANSFER.

protocol conversion The process entailed in converting the information used to support transmission of a MESSAGE, as it is required by one PROTOCOL, into the form required by another protocol.

PSDS See PUBLIC SWITCHED DIGITAL SERVICE.

PSE See PACKET SWITCHING EXCHANGE.

psophometric weighting function See PSOPHOMETRY.

psophometry The name given to the studies concerned with the effect upon USERS of NOISE interference on a TELEPHONE LINE. The different frequencies at which noise may arise create different levels of annoyance to users. As a result of such studies, a weighting function has been given to noise at different frequency levels; this is known as the psophometric weighting function.

PSS See PACKET SWITCHING SERVICE.

PSTN See PUBLIC SWITCHED TELEPHONE NETWORK.

PTT See POSTAL, TELEGRAPH AND TELEPHONE AGENCY.

public data networks The first public data networks began commercial service around 1970. Public data networks are designed to provide low ERROR RATES and better line utilization using DIGITAL TECHNIQUES rather than ANALOG TECHNIQUES that were previously used.

Public data networks have progressed through three distinct stages throughout this period: (a) DIGITAL LEASED CIRCUITS, (b) DIGITAL SWITCHED CIRCUITS and (c) PACKET SWITCHING NETWORKS. Each of these transmission schemes are used today. A fourth stage is emerging with the advent of FAST PACKET SWITCHING.

Digital leased circuits: In the early stages of this development, USERS wishing to transmit DIGITAL DATA over public networks were required to lease circuits from CARRIERS to provide a permanent TERMINAL-to-terminal connection over a PRIVATE LINE. However, by using TIME DIVISION MULTIPLEXING, more than 20 separate DIGITAL DATA CHANNELS can be transmitted in the BANDWIDTH normally devoted to one VOICE CHANNEL. Prior to the advent of these digital leased circuits, an analog transmission system normally produced a relationship of one data channel to one voice channel. In a digital network, DATA SIGNALS are maintained in digital form, whereas in an analog system the signals are converted to analog form for transmission and reconverted to digital form on arrival at the destination. A major advantage of digital circuits over analog transmission is the ease with which the original signal can be regenerated along the channel to arrive at the destination in its original form. The introduction of digital circuits improved the ERROR RATE to 1 BIT in 10^7 bits, compared to 1 in 10^5 as experienced in the use of analog circuits.

Digital switched circuits: The next stage in the evolution of public data networks was the provision of SWITCHED CIRCUITS, i.e., users could dial a connection and be charged only for connect time. At the same time, carriers were able to provide fast CALL SETUP and CALL CLEARING mechanisms. Typically, the BILLING charges in such digital systems can be recorded in one-second increments, thus providing greater efficiency to the end user. The terminal-to-terminal connection is for the duration required rather than a permanent terminal-to-terminal connection.

Packet switching networks: A further stage of evolution took place with the introduction of packet switching networks. Where messages are short and the data volumes are not high, an even greater utilization of the carrier network can be achieved by using packet switching. Essentially, the paths through the network are shared by a number of users at the same time. It is not apparent to the users that this is taking place, but, in fact, their individual MESSAGE SIGNALS are each divided into PACKETS consisting of from 16 to 1,024 bits. Each packet contains sufficient leading information to enable the system to control delivery to the CALLED TERMINALS. Packet networks provide a VIRTUAL CIRCUIT, i.e., to a pair of terminals it appears that a point-to-point connection exists. In fact, major paths in the TRUNK ROUTING are also being used momentarily to transmit packets forming parts of other signals. See also PACKET SWITCHING.

A family of PROTOCOLS known as the X SERIES INTERFACES has been drawn up by the CCITT to govern connection to public data networks. An earlier series, known as the V SERIES INTERFACES, was introduced c. 1960 to govern attachment to analog facilities. See also FAST PACKET SWITCHING.

public data transmission service A service supplied to the public for the transmission of DATA TRAFFIC using a public DATA NETWORK operated by a communications authority or COMMON CARRIER.

Public Switched Digital Service (PSDS) A service offering of the BELL OPERATING COMPANIES, PSDS allows full-duplex dial-up circuits at 56 kbps throughout the connection from end to end. See also FULL-DUPLEX, DIAL-UP, CIRCUIT.

public switched network (PSN) A SWITCHED SYSTEM that provides CIRCUIT SWITCHED CONNECTIONS to public customers. The telephone network is a public switched network, as is TELEX. See also TELEPHONE, NETWORK.

Public Switched Telephone Network (PSTN) The term used to describe the public TELEPHONE SYSTEM, including the TELEPHONES, LOCAL LINES, LOCAL EXCHANGES and the complete system of TRUNKS and the EXCHANGE HIERARCHY that makes up the NETWORK.

public telegraph network A NETWORK established to provide a TELEGRAPH SERVICE for public use and supplied by a TELECOMMUNICATIONS operating authority or COMMON CARRIER.

Public Utilities Commission (PUC) A state regulatory body governing companies that provide utility services, such as communications facilities or power, for a fee to the public.

public videotex system A communications system intended to be a public information service and to provide for an interactive service over the public telephone network to members of the public and the business community in which information is displayed on an adapted television receiver. See also VIDEOTEX SYSTEM. Contrast with PRIVATE VIDEOTEX SYSTEM.

public viewdata system See PUBLIC VIDEOTEX SYSTEM.

PUC See PUBLIC UTILITIES COMMISSION.

pulse amplitude modulation (PAM) The name given to a technique that forms the basis of PULSE CODE MODULATION (PCM). The technique consists of SAMPLING an analog SPEECH SIGNAL at specific short intervals to produce a series of pulses of identical duration but varying in AMPLITUDE in accordance with the original speech waveform; see also Appendix 8. The number of pulses required to represent an ANALOG SIGNAL accurately depends on the frequency of the analog signal, but, to give a good reproduction of speech, 8,000 pulses per second are required. In practice, these pulses are modified to a coded form to avoid DISTORTION in transmission. See also PULSE CODE MODULATION and QUANTIZATION.

pulse code modulation (PCM) A method of converting an ANALOG SIGNAL (e.g., a VOICE SIGNAL) to a DIGITAL SIGNAL. This process entails SAMPLING the analog signal and encoding to represent the signal levels of the waveform of the analog signal in digital form. The sampling technique is based upon a principle known as PULSE AMPLITUDE MODULATION (PAM); see also Appendix 8.

In general, the sampling rate is at least twice the frequency present in the analog waveform, and a practical rate for speech is 8,000 samples per second. In fact, digital signals of varying AMPLITUDE, but identical duration, are produced by PAM; such signals are prone to DISTORTION in transmission. Each pulse representing a sample is thus further coded as a GROUP of BINARY DIGITS with only two levels of amplitude. A CCITT recommendation proposes that each sample consist of an 8-BIT code; thus a SPEECH CHANNEL, after digital encoding, would have a BIT RATE of 64,000 bits per second. PCM techniques are used in association with TIME DIVISION MULTIPLEXING (TDM) to carry many speech signals along a TRANSMISSION SYSTEM as interleaved digital signals. At the receiving end, the encoded digital signals are reconverted to analog signals and delivered to USERS. The great advantage of TDM is that it avoids many CROSSTALK limitations that arise with analog signals on TWISTED WIRE PAIRS, and it provides a very efficient form of MULTIPLEXING. See also TIME DIVISION MULTIPLEXING.

pulse stuffing See JUSTIFICATION.

punched card A card, usually measuring 7⅜″ × 3¼″ and .007″ thick in which holes are punched to represent DATA. One of the earliest forms of COMPUTER input, they have been extensively replaced by direct entry systems in which the data entry staff are on-line to a processor, which collects and validates data.

punched paper tape A method for preparing INFORMATION for a slow-speed COMMUNICATION CHANNEL (e.g., TELEX) in which information is represented as patterns of holes punched as rows across a narrow strip of paper tape. Various standards exist, and paper tape may have five, six, seven or eight holes in each row. For use in the telegraph service, 5-channel tape is common but, for COMPUTER input where a large CHARACTER SET is often needed, 7- or 8-channel PAPER TAPE is used. See also TORN TAPE CENTER.

pure ALOHA A variation of ALOHA in which a STATION does not listen to the CHANNEL before transmitting.

push-button dialing A method of generating DIGITAL SIGNALS using push buttons rather than a dial. The pulses are generated either by disconnection of a CIRCUIT when each button is pressed or by activation of OSCILLATORS, which send distinctive tones to the LINE. See also MULTIFREQUENCY TONE SIGNALING and LOOP-DISCONNECT SIGNALING.

push-button telephone (PBT) A TELEPHONE in which the USER is able to obtain an ADDRESS by pushing buttons rather than by operating a dial. This method may be associated with LOOP-DISCONNECT SIGNALING and MULTIFREQUENCY TONE SIGNALING.

PWR Abbreviation for power, used in specifications and on fascia plates of communication devices.

Q

QAM See QUADRATURE AMPLITUDE MODULATION.

quadrature amplitude modulation (QAM) A form of MODULATION which uses combined techniques of PHASE MODULATION and AMPLITUDE MODULATION. The system is based upon SIGNALS of constant frequency, but four signal variations are possible by creating a phase difference of 90°. Each of these signals can also be varied in AMPLITUDE and, for example, if four amplitude variations are allowed, the signals can be used to represent up to 16 separate values. Used for the transmission of BINARY CODED INFORMATION.

quality of a circuit The description of a CIRCUIT is usually given in technical terms which describe its limitations for transmission of SIGNALS of a particular type. It is difficult to define the precise quality of a circuit without considering the equipment to be attached to it.

Communications providers generally publish circuit specifications for equipment manufacturers so that they can design equipment to make good use of the circuit characteristics. The communications authorities generally aim to maintain the quality of circuits to conform to these specifications, but in SWITCHED SYSTEMS (e.g., the public TELEPHONE NETWORK), the equipment used is selected for each CALL on a random basis. The increasing use of the telephone network for DATA COMMUNICATIONS has also introduced the need for different levels of specification. The main topics covered in such specifications are: FREQUENCY BAND, LOSS/FREQUENCY RESPONSE, GROUP DELAY/FREQUENCY RESPONSE, RANDOM NOISE, SIGNAL-TO-QUANTIZING NOISE, MAXIMUM FREQUENCY ERROR, TRANSMIT-TO-RECEIVE CROSSTALK, SIGNAL-TO-LISTENER ECHO RATIO, VARIATION OF INSERTION LOSS with time, ERROR RATE.

quality of service A measure of the difficulties a USER experiences in using a system as shown by the quality of the LINES and the extent of CALL BLOCKING that takes place. See also AVAILABILITY OF SERVICE and RELIABILITY OF SERVICE.

quantization A process associated with PULSE AMPLITUDE MODULATION (PAM), involving the division of an ANALOG SIGNAL into digital form by SAMPLING and the reassembly of the DIGITAL SIGNALS after transmission into an analog waveform. In this quantization process, samples are classified into intervals, each having a single value to represent the AMPLITUDE of the sample. In a practical system for VOICE transmission, each sample pulse may be represented by seven BITS, giving up to 128 QUANTIZATION LEVELS to represent one sample. See also Appendix 8.

quantization distortion The DISTORTION that can occur in an ANALOG SIGNAL from the process known as QUANTIZATION. See also QUANTIZATION ERROR.

quantization distortion power The power of the DISTORTION component of an output SIGNAL from the QUANTIZATION process.

quantization error Relates to PULSE CODE MODULATION (PCM); an error arising in the reassembly of a DIGITAL SIGNAL to an ANALOG SIGNAL in the process known as QUANTIZATION. Such an error would arise if too few QUANTIZATION LEVELS were selected; the effect for the USER would be DISTORTION of the resulting analog signal. See also QUANTIZATION DISTORTION.

quantization interval The interval between two adjacent values in the process known as QUANTIZATION. See also QUANTIZATION LEVEL.

quantization level In the technique known as PULSE CODE MODULATION, signals representing speech are converted from ANALOG to DIGITAL form for transmission. Samples taken of the ANALOG SIGNALS result in pulses of varying AMPLITUDE, which are then each represented by a group of BITS that describe the amplitude value of the pulse. This process is known as QUANTIZATION. Using 7 bits, up to 128 levels of amplitude can be represented. Thus, such a system has 128 quantization levels.

quantization noise An interference that arises during the process of PULSE CODE MODULATION in which NOISE is generated during the conversion of ANALOG SIGNALS to DIGITAL SIGNALS and vice versa.

quarternary trunk exchange One of a set of TRUNK EXCHANGES providing a means of communication in a TELEPHONE NETWORK at the fourth level. In an EXCHANGE HIERARCHY, they would be fully interconnected to one another, and each would represent the convergence of lower levels of the hierarchy, including TERTIARY, SECONDARY, PRIMARY and LOCAL EXCHANGES.

queue A sequence of telephone calls or data messages in which new ones are added to the tail end as they wait for service or transmission. See also TELEPHONE, CALL, DATA, MESSAGE.

quiescent phase The nonactive phase during the establishment of a CALL using a SWITCHED or LEASED CIRCUIT, in which the NETWORK and the CALLED TERMINAL indicate the ready or not-ready status.

R

radar A system that detects distant objects by measuring the deflection of MICROWAVE frequencies, used, for example, to provide information about the movement of aircraft, ships or vehicles.

radio frequencies The spectrum of frequencies used for RADIO TRANSMISSION and generally considered to be within the range from 30 kHz to 3 GHz. See also ELECTROMAGNETIC WAVES.

radio frequency carrier wave A RADIO FREQUENCY SIGNAL used to carry another signal imprinted upon it by the techniques of MODULATION.

radio frequency signal Any signal falling within the RADIO FREQUENCY SPECTRUM and used to radiate information through SPACE. See also ELECTROMAGNETIC WAVES.

radio frequency spectrum The range of ELECTROMAGNETIC WAVES associated with radio and television broadcasting, including transmission in the following BANDWIDTHS:

low frequency (LF)	30 kHz to 300 kHz
medium frequency (MF)	300 kHz to 3 MHz
high frequency (HF)	3 MHz to 30 MHz
very high frequency (VHF)	30 MHz to 300 MHz
ultra high frequency (UHF)	300 MHz to 3 GHz

This spectrum covers the present range of frequencies used for commercial and military/civil communications. See also FREQUENCY SPECTRUM.

radio receiver A device that can be tuned to receive RADIO FREQUENCY SIGNALS and to detect SOUND SIGNALS carried in the broadcast RADIO SIGNAL for audible presentation to listeners.

radio transmission A form of TELECOMMUNICATION in which MESSAGE SIGNALS are radiated as energy in the form of RADIO WAVES. Examples of radio transmission include sound and television public BROADCAST systems established to serve a particular geographic area as well as directional radio systems designed to provide a CHANNEL for point-to-point communication.

radio transmitter A device capable of capturing SIGNALS representing SOUND or light and converting them by a process of MODULATION into a form suitable for transmission as ELECTROMAGNETIC WAVES in the RADIO FREQUENCY SPECTRUM.

radio waves A range of ELECTROMAGNETIC WAVES, in the FREQUENCY SPECTRUM from 30 kHz to 3GHz, which are suitable for carrying SIGNALS across SPACE.

radiometry The measurement of light energy from a source, irrespective of human factors involving the perception of light. Studies concerned with consideration of the human factors are known as PHOTOMETRY.

RAM See RANDOM ACCESS MEMORY.

random access memory (RAM) A type of storage device used in COMPUTERS to retrieve information directly with very short access times measured in milliseconds. Any particular retrieval operation will produce information within a more or less constant access time, regardless of the last location addressed. Magnetic disk storage is an example of such a storage medium, but MAGNETIC TAPE is not a random access memory medium. See also MAIN MEMORY.

random noise A form of interference that may be noticed in a TELEPHONE CHANNEL as a hissing sound. If the noise level is high in a particular CIRCUIT, it can severely impair SIGNAL quality at the RECEIVING TERMINAL. NOISE is measured in DECIBELS and expressed as a ratio of noise power to the power of a test signal. A most important ratio is the power of the random noise relative to signal power (the SIGNAL-TO-NOISE RATIO). Also known as WHITE NOISE or GAUSSION NOISE.

RAP See REMOTE ACCESS POINT.

raster The pattern formed by the movement of an ELECTRON BEAM inside a television camera tube (or TV RECEIVER tube) to scan a picture and form a SIGNAL relating to the light emanating from objects being televised. See also VIDEO SIGNAL.

RBOC See REGIONAL BELL OPERATING COMPANY.

RBT See REMOTE BATCH PRINTER.

read only memory (ROM) A storage device containing information that is fixed during a special process and that cannot be overwritten by a USER of the device or by any COMPUTER program during the normal operation of the device.

Usually used to build programs such as COMPILERS into a MICROPROCESSOR or TERMINAL.

ready state A condition in which a DATA TERMINAL (DTE) and its MODEM (or DCE) are operable, are not engaged in any activity associated with a CALL and the DCE is ready to accept an INCOMING CALL or a CALL REQUEST signal from the DTE.

ready to send An INTERCHANGE SIGNAL that passes from a MODEM to its associated DATA TERMINAL (DTE) to indicate that the modem has established contact with a distant modem and that DATA TRANSMISSION from the DTE to the distant location can take place. See also CARRIER DETECTOR.

ready-for-data signal A control SIGNAL transmitted by a MODEM to a DATA TERMINAL to indicate that a connection is available to allow DATA to be transferred to or from another data terminal. The ready-for-data condition in a DATA NETWORK occurs when all connections involved in the CALL have been completed.

real-time system A special class of ON-LINE SYSTEM in which the processing of transactions occurs simultaneously with the events which give rise to transactions. The relationships between the various USERS and the COMPUTER system is such that business cannot be conducted at all without the system being available, and any user who accesses the DATABASE will always find an up-to-the-second picture of the events and objects being controlled by the system. An airline ticket reservation system is an example of a real-time application.

receive only (RO) Pertaining to a TERMINAL device that can receive INFORMATION but not transmit information. It might, for example, be a DATA PRINTER or a PAPER TAPE PUNCH.

receiver clock In SYNCHRONOUS TRANSMISSION, a device that takes its timing from line conditions and establishes the TIME INTERVALS within a RECEIVING TERMINAL to keep the terminal in SYNCHRONIZATION with signal pulses sent by the TRANSMITTING STATION. See also TRANSMITTER CLOCK.

receiving aerial A device designed to receive RADIO WAVES to be input to a RADIO RECEIVER where selection and AMPLIFICATION of specific frequencies may take place.

receiving earth station A system forming part of a communications NETWORK and equipped with a dish-shaped AERIAL to receive RADIO SIGNALS reflected from a SATELLITE orbiting the earth. The EARTH STATION may distribute the received signals over an EARTH NETWORK or pass them to another TRANSMITTING EARTH STATION to be beamed at another orbiting COMMUNICATIONS SATELLITE.

receiving terminal A TERMINAL receiving SIGNALS from another or from a network NODE at a particular instant.

record Any unit of DATA representing a complete item of information or a transaction to be processed by a COMPUTER system and consisting of a defined set of related FIELDS of INFORMATION.

record separator (RS) A special CODE under the general classification known as INFORMATION SEPARATORS and used in a DATA COMMUNICATIONS CODE to denote the boundary between RECORDS in BINARY CODED form.

recorded information service A service that allows members of the public to dial into a special TERMINAL using the TELEPHONE NETWORK to receive prerecorded information, e.g., sports news or a speaking clock.

recovery procedures Procedures, usually implemented by SOFTWARE, that are designed to protect an ON-LINE or REAL-TIME SYSTEM from major failure. Should any component of the system fail, potentially causing a major interruption of service to the USERS, the recovery procedures will automatically record the status of current transactions and will write to BACKING STORE the contents of any MAIN MEMORY locations. Any reserve equipment may be brought into operation automatically and faulty units identified and isolated for the attention of system engineers. The system may then recover automatically by retrieving the information previously stored.

The complexity and sophistication of such recovery systems depends upon the importance of the APPLICATION to the end users, but in any real-time DATA PROCESSING application or in a communications system, it is expected that large sums would be invested to prevent a major failure, and automatic recovery would be effective in seconds or minutes at the most. This would entail the employment of redundant HARDWARE units ready to be brought into service by the operating system and the ongoing maintenance of duplicate file systems and TRANSACTION records.

Recovery systems must be prepared for the possibility of failure by frequently taking copies of FILES and RECORDS and maintaining a TRANSACTION LOG. Thus, in the event of a serious failure, the recovery routines can reconstitute the status of files quickly and efficiently without loss of DATA and without requiring the users to repeat previous work.

Red, Green, Blue (RGB) See RGB.

redundancy A concept used in the design of communications systems in which more functional units are provided in the system than are strictly needed to handle the planned workload. The units are arranged such that each is easily and automatically substituted for any other. Several parts of the system may fail, but the system continues to operate by falling back on spare, or lightly loaded, units.

redundancy checking A method of ERROR DETECTION in DATA TRANSMISSION in which additional BITS or CHARACTERS are computed from the DATA and are added to BLOCKS of data transmitted over a NETWORK. The RECEIVING TERMINAL is able to carry out checks by comparing BIT PATTERNS formed in the data blocks in such a manner that it is possible to detect lost or incorrectly received bits. The receiving terminal usually requests automatic retransmission of ERROR BLOCKS; but see also FORWARD ERROR CORRECTION and CYCLIC REDUNDANCY CHECKING.

reed relay A device used to provide a CROSSPOINT in a CIRCUIT SWITCHING EXCHANGE. Reed relays are cheap and reasonably compact devices, and they can be combined to make up a switching matrix of any desired capacity. A reed relay consists of a glass tube surrounded by a coil. Within the tube are two nickel/iron reeds with gold-plated tips. When a current is passed through the coil, the reeds are magnetized and come together to form a contract.

In more modern DIGITAL EXCHANGES, reed relays are replaced entirely by ELECTRONIC CROSSPOINTS.

reference carrier See REFERENCE WAVE.

reference wave A SIGNAL transmitted over a MULTIPLEXED CHANNEL and used to detect MESSAGE SIGNALS that have been generated by the process of MODULATION. In the process of DEMODULATION, it is necessary to use a replica of a CARRIER SIGNAL to detect the original message signal. Sometimes the carrier is generated locally in the DEMODULATOR, but in other cases (particularly where a large number of CHANNELS are created over a suitable physical path), one channel is used to transmit a REFERENCE CARRIER so that other carriers can be generated from it to demodulate signals on the various channels. Also called reference carrier.

refresh The process of repeatedly producing a display image on a CATHODE RAY TUBE (CRT).

regeneration unit A device used in DIGITAL TRANSMISSION to reconstitute a distorted SIGNAL as it passes along the TRANSMISSION PATH.

regenerative repeater A REPEATER that operates in TRANSMISSION SYSTEMS using binary DIGITAL SIGNALS. It examines signals and identifies each element as 0 or 1 and automatically regenerates appropriate 0 or 1 elements for output to the LINE. It has the advantage of generating virtually noise-free signals which are exactly synchronized with the pulses of the incoming MESSAGE SIGNAL.

Regional Bell Holding Company (RBHC) DIVESTITURE created seven independent RBHCs, sometimes called Regional Bell operating companies (RBOCs), to oversee the 22 BELL OPERATING COMPANIES that had previously been owned by AT&T. The seven RBHCs are: Ameritech, Bell Atlantic, BellSouth, Nynex, Pacific Telesis, Southwestern Bell Corp. and U S West.

Regional Bell operating company See REGIONAL BELL HOLDING COMPANY.

regional center A NODE in a TELECOMMUNICATIONS NETWORK that connects SECTIONAL CENTERS and controls TRAFFIC between them. Sometimes called regional exchange. See also EXCHANGE HIERARCHY.

regional exchange See REGIONAL CENTER.

register 1. A CONTROL device used to receive and store ADDRESS INFORMATION during the setup of a CALL.

2. In any COMPUTER-controlled system, a special store location having special properties used for arithmetic or local operations.

register translators Units incorporated into the old STROWGER telephone exchanges to assist USERS by simplifying the dialing process. See also DIRECTOR EXCHANGE.

relational database A way of structuring a database FILE so that information from separate RECORDS can be linked together.

reliability of service A measure of the extent to which USERS can rely on the service as shown by the effective operation of TERMINALS and transmission equipment. The reliability of a communications system is generally expressed as a set of target PROBABILITIES OF FAILURE for various parts of the NETWORK. For example, in a TELEPHONE NETWORK, target probabilities for failure per annum might be: telephone terminal 0.1, LOCAL LINE 0.075, LOCAL EXCHANGE SWITCHING EQUIPMENT 0.01, and so on for other system components. See also AVAILABILITY OF SERVICE and QUALITY OF SERVICE.

reliability target In order to plan for an acceptable level of satisfaction for USERS of a communications system, it is customary to establish reliability targets for the system and for key system components. The targets are expressed as the PROBABILITY OF FAILURE per unit time. For example, the reliability target for a NODE in a NETWORK might be 0.02 per annum. With 50 such nodes in a network, the expectation is that one year, 50×0.02 (or 1) failure would occur. See also MEAN DOWN TIME and FAULT RATE.

remote access point (RAP) A MULTIPLEXER or CONCENTRATOR established in a particular location to provide access to a NETWORK in areas not directly covered by NODES having full NETWORK FACILITIES. The RAP will normally be connected to a main node by a high-speed CHANNEL, capable of carrying a volume of MULTIPLEXED TRAFFIC to the MAIN NETWORK.

remote batch printer (RBT) A printer connected as a remote TERMINAL under control of a central COMPUTER and used to print INFORMATION in batches after the information has been prepared by the computer.

remote batch terminal A TERMINAL used to collect DATA that is entered from a KEYBOARD or some other local data input device. The data is stored on a local storage medium (e.g., a magnetic disk) and is later transferred as a complete batch of RECORDS over a TRANSMISSION CHANNEL to a central computer installation. Such a terminal may also receive batches of data from a central COMPUTER.

remote job entry (RJE) The process of sending units of work for a COMPUTER, such as programs, FILES and instructions for the OPERATING SYSTEM, to the computer via an input device that accesses the computer through a data communications LINK.

remote printer A mechanism used for printing INFORMATION at a location remote from the center at which the information is stored.

remote printing The production of printed output in a communications system at a point remote from the location at which the INFORMATION is stored or entered into the system.

repeater A type of AMPLIFIER used at regular intervals along a TRANSMISSION CHANNEL to regenerate MESSAGE SIGNALS and overcome various impairments, such as ATTENUATION and CROSSTALK. See also ANALOG REPEATER and DIGITAL REPEATER.

replicated database A computer networking APPLICATION in which duplicate copies of a DATABASE are transmitted to be available at regional centers for local inquiry. The updating of such FILES is usually done centrally to simplify control problems, and corrected versions of the database (or parts of it) are transferred periodically to the regional centers. Such designs are best used with DATA that is relatively slow to change and where the operational requirements of USERS do not require an up-to-the-minute view of the information. Contrast with PARTITIONED DATABASE.

request-response unit In a PACKET SWITCHING NETWORK, this term refers to the APPLICATION information being transferred between USERS as part of a PACKET, which is, in turn, part of a TRANSACTION between the users. The packet itself is completed by the addition of HEADER INFORMATION, e.g., for DATA LINK CONTROL, PATH CONTROL and TRANSMISSION CONTROL within the NETWORK.

request-to-send An INTERCHANGE SIGNAL that passes from a DATA TERMINAL (DTE) to its DCE, indicating that it wishes the DCE to transmit information to the LINE. The DCE must reply with a READY-TO-SEND signal, indicating that it has established a connection with the DCE at the distant terminal. The data terminal cannot send DATA to its DCE until this condition is established. See also CARRIER DETECTOR.

request-unit See REQUEST-RESPONSE UNIT.

reserve link A CIRCUIT used as a standby for a regular LINK that normally carries the TRAFFIC for some designated purpose.

residential terminal A TERMINAL used in the home rather than in a business environment. The implication is that a residential terminal will originate and accept a lower TRAFFIC VOLUME than a business terminal.

resolution A term denoting the degree of detail that can be created in a particular VISUAL DISPLAY system, e.g., a television system or a visual display used to form TEXT, DATA, or graphical images. The degree of resolution is indicated by the number of PICTURE ELEMENTS that make up the image. For example:

system	matrix of PIXELS
US 525-line TV	340×422
British 625-line TV	402×572
French 819-line TV	527×786

The term HIGH RESOLUTION DISPLAY is often used in relation to information systems. Factors affecting human perception of images include the nature and shape of images to be drawn, the size of the viewing screen, whether color or monochrome is desirable, the viewing distance and the distance between picture elements. See also VISUAL ACUITY and KELL FACTOR.

response frames A PAGE of INFORMATION, designed by an INFORMATION PROVIDER for display on a VISUAL DISPLAY terminal to act as an order form, or some such document, and allowing a USER of the system to enter details for the ordering or reservation of goods and services. See also VIDEOTEX SYSTEM.

response header A unit of DATA attached to a PACKET so that it may be identified to the TRANSMISSION CONTROL and DATA LINK CONTROL procedures in a PACKET SWITCHING NETWORK.

response-unit See REQUEST-RESPONSE UNIT.

restart A term used to describe the processes involved in recommencing the operation of a DATA PROCESSING system (particularly one that uses DATA COMMUNICATIONS techniques) after a system failure. This often creates a PEAK LOAD on the system because MESSAGES and TRANSACTIONS that have previously been interrupted are waiting in queues to be serviced.

return path A CHANNEL used to convey INFORMATION back to a TRANSMITTING TERMINAL to provide CONTROL INFORMATION about a CALL in progress. For example, to send information about the status of the RECEIVING STATION or to send back a copy of the transmitted MESSAGE SIGNAL to enable the accuracy of the transmission to be verified.

revertive error checking A system of ERROR CHECKING in which the TRANSMITTING TERMINAL generates a sequence of CHECK DIGITS derived from an algorithm performed on the content of a FRAME to be transmitted. The RECEIVING TERMINAL uses the same procedure to check the incoming information, including the check digits, and reverts to the transmitting terminal, using the same CHANNEL, to request a retransmission if an error has been detected. Contrast with NONREVERTIVE ERROR CHECKING.

rf carrier wave See RADIO FREQUENCY CARRIER WAVE.

rf filters Devices intended to accept specified frequencies in a RADIO FREQUENCY bandwidth and to reject frequencies falling outside the specified BANDWIDTH, e.g., to provide a means of tuning reception to a particular SIGNAL.

RGB Abbreviation of red, green, blue, the three primary colors that are fundamental to color television systems. During the transmission of picture information, the light from a televised scene is separated into three outputs corresponding to red, green and blue. These outputs are transmitted upon a CARRIER WAVE to the receivers. Each TV color receiver has patterns of red, green and blue phosphor dots on the surface of the viewing screen. The DEMODULATED signals are used to drive separate RGB GUNS, which control the direction of beams onto the appropriate color dots on the screen. The illuminated dots on the screen form combinations of primary colors to reproduce the color of the original televised scene.

RGB guns ELECTRON GUNS used in COLOR TELEVISION RECEIVERS to activate colored phosphors on a television screen.

ring See RING NETWORK.

ring network A NETWORK in which the various NODES are interconnected along a TRANSMISSION LINK that can be diagrammatically represented as the circumference of a wheel. The nodes appear as points along the circumference, and communication between two nodes must proceed via any intermediate nodes along the ring. Also known as LOOP NETWORK. Contrast with MESH-NETWORK, and see also NETWORK TOPOLOGIES.

ringing tone The SIGNAL heard by the USER of a TELEPHONE when the called telephone is being rung.

RJE See REMOTE JOB ENTRY.

RO See RECEIVE ONLY.

roll-call polling A system of POLLING in which each TERMINAL device is addressed in strict sequence by the CONTROLLER to see which, if any, device is ready to send or receive a FRAME of INFORMATION, starting at the nearest terminal and working out toward the most distant. See also HUB POLLING.

ROM See READ ONLY MEMORY.

round-trip propagation time See PROPAGATION TIME.

router 1. In a MESSAGE SWITCHING SYSTEM, that part of a NODE (or EXCHANGE) that examines incoming MESSAGES, interprets the ADDRESS INFORMATION contained in each message and determines which of the outgoing LINKS are to be used. The router is usually a COMPUTER program that selects messages from INCOMING BUFFERS and places them into appropriate outgoing MESSAGE QUEUES.

2. In LANs, a device that interconnects NETWORKS. A router forwards only the DATA TRAFFIC that is destined for remote sites, not the local traffic. It is hardware independent and relays information at layer three of the OSI model. Unlike BRIDGES, routers must be compatible with the PROTOCOL used for the DATA being sent.

routing The operation that takes place to connect two USERS in response to the ADDRESSING INFORMATION contained in a transmission request. The combination of TRANSMISSION PATHS used for a particular CALL is also known as the routing. See also BASIC ROUTING and ALTERNATIVE ROUTING.

routing rules Used in times of high TRAFFIC to determine when, and in what sequence, ALTERNATIVE ROUTES are attempted.

RS See RECORD SEPARATOR.

RS-232 A technical specification established by the Electronics Industries Association defining the communications lines that interface between COMPUTERS, TERMINALS and MODEMS.

S

S interface In an ISDN network, the juncture where a TERMINAL and the network meet. See also ISDN, NETWORK.

sampling A process in which the value of a variable factor (e.g., a current of fluctuation frequency) is examined at periodic intervals and in which the variable may be further represented by a system of coding, derived from the samples. See also PULSE AMPLITUDE MODULATION.

satellite See COMMUNICATIONS SATELLITE.

satellite channel A TRANSMISSION PATH provided by an Earth satellite system. See also COMMUNICATIONS SATELLITE.

satellite station A transmitting and receiving center capable of communicating with an artificial body placed into Earth orbit for the purpose of long-distance communication. A highly directional ANTENNA is used to control precisely the transmission of RADIO FREQUENCY SIGNALS to and from the SATELLITE.

scanning beam In a television camera, a beam of electrons that is passed over an electrically charged surface to create an electrical current that represents light emanating from a televised scene.

scattering In DATA TRANSMISSION that uses FIBER-OPTIC CABLE, a loss in the light-wave SIGNAL is caused by a type of distortion called scattering, which is the result of tiny variations in the density of the cable.

SCL See SUPERVISORY CONTROL LANGUAGE.

screened cable A cable in which the CONDUCTOR used to carry MESSAGE SIGNALS is encased in a sleeve of which the outer layer is an earthed metal skin. The purpose of the screen is to reduce the background noise arising from electrical interference along the cable.

SCU See SYSTEM CONTROL SIGNAL UNIT.

SD See SPACE DIVISION.

SDLC See SYNCHRONOUS DATA LINK CONTROL.

SECAM Acronym for *sequential couleur a memoire.* A color broadcasting system developed in France but used also in the Soviet Union. It is distinctive in that the two color difference signals are transmitted sequentially rather than simultaneously as is the case with the PAL and NTSC systems. SECAM uses 625 picture lines and a 50 Hz FIELD FREQUENCY. See also PAL and NTSC.

secondary center An exchange in a PUBLIC SWITCHED TELEPHONE NETWORK that links the TRUNK CIRCUITS arising from several REGIONAL EXCHANGES to the main TERTIARY TRUNK EXCHANGE network. See also EXCHANGE HIERARCHY.

secondary channel A CHANNEL attached to a device, such as a MODEM, to enable tests and diagnostic information to be obtained about the performance of the modem without interrupting the PRIMARY CHANNEL, which is used for DATA TRANSMISSION.

secondary characters A set of special CHARACTERS occurring in the FIGURES SHIFT of a TELEGRAPH CODE including, for example, punctuation symbols.

secondary route An alternative path for transmission of a MESSAGE between two TERMINALS over a NETWORK; used when the PRIMARY ROUTE is unavailable due to congestion or maintenance.

secondary trunk exchange An EXCHANGE that handles major ROUTINGS in a public TELEPHONE NETWORK and that is connected only to other TRUNK EXCHANGES. See also EXCHANGE HIERARCHY.

sectional center A TELECOMMUNICATIONS provider's CONTROL CENTER for linking PRIMARY CENTERS. Categorized as a class 2 OFFICE.

selection digits A group of signal elements representing the DIGITS of a telephone NUMBER of a CALLED PARTY.

selection signals A sequence of CHARACTERS that appear in a FACILITY REQUEST and that define the ADDRESS required for a CALL and also the particular NETWORK FACILITIES needed in making the call.

selector An electromechanical switching device used in the old STROWGER exchanges, in which moving contacts are used to create connections for switching LINES.

self-test A test undertaken by an item of line terminating equipment, such as a MODEM, in which the modem is instructed to establish a LOOP BACK path through itself. This instruction is normally conveyed to the modem by a specialized NETWORK DIAGNOSTIC CONTROLLER, which transmits a test pattern through the modem and analyzes the returning pattern to assess the performance of the modem under various conditions.

semaphore An early method for telegraphing SIGNALS between locations in visual contact, aided by the telescope or binoculars. The physical positioning of arms, flags or spars was used to represent information. Later inventions included the optical semaphore (attributed to Claude Chappe), in which coded information was transmitted as light signals. These developments led to the later introduction of the ELECTRICAL TELEGRAPH by Samuel MORSE.

send channel Most communication CIRCUITS consist of two CHANNELS to allow simultaneous two-way transmission between TERMINALS. The send channel is used for transmission in a particular direction at any instant; the other channel is known as the return or BACKWARD CHANNEL and is mainly used for ERROR CONTROL and supervisory purposes.

sender A device in an EXCHANGE that controls the transmission of SIGNALS to and from a LINE.

separate channel signaling A system of SIGNALING in which a dedicated CIRCUIT is used to carry CONTROL signals related to a large group of circuits carrying MESSAGE SIGNALS. See also CENTRALIZED CONTROL SIGNALING and COMMON CHANNEL SIGNALING.

serial attribute coding A system of coding in which the attributes of a CHARACTER to be displayed (e.g., its color, height or flashing/steady indicator) are stored as nondisplayable CODES in the PAGE STORE serially with characters to be displayed. This means that the attribute characters must appear as spaces in the TEXT at the beginning of each new sequence although, in practice, this is not a serious problem because it is usual to change attributes at the beginning of a WORD or phrase where the space is needed anyway. This system is not quite so flexible as the PARALLEL ATTRIBUTE CODING methods, but the method requires less storage in each terminal and is therefore cheap. The first public trials of VIDEOTEX SYSTEMS have all used serial attribute coding.

serial bit-stream A series of BINARY DIGITS occurring in sequence one after the other in which the pattern of BITS within a particular sequence may have a specific meaning.

serial mode Relating to the transfer or transmission of coded information in which the signal elements (BITS) pass one after another along a single path. Contrast with PARALLEL MODE, in which separate paths are provided for each bit forming a CHARACTER or BYTE.

serial transmission The most common sequence of DATA TRANSMISSION in which pulses representing BITS are sent one after another along the TRANSMISSION LINE. Contrast with PARALLEL TRANSMISSION.

server A COMPUTER program and/or PROCESSOR that provides a service to USERS on a LOCAL AREA NETWORK, for example, accessing a FILE or controlling a printer. Servers vary according to whether the NODES and NETWORK are of a like ARCHITECTURE or different architectures.

service area See LATA.

session A period during which an ACCESS PATH is maintained between a TRANSMITTING and a RECEIVING STATION to allow a series of related TRANSACTIONS to be progressed.

session layer Layer five of the OSI model, the session layer manages the LOGICAL INTERFACE between APPLICATIONS. It controls when USERS can send and receive DATA.

shadow mask tube A type of CATHODE RAY TUBE (CRT) used in the construction of COLOR TELEVISION RECEIVERS in which a metal mask containing holes is placed between the RGB GUNS and the groups of three colored phosphor dots known as TRIADS on the screen surface. The mask is constructed so that the red gun can only activate red phosphor dots, the blue gun the blue phosphors, and the green gun the green phosphors.

Shannon, Claude In 1948 Claude Shannon expanded on the NYQUIST THEOREM regarding the theoretical limit of the DATA TRANSFER RATE. He extended the theorem to the case of a CHANNEL experiencing RANDOM NOISE.

shared database A DATABASE used in a COMPUTER networking environment that can be updated and accessed simultaneously by USERS in different locations, using programs which provide updating and CONTROL PROCEDURES operating independently of the location of the DATA. For example, RECORDS may be stored in regional centers that have a primary responsibility for designated records, but the system may have to accommodate changes to records related to a region by TRANSACTIONS arising outside the region. Such systems are also known as DISTRIBUTED SYSTEMS and have particularly challenging control problems, which have to do with the orderly management of communications TRAFFIC in the NETWORK.

shared service In a TELEPHONE SYSTEM, this term describes the condition that exists when two USERS are sharing the same LOCAL LINE. This arrangement is sometimes necessary to economize in the use of local lines. The system is usually applied to residential users who have low volume utilization, and special arrangements are made to ring the bell of each TERMINAL independently and to measure OUTGOING CALLS for BILLING purposes.

SHF See SUPERHIGH FREQUENCY.

shielded twisted pair Two insulated wires encased in a cable that prevents electromagnetic interference and provides virtually noise-free transmission. Compare with UNSHIELDED TWISTED PAIR.

shift character A CHARACTER in a DATA COMMUNICATIONS CODE that is used to designate a following group of CODES in a transmission sequence as having a specific significance. These codes retain that significance until another shift character occurs to revert to the original case, e.g., LETTERS SHIFT and FIGURES SHIFT used in INTERNATIONAL ALPHABET NO. 2.

shift in (SI) A CHARACTER in a DATA COMMUNICATIONS CODE that is used to indicate that the following codes have the meaning specified in the standard code set. Contrast with SHIFT OUT.

shift out (SO) A CHARACTER in a DATA COMMUNICATIONS CODE that is used to depart from the standard set and denotes that all following characters have a meaning other than the standard set until a SHIFT IN code is detected.

short haul modem A device used to connect a TERMINAL to a communications CIRCUIT in which the SIGNAL frequencies to the LINE are suitable for transmission over only relatively short distances. Used mainly for in-plant systems rather than for connection to a PUBLIC NETWORK.

SI See SHIFT IN.

sideband A SIGNAL that arises when a RADIO FREQUENCY SIGNAL is MODULATED by a second signal in order to carry the second signal in a TRANSMISSION SYSTEM. Sidebands are generated by the process of MODULATION above and below the frequency of the CARRIER SIGNAL and are displaced from the frequency of the carrier according to the frequency of the modulating signal. They are known as UPPER SIDEBANDS and LOWER SIDEBANDS.

signal 1. In TELEPHONY and in public networks, an instruction forming part of the process in setting up, maintaining or clearing a CALL. See also, for example, SIGNALING and SIGNALS.

2. In general, any electrical pulses transmitted in a network to represent MESSAGE information or CONTROL INFORMATION in handling the process of communications.

signal bandwidth The range of frequencies required to convey a particular MESSAGE SIGNAL accurately over a CHANNEL. For example, a SPEECH CHANNEL allows up to 4 kHz for transmission of ELECTRICAL SIGNALS representing voices; a TELEVISION CHANNEL may require up to 5 MHz to contain all the information necessary in a VIDEO SIGNAL.

signal element A discrete pulse forming part of a DIGITAL SIGNAL and having a value determined by the PULSE AMPLITUDE.

signal message A MESSAGE made up of a number of SIGNAL UNITS and transmitted on a SIGNALING channel to control the setup, maintenance or termination of a CALL in a DATA NETWORK.

signal phase See PHASE.

signal power A measure of the strength of any ELECTRICAL SIGNAL and expressed in BELS or DECIBELS (dB).

signal unit (SU) A unit of information in a SIGNALING SYSTEM for a PUBLIC DATA NETWORK and consisting of a defined number of BITS that provide INFORMATION to control the progress of CALLS. See also ACKNOWLEDGMENT SIGNAL UNIT, INITIAL SIGNAL UNIT, LONE SIGNAL UNIT, MULTI-BLOCK SYNCHRONIZATION UNIT, SUBSEQUENT SIGNAL UNIT, SYNCHRONIZATION SIGNAL UNIT and SYSTEM CONTROL SIGNAL UNIT.

signaling This term is given to the procedures concerned with the establishment, maintenance and termination of CALLS in a NETWORK. SIGNALING SYSTEMS have evolved to accommodate the development of all classes of communications systems, including TELEPHONY, TELEGRAPHY and DATA COMMUNICATIONS.

The simplest form of signaling occurs in a LOCAL TELEPHONE NETWORK in which various signals are transferred between the telephone instrument and the LOCAL EXCHANGE. For example, when a SUBSCRIBER lifts the HANDSET from the SWITCH HOOK, an automatic CALL REQUEST SIGNAL is sent to the LINE. The response from the exchange is a PROCEED-TO-SEND SIGNAL, which is recognizable as a DIAL TONE. Individual ADDRESS DIGITS dialed by the subscriber are also signals. Other signals include: CALLED TERMINAL FREE—ringing tone; CALLED TERMINAL ANSWERED—ringing tone stops; CLEAR—a party replaces handset. This illustration is oversimplified, and the signaling process includes complexities concerned with MULTI-EXCHANGE CONNECTIONS and INTER-EXCHANGE SIGNALING.

The methods of effecting signaling vary considerably with the evolution of SWITCHING technology, and in any particular TELEPHONE NETWORK various forms may be encountered.

DIRECT CURRENT signaling is dependent upon a DC path being created for signals through the TRANSMISSION PATH used for each call. It has tended to be replaced by ALTERNATING CURRENT signaling in which different signals are represented by AC tones applied to the transmission path. This form of signaling can itself be classified into IN-BAND SIGNALING and OUT-BAND SIGNALING.

In the former case, the tones are conveyed within the BANDWIDTH allocated to each SPEECH CHANNEL and, in the latter case, conveyed in a gap of 900 Hz between speech channels. Signals can be distinctly conveyed as specific tones, and the duration of the tone can also serve to define the specific meaning.

It has been usual for signaling to be carried on the actual TRANSMISSION CHANNEL or on a subsidiary channel directly associated with it. Various names are given to this technique, including: ASSOCIATED CHANNEL SIGNALING, CHANNEL ASSOCIATED SIGNALING, DECENTRALIZED SIGNALING.

With the use of modern digital techniques, specific signaling channels are designated to control a large number of transmission paths. This is particularly used between exchanges. Terms applied to this technique include: COMMON CHANNEL SIGNALING, CENTRALIZED CONTROL SIGNALING, SEPARATE CHANNEL SIGNALING, NONASSOCIATED SIGNALING. In such systems, each signal is represented by a group of BITS that includes the CHANNEL IDENTIFICATION and the specific signal intended. The exchanges concerned in such a system are able to carry out digital processing and are connected by a DIGITAL DATA LINK.

An example is the CCITT system, recommended for INTERNATIONAL EXCHANGES, known as SIGNALING SYSTEM NO. 6.

signaling interworking A concept that arises when an existing NETWORK has to be extended or gradually replaced by a more modern network that uses different technology and therefore different SIGNALING standards. There is a need during the period of changeover to provide subsystems capable of recognizing the new and old signaling systems.

signaling rate The rate at which a device can transmit or receive INFORMATION, usually expressed in BITS per second. For example, 1,200 bits per second implies the ability to send/receive 1,200 pulses per second.

signaling system No. 6 A COMMON CHANNEL SIGNALING system defined by the CCITT for use on international NETWORKS, in which each SIGNAL is represented by 28 BITS, including the signal itself, the CHANNEL IDENTIFICATION and ERROR CONTROL bits. Exchanges operating to this method have computerlike facilities and are linked by a DATA CHANNEL over which signals are exchanged as MESSAGES. See also SIGNALING.

signaling system No. 7 (SS#7) A CCITT recommendation for COMMON CHANNEL SIGNALING designed for use in, but not limited to, networks conforming to INTEGRATED SERVICES DIGITAL NETWORK standards. SS#7 provides internal CONTROL and NETWORK intelligence but not the transfer of SUBSCRIBER DATA. Developed during the 1970s and based on SIGNALING SYSTEM NO. 6, SS#7 is basically a way to control telephone SWITCHING EQUIPMENT. SS#7 defines the format and content of PACKETS on the D CHANNEL and is being modified continually so that the protocol hierarchy on the ISDN D channel can better fit the OSI model.

signals INFORMATION transmitted within a NETWORK to control the handling of MESSAGES and the setup, clearing and maintenance of connections. See also SIGNALING, ACCESS-BARRED SIGNAL, ADDRESS-COMPLETE SIGNAL, ADDRESS-INCOMPLETE SIGNAL, ADDRESS SIGNAL, ANSWER SIGNAL, BLOCKING SIGNAL, CALL ACCEPTED SIGNAL, CALL ANSWERED SIGNAL, CALL CONNECTED SIGNAL, CALL FAILURE SIGNAL, CALL NOT ACCEPTED SIGNAL, CALL PROGRESS SIGNAL, CALL REQUEST SIGNAL, CALLED TERMINAL ANSWERED SIGNAL, CALLED TERMINAL ENGAGED SIGNAL, CALLED TERMINAL FREE SIGNAL, CALLING INDICATOR SIGNAL, CHANGED NUMBER SIGNAL, CHARACTER SIGNAL, CIRCUIT GROUP CONGESTION SIGNAL, CLEAR BACK SIGNAL, CLEAR CONFIRMATION SIGNAL, CLEAR FORWARD SIGNAL, CLEAR REQUEST SIGNAL, CONFUSION SIGNAL, CORRECT SIGNAL, CONTINUITY-FAILURE SIGNAL, DATA TRANSFER REQUESTED SIGNAL, DISTRIBUTED FRAME ALIGNMENT SIGNAL, END-OF-ADDRESS SIGNAL, END-OF-BLOCK SIGNAL, END-OF-PULSING SIGNAL, FRAME ALIGNMENT SIGNAL, HANG-UP SIGNAL, LINE-OUT-OF-SERVICE SIGNAL, NO CHARGE ANSWER SIGNAL, OCTET TIMING SIGNAL, OUT-OF-ORDER SIGNAL, PROCEED-TO-SEND SIGNAL, READY-FOR-DATA SIGNAL.

These and other signals are used variously in TELEGRAPHY, TELEPHONY and DATA COMMUNICATIONS. There are standard systems of SIGNALING, and particular reference should be made to a CCITT standard for the appreciation of such systems. There are also variations of international standards used in national networks, and in most countries one finds more advanced systems having to operate alongside older, and even outdated, SIGNALING SYSTEMS.

signal-to-listener echo ratio The ratio of SIGNAL POWER to the power of ECHO signals reflected back to the TRANSMITTING STATION and caused by changes in the electrical characteristics of a CIRCUIT. A form of signal impairment in transmission over long-distance TRANSMISSION PATHS, e.g., intercontinental TELEPHONE CIRCUITS.

signal-to-noise ratio In any RADIO TRANSMISSION, or in any communication LINK, a certain amount of NOISE is generated and is carried as background interference to the desired MESSAGE SIGNAL. If the signal-to-noise ratio is high, then the message is unlikely to be impaired; if it is low, the signal may well be severely impaired.

The problem is intensified by the use of AMPLIFIERS, which will amplify both noise and signal. REPEATERS containing amplifiers are spaced at intervals along transmission cables to maintain an appropriate signal-to-noise ratio. These amplifiers are designed to amplify signals occurring in a critical frequency BANDWIDTH in which the message signal arises; the bandwidth of the amplifier is restricted so that noise outside the critical bandwidth is rejected.

signal-to-quantizing noise ratio QUANTIZING NOISE occurs in PULSE CODE MODULATION (PCM) systems and arises as part of the process of converting an AUDIO SIGNAL to digital form and vice versa. See also SIGNAL-TO-NOISE RATIO.

silicon chip A very small device composed of silicon and used for the construction of micro-electronic circuits in electronic machines. Silicon materials are very cheap; their main property is that they are semiconductors and can be used to provide very high-speed SWITCHING operations necessary in digital storage and processing systems.

simplex 1. Sometimes used to indicate a transmission CIRCUIT in which MESSAGES can be sent only in one specific direction.

2. The CCITT definition states that a simplex circuit allows transmission in either direction but only one way at a time. See HALF DUPLEX, definition 1.

single bit error An error occurring in a DATA TRANSMISSION sequence in which a single BIT is inverted, i.e., a 0 becomes a 1 or a 1 becomes a 0. See also TRANSMISSION ERRORS.

single current circuit A CIRCUIT used for DATA TRANSMISSION in which voltages are applied directly to a LINE to represent BINARY NUMBERS, i.e., positive voltage to represent 1 and zero voltage to represent 0. Contrast this with a DOUBLE CURRENT CIRCUIT in which 1 and 0 are represented by positive and negative voltages respectively. Either system can be used for transmission over short distances (a few kilometers), but for long-distance communication over a NETWORK, a MODEM or NETWORK INTERFACE UNIT is needed. Such circuits are often used between a DATA TERMINAL (DTE) and its DCE, when they are referred to as INTERCHANGE CIRCUITS.

single mode fiber A data transmission medium. In DATA TRANSMISSION using FIBER OPTIC CABLE, the core size of single mode fiber accommodates only one path of light.

single sideband modulation A CARRIER WAVE modulated at a single frequency produces three simultaneous SIGNALS: the unmodulated CARRIER and two associated steady frequencies spaced on either side of the carrier by the frequency of MODULATION. If a carrier wave is modulated by a signal that is not steady (e.g., an AUDIO SIGNAL), a SPECTRUM ENVELOPE of associated frequencies known as a SIDEBAND is generated. To BROADCAST and receive accurately AUDIO FREQUENCIES up to 15 kHz, the sidebands will spread 15 kHz on each side of the carrier wave.

These sidebands are known as UPPER SIDEBANDS and LOWER SIDEBANDS. It is common practice to select one of these sidebands when transmitting modulated signals over a TRANSMISSION CHANNEL and to suppress the carrier and the other sideband. This economizes on the use of power and BANDWIDTH in transmission. See also MULTIPLEXING.

sinusoidal Pertaining to a SIGNAL that is in the form of a pure sine wave and in which there is one complete reversal of phase in a cycle of given duration.

SITA See SOCIETE INTERNATIONALE DE TELECOMMUNICATION AERONAUTIQUE.

sky-waves Radio broadcast signals that are reflected from the IONOSPHERE, usually in the MEDIUM FREQUENCY and HIGH FREQUENCY bands.

slotted ALOHA A variation of the ALOHA TRANSMISSION technique, slotted ALOHA restricts a TERMINAL from sending DATA continuously. Instead, the terminal must wait for the beginning of the next TIME SLOT.

SNA See SYSTEMS NETWORK ARCHITECTURE.

SO See SHIFT OUT.

Societe Internationale de Telecommunication Aeronautique An international body that has introduced standards for a communication system that is the MAIN NETWORK used by world airlines for MESSAGE SWITCHING. A number of computer NODES are installed in major cities, and service TERMINALS in airline offices, airports and centers of administration.

soft copy A MESSAGE produced in a communications system but not in physical form, e.g., a message displayed on a VISUAL DISPLAY. Also known as TRANSIENT COPY. Contrast with HARD COPY or PERMANENT COPY.

software Relating to any logical rules that are built into a device by COMPUTER programs rather than by the physical arrangement of HARDWARE components. The scope and application of the software varies greatly. It can be the OPERATING SYSTEM provided by the computer manufacturer or an APPLICATION written by a USER for a specific purpose.

Software Defined Network (SDN) A TELECOMMUNICATIONS service that provides a virtual PRIVATE NETWORK based on a PUBLIC SWITCHED TELEPHONE NETWORK.

software interface The specification of the logical rules that will allow two COMPUTER programs to interact with each other and to ensure the accurate and efficient transfer of information between the programs.

SOH See START OF HEADING.

solenoid A type of switch, the operation of which depends upon the principles of electromagnetism. A current passes through a coil constructed around an armature that moves under the influence of the current to open or close a contact.

SOM See START OF MESSAGE.

SONET See SYNCHRONOUS OPTICAL NETWORK.

sound See SOUND WAVES.

sound bandwidth Relating to the range of frequencies occupied by ELECTRICAL SIGNALS corresponding to SOUND WAVES and generally considered to be within the BAND from 20 Hz to 20 kHz.

sound carrier A CARRIER WAVE used to carry an AUDIO SIGNAL and used particularly to distinguish from a VISION CARRIER in the composite signal used for television broadcasting. See also TELEVISION TRANSMISSION SIGNAL.

sound signal An ELECTRICAL SIGNAL corresponding to acoustic signals in the range audible to humans: 20 Hz to 20 kHz.

sound waves Waves transmitted through air (or any other gas, solid or liquid) as a result of vibration through the medium in which it is traveling. In communication systems, sound waves are generally considered to be within the range of frequencies that human beings can perceive: 20 Hz to 20 kHz.

sound-program Signals within a range of frequencies human beings can hear (i.e., from 20 Hz to 20 kHz) and representing music or speech prepared for transmission as a radio program or as the sound component of a television program.

sound-program circuit A one-way AUDIO CIRCUIT for the transmission of a SOUND-PROGRAM.

source address field A FIELD of INFORMATION in a FRAME that identifies the STATION sending the frame to the NETWORK.

Southwestern Bell Corp. See REGIONAL BELL HOLDING COMPANY.

space In ALPHABETIC TELEGRAPHY, one of two possible line conditions occurring in a SIGNAL, the other condition being known as a MARK. All CHARACTERS in telegraphy are made up of combinations of spaces and marks, i.e., patterns of BITS represented by BINARY DIGITS 0 and 1. In a transmission sequence, the first bit of each character is always a space that acts as a START PULSE. The final bit is always a mark (a STOP PULSE), and the line condition remains as a mark until another character is transmitted.

space switched systems Used to refer to SWITCHING systems in which FREQUENCY DIVISION MULTIPLEXING is used rather than TIME DIVISION MULTIPLEXING. See also SWITCHING EQUIPMENT.

space switching In TRANSMISSION SYSTEMS using FREQUENCY DIVISION MULTIPLEXING, the process of SWITCHING to make physical connections through an EXCHANGE is often referred to as space switching. This distinguishes from TIME SWITCHING, which arises in systems using TIME DIVISION MULTIPLEXING (TDM). In both cases, a physical switching operation is still necessary, but furthermore with TDM, a SYNCHRONIZATION OF TIME SLOTS is also necessary.

space waves Radio broadcast SIGNALS used in short-range communication by means of VHF and UHF signals, in which the waves are propagated as a combination of direct and ground-reflected waves.

space-division systems This term refers to systems in which MULTIPLEXING is achieved by FREQUENCY MODULATION (FM) rather than by TIME DIVISION MULTIPLEXING (TDM). Thus, terms such as space-division interface arise, to distinguish from a TDM INTERFACE.

space-time-space network Relates to a SWITCHING process sometimes used in DIGITAL EXCHANGES handling TIME DIVISION MULTIPLEXED traffic, in which incoming SIGNALS first pass through a SPACE SWITCH, then a TIME SWITCH, and then a space switch. This method can be compared with the time-space-time network, which is perhaps more commonly used. See also TIME SHIFTING.

SPC See STORED PROGRAM CONTROL.

spectral colors Colors generated directly from the narrow BANDS representing the color stages of the VISIBLE COLOR SPECTRUM rather than colors arising as combinations of these stages, which are known as NONSPECTRAL COLORS.

spectrum envelope When a SIGNAL is MODULATED onto a CARRIER WAVE, a complex pattern of signals is generated; this would include the carrier wave plus SIDEBAND signals, which are displaced in frequency on either side of the carrier and known as UPPER SIDEBAND and LOWER SIDEBAND. The total pattern of signals is known as the spectrum envelope. There are different methods for applying the basic modulation techniques resulting in different forms of the spectrum envelope. See also MODULATION, SINGLE SIDEBAND MODULATION and VESTIGIAL SIDEBAND MODULATION.

speech channel A COMMUNICATIONS CHANNEL designed to occupy a very NARROW BANDWIDTH equivalent to the range of sounds necessary for humans to speak to one another, i.e., an AUDIO FREQUENCY bandwidth of 3 or 4 kHz.

speech circuit A CIRCUIT designed to carry ELECTRICAL SIGNALS as a representation of human speech and offering a BANDWIDTH of from 300 Hz to 3,300 Hz.

speech communication Relating to a system designed to permit communication of human speech, i.e., to switch and transmit ELECTRICAL SIGNALS up to 4 kHz in BANDWIDTH. See also SPEECH TRAFFIC.

speech path A TRANSMISSION CHANNEL, up to 4 kHz in bandwidth, used in a TELEPHONE NETWORK intended to carry VOICE ANALOG SIGNALS representing human speech.

speech signal An ANALOG ELECTRICAL SIGNAL representing the sound of human speech. Same as VOICE SIGNAL.

speech traffic Relating to MESSAGES being transmitted to represent human speech in a TELEPHONE SYSTEM, where each SPEECH CHANNEL consists of ANALOG ELECTRICAL SIGNALS in a BANDWIDTH of from 300 to 3,300 Hz. Note, however, such signals can be converted to digital signals using PULSE AMPLITUDE MODULATION, and therefore speech traffic can be carried by TIME DIVISION MULTIPLEXING.

spill-over traffic Traffic in a SWITCHED SYSTEM that cannot be handled by the BASIC ROUTE during a PEAK LOAD and therefore is transmitted via an alternative TRANSMISSION PATH.

split screen transmission A technique for entering DATA over a NETWORK in which an operator completes entries onto a form displayed on a VISUAL DISPLAY unit; but when the details are sent, only the variable data on the form is transmitted to the LINE. Also known as PARTIAL TRANSMISSION.

SQL See STRUCTURED QUERY LANGUAGE.

SSB See SINGLE SIDEBAND MODULATION.

SSU See SUBSEQUENT SIGNAL UNIT.

stability When a high proportion of the OFFERED TRAFFIC in a NETWORK is delivered within the standards set, and this proportion is maintained at all levels of loading planned for the network.

standard code sets A set of internationally agreed upon CODES and their approved significance within an approved DATA COMMUNICATIONS CODE. Sometimes these code sets can be extended with nonstandard codes used in local or national situations. The standard code is then a subset used for international purposes.

standing charge A charge made to a USER for being a registered SUBSCRIBER to a communications service. The charge may be levied as an annual fee, which may or may not include rental of a TERMINAL and the allocation of reference numbers to allow access to facilities on the system. Contrast with USAGE CHARGE.

star See STAR NETWORK.

star network A NETWORK in which the USERS in the system are connected by means of communication LINKS radiating out, like spokes of a wheel, from a central hub or controlling NODE, which handles all communication between users. See also NETWORK TOPOLOGIES.

start bit A BINARY DIGIT at the beginning of a series of BITS representing a CHARACTER. See also START CODE and START-STOP SIGNALS.

start code 1. A BIT at the beginning of a series of bits representing a single CHARACTER. The start code signifies the beginning of the character to maintain SYNCHRONIZATION between the TRANSMITTING and RECEIVING TERMINALS.

2. Any bit sequence or character sequence used to signify the beginning of a unit of INFORMATION in a transmission sequence. See also STOP CODE.

start of heading (SOH) An international TRANSMISSION CONTROL CODE. This identifies a succeeding group of CHARACTERS as a HEADER, e.g., containing ROUTING or other CONTROL INFORMATION relevant to an ensuing TEXT.

start pulse A pulse at the beginning of a CHARACTER in an ASYNCHRONOUS transmission system and used to establish SYNCHRONIZATION between TRANSMITTING and RECEIVING TERMINALS. See also START CODE and START-STOP SIGNALS.

start-stop signals Pulses used to indicate the beginning and end of a group of pulses that represent INFORMATION. The pulses are used to synchronize the RECEIVING TERMINAL to the incoming stream of pulses representing information. For example, a standard TELEPRINTER reacts to groups of seven pulses, five of which are coded to represent a single character of information, and two are the start and stop pulses. Each stop pulses is identified because it is of longer duration than the others. See also ASYNCHRONOUS OPERATION.

start-stop transmission A mode of transmission in which CHARACTERS of INFORMATION on the LINE are delineated by START-STOP SIGNALS, which synchronize the RECEIVING TERMINAL to the incoming stream of pulses representing characters. See also ASYNCHRONOUS OPERATION.

state One of the conditions which can exist during the establishment, maintenance or clearance of a CALL, e.g., CALLED TERMINAL ALERTED STATE.

station A location connected to a NETWORK and having a unique ADDRESS to enable signals to be routed to it from other stations. A station may be able both to send and to receive INFORMATION and could be implemented as a COMPUTER or a TERMINAL.

statistical multiplexer A development of the TDM MULTIPLEXER in which increased efficiency in the use of DATA CIRCUITS is achieved by giving increased priority to certain CHANNELS in the TRANSMISSION PATH according to the expected transmission load. See also MULTIPLEXER and TIME DIVISION MULTIPLEXING.

statmux See STATISTICAL MULTIPLEXER.

STD See SUBSCRIBER TRUNK DIALING.

stop bit A BINARY DIGIT occurring at the end of a CHARACTER and used to synchronize TRANSMITTING and RECEIVING TERMINALS. See also START-STOP SIGNALS.

stop code 1. A BIT, or series of bits, at the end of a group of bits representing a single CHARACTER. The stop code signifies the end of character to maintain SYNCHRONIZATION between the TRANSMITTING and RECEIVING TERMINALS.

2. Any bit sequence or character sequence used to signify the end of a unit of INFORMATION in a transmission sequence. See also START CODE.

stop pulse A pulse occurring at the end of every CHARACTER to establish synchronization between TRANSMITTING and RECEIVING TERMINALS. See also START-STOP SIGNALS.

store and forward systems A communication system in which MESSAGES may be transmitted, even though a complete TRANSMISSION PATH to the RECEIVING TERMINAL is not available. The system will entail one or more COMPUTER-controlled EXCHANGES (or NODES) that are able to store messages and release them for transmission to the receiving terminal when a transmission path is available.

stored program control (SPC) This concept refers to the application of DATA PROCESSING and COMPUTER control techniques in the operation of an EXCHANGE. The techniques can be applied to any service, e.g., TELEX, TELEPHONE or INTEGRATED DIGITAL EXCHANGE.

SPC provides the means of using a computer program to give CENTRALIZED CONTROL over the operational, administrative and maintenance functions. It interprets SIGNALS received from SUBSCRIBERS and other exchanges, arranges the setup and clearing procedures and paths through the switching unit and determines what MESSAGES are sent to the various subscribers or other exchanges connected to the particular exchange.

Strowger Almon B. Strowger developed a mechanical relay in 1891, the principles of which are still used in many countries as the basis of electromechanical SWITCHING operations in TELEPHONE EXCHANGES.

Strowger selectors Electromechanical devices used in early CIRCUIT SWITCHED TELEPHONE EXCHANGES to make connections between INCOMING LINES and OUTGOING LINES. Each SELECTOR in such a system is activated by a SOLENOID or a motor. The system was first developed by Almon B. Strowger in 1891 but has seen many refinements. The benefits of the system are the reliability and simplicity of the selector devices, which can be activated directly by SIGNALS originated from the telephone dialing mechanism. In recent times, Strowger exchanges have been replaced by ELECTRONIC EXCHANGES, which are more efficient when used in conjunction with digital forms of transmission.

Structured Query Language (SQL) An ANSI standard for retrieving DATA from a RELATIONAL DATABASE.

S-T-S network See SPACE-TIME-SPACE NETWORK.

STX See START OF TEXT.

SUB A special CHARACTER used in a DATA COMMUNICATIONS CODE to present a character that is to be substituted for an erroneous or invalid character.

sub-address A suffix added to a NETWORK USER ADDRESS to identify a particular TERMINAL, USER, or class of use available within a communications complex.

submarine cable A cable submerged beneath the ocean to provide communication between landmasses separated by sea. This is one of the earliest forms of TRANSMISSION LINK between the major continents of the world, and such cables are still being laid down, despite the rapid growth of SATELLITE communication. Submarine transmission links usually consist of COAXIAL CABLES with REPEATERS sealed into the construction of the cable at regular intervals. MULTIPLEXING techniques are used so that a single CHANNEL can be used for thousands of simultaneous CALLS.

subscriber Any person or organization registered as a USER of a TELECOMMUNICATIONS service and who is entitled to send and receive INFORMATION over a NETWORK. The subscriber is usually identified by an ADDRESS, which is typically a NUMBER providing a unique identifier for a particular TERMINAL or a password related to a named individual or organization.

subscriber instrument A TERMINAL registered for use by an individual or an organization over a PUBLIC NETWORK, e.g., a TELEPHONE.

subscriber line The TRANSMISSION LINK between a subscriber's TERMINAL and the LOCAL EXCHANGE with which it is permanently associated. Also known as CUSTOMER LOOP.

subscriber switching subsystem Provides for the concentration of TRAFFIC from lightly utilized SUBSCRIBERS' LINES at a LOCAL EXCHANGE onto the heavily used common CIRCUITS.

subscriber trunk dialing A service provided to SUBSCRIBERS in a TELEPHONE NETWORK in which they are able to call distant subscribers over TRUNK CIRCUITS without the intervention of a human operator.

subsequent signal unit (SSU) In some systems, groups of SIGNALS may be transmitted as a unit known as a MULTIBLOCK. Any signal, other than the initial signal of the BLOCK, is referred to as a subsequent signal unit.

supergroup In relation to FREQUENCY DIVISION MULTIPLEXING, an assembly of equipment providing a means of transmission for 60 separate VOICE CHANNELS along a single COAXIAL TUBE.

superhigh frequency (SHF) A range of ELECTROMAGNETIC WAVES in the range of from 3 to 30 GHz and having WAVELENGTHS from 1 to 10 centimeters.

supervisory control language A type of PROGRAMMING LANGUAGE used by system managers responsible for customizing the facilities provided in a communications network based upon a STORED PROGRAM CONTROL computer.

supervisory frame See TOKEN RING.

surface waves RADIO WAVES are guided over the earth's surface and usually occur in the LOW FREQUENCY and MEDIUM FREQUENCY bands of the RADIO FREQUENCY SPECTRUM.

switch fabric A term used to refer to the details of how DATA is switched from one NODE to another within a NETWORK rather than at the periphery of the network.

switch hook The contacts that are activated when a telephone HANDSET is raised or set down. Sometimes called a CRADLE SWITCH.

switched circuits CIRCUITS are formed by activating switches within an EXCHANGE to connect one set of LINES with another. The implication is that a SWITCHING operation is performed to make a particular CALL possible and that the connection is automatically maintained until either party CLEARS. Contrast with PACKET SWITCHING and MESSAGE SWITCHING.

switched connection A TRANSMISSION PATH established by an EXCHANGE and entailing the physical connection of CIRCUITS in the exchange by means of electromechanical switches or entailing the SYNCHRONIZATION of timing between an incoming and an outgoing DIGITAL CHANNEL to complete an ACCESS PATH between a CALLING TERMINAL and a CALLED TERMINAL.

switched network A multipoint communications NETWORK that provides circuit SWITCHED CONNECTIONS. TELEX is an example. See also SWITCHED TELECOMMUNICATIONS SYSTEM.

switched telecommunications system In a switched telecommunications system, there are three basic elements: TERMINALS, TRANSMISSION LINKS and at least one EXCHANGE.

The objective of a switched system is to enable a USER to communicate with any other user at any time.

In the TELEPHONE SYSTEM, a user is able to talk to another by dialing a connection to the LOCAL EXCHANGE, and then by transmission links (possibly including other exchanges) to the user required. Once a TRANSMISSION CHANNEL is established between the two users, it remains available until the CALL is finished. This is an example of CIRCUIT SWITCHING.

There are, however, switching systems in which transmission links are used but not allocated exclusively for the duration of a particular call. Such systems are more often used in the transmission of DATA.

In a packet switched system, data is transmitted in BLOCKS which contain identifying information, allowing the PACKET to be associated with a particular call to a particular user. As they pass over the transmission links, the packets forming the elements of a MESSAGE may be interspersed with packets related to entirely different calls, destined for other users. No continuously available CHANNEL exists between two terminals in such a system, yet such systems, working at high speeds, can conduct communications in CONVERSATIONAL MODE, as well as carry messages from a source to a destination. (See also PACKET SWITCHING NETWORK, FAST PACKET SWITCHING.)

In a MESSAGE SWITCHED SYSTEM, a user can transmit a message to the network, where it may be stored and delivered to the intended recipient at a later time.

Message switched systems can be used to attempt to optimize the cost of the telecommunications activity by delivering messages by an available ROUTE, taking advantage of differential TARIFFS that may apply in different time zones and through different CARRIERS.

The distinction between a message switched system and a circuit switched system is determined largely by the design of the exchange.

An exchange that establishes a physical transmission channel between two terminals for the duration of a call is known as a CIRCUIT SWITCHED EXCHANGE and is necessary for person-to-person communication.

An exchange that stores messages until it can establish a transmission channel is a MESSAGE SWITCHED EXCHANGE and is generally used for transmission of messages or small units of data. See also SWITCHING EQUIPMENT, CIRCUIT SWITCHING, TELEGRAPH SYSTEM and TELETYPEWRITER.

switched telephone exchange A NODE in a TELEPHONE NETWORK in which CIRCUITS are connected automatically in response to SIGNALS generated by USERS dialing ADDRESSES upon a telephone instrument.

switched virtual circuit Same as VIRTUAL CIRCUIT.

switching equipment For many years the technology used in TELEPHONE EXCHANGES to switch connection between CIRCUITS was based on electromechanical devices made up of rotary switches and called SELECTORS. The concept of the automatic telephone exchange, using such principles, was invented in 1889 by an American undertaker, Almon B. Strowger.

An improved electromechanical system, known as CROSSBAR EXCHANGE, was introduced in the late 1920s.

With the introduction of ELECTRONIC EXCHANGES, the principles of crossbar systems have been adapted most successfully to provide the design basis for the early electronic switching systems. These electronic exchanges have the advantage of relative cheapness and are more easily maintained than electromechanical systems as well as having the ability to record activities automatically, e.g., for providing BILLING INFORMATION or TRAFFIC STATISTICS. See also COMMON CONTROL.

Many electronic exchanges have DIGITAL COMPUTERS controlling them, and the common control features of the crossbar exchange are now provided by computer programs in what is known as STORED PROGRAM CONTROL (SPC) exchanges.

There is now a rapid change taking place in exchange and transmission technology, and this is concerned with the introduction of TIME DIVISION SYSTEMS, which use transmission techniques based upon TIME DIVISION MULTIPLEXING (TDM). Such systems must use DIGITAL TRANSMISSION, not ANALOG transmission, and TDM was first applied to DATA NETWORKS.

In time division systems, a number of CALLS are able to share the transmission highway; in effect, the use of the HIGHWAY is available as a series of TIME SLOTS.

A time slot might be 8 BITS in length and, typically, 30 active channels might share a 2 Mbit highway.

Now, time division techniques have been extended to VOICE networks in which each human CONVERSATION is converted to a string of BINARY DIGITS for TRANSMISSION and reconverted to audio ANALOG SIGNALS for the SUBSCRIBER.

The crosspoints in such a TDM system are referred to as TIME SHARED DIGITAL CROSSPOINTS; to connect two such channels in an exchange requires two processes: SPACE SWITCHING (i.e., making the connection from one channel to the other) and TIME SWITCHING (i.e., SYNCHRONIZING the time slots occupied in the two channels).

It is common to refer to TDM systems as TIME SWITCHED SYSTEMS and to non-TDM systems as SPACE SWITCHED SYSTEMS. Time switching techniques enable several conversations or messages to share the same line; they can likewise efficiently time-share the crosspoints in an exchange.

TDM systems are expected gradually to replace the so-called space switched systems; but this will take time, due to the heavy investments made by TELECOMMUNICATIONS companies in the earlier systems. There are, however, great efficiencies in the utilization of lines to be obtained with time switching, and a far greater potential to extend a whole range of services—digital, voice and GRAPHICS to the individual office or home.

Telecommunications networks will, in future, combine speech, DATA and other services; this concept is referred to as an *integrated digital transmission and switching system*. The following are included in the benefits to be derived from it: fast setup for MULTILINK CALLS, common SIGNALING SYSTEMS with high capacity, transmission loss independent of the length of circuit, low DISTORTION and NOISE, high reliability and an extensive selection of services to the subscribers.

All the topics discussed above are examples of CIRCUIT SWITCHING. See also SWITCHED TELECOMMUNICATION SYSTEM, MESSAGE SWITCHING, which operates on different principles, and INTEGRATED SERVICES DIGITAL NETWORK.

SYN See SYNCHRONOUS IDLE.

sync bytes Units of INFORMATION that precede each transmission in a SYNCHRONOUS system to notify the RECEIVING STATION that a SIGNAL is about to be transmitted. The RECEIVER CLOCK in the RECEIVING TERMINAL uses these pulses to establish SYNCHRONIZATION with the TRANSMITTER CLOCK.

sync pulse See SYNCHRONIZATION PULSE.

sync pulse separator A device in a TELEVISION RECEIVER that is used to extract SYNCHRONIZATION information representing FIELD SCAN and LINE SCAN instructions so that a scanning operation can be generated to produce an accurate picture.

synchronization The process by which DATA TERMINALS connected to a NETWORK can communicate with one another. The methods vary from one class of system to another, but the principles are discussed under the following headings: BIT SYNCHRONIZATION, CHARACTER SYNCHRONIZATION and MESSAGE SYNCHRONIZATION.

synchronization pulses In a television system, these are pulses generated during the camera scanning process, transmitted as part of the COMPOSITE VIDEO SIGNAL and used to maintain SYNCHRONIZATION between the camera and the TV RECEIVER. In practice, these pulses enable the SCANNING BEAM in the receiver to be related to the equivalent scanning points traced by the scanning beam in the camera. See also VIDEO SIGNAL.

synchronization signal unit (SYU) A unit of SIGNAL information that contains

INFORMATION to synchronize a number of other SIGNAL UNITS transmitted as a MULTIBLOCK on a SIGNALING channel.

synchronized network A NETWORK in which the timing of all operations is governed by one MASTER CLOCK. Also known as a DESPOTIC NETWORK; contrast with DEMOCRATIC NETWORK.

synchronous data link control (SDLC) A LINE CONTROL protocol developed by IBM that is a subset of the HIGH LEVEL DATA LINK CONTROL developed by the International Organization for Standardization. It performs transmission ERROR CHECKING functions and automatically requests retransmission of error FRAMES.

synchronous data transmission A system used for high-speed DIGITAL TRANSMISSION in which SYNCHRONIZATION is maintained by CLOCKS in the TRANSMITTING and RECEIVING TERMINALS, and BINARY SIGNALS are transmitted without gaps. This continues for as long as necessary and, if there are gaps in the DATA, the transmitting terminal must insert idle BITS. Synchronization is established at the beginning of each transmission by special SYNC characters, which are used to align the clocks at each STATION. Contrast with ASYNCHRONOUS OPERATION.

synchronous detection A method of DETECTION used in DEMODULATION where the method of transmission involves suppression of the CARRIER and UPPER SIDEBAND signals. It involves the generation in the DEMODULATOR of a local CARRIER SIGNAL. See also MODULATION.

synchronous digital system Any communication system in which communication is in BITS and in which SYNCHRONIZATION between TRANSMITTING and RECEIVING STATIONS is achieved by arranging for their CLOCKS to be synchronized following the transmission of SYNCHRONIZATION PULSES at the beginning of each MESSAGE SIGNAL. Contrast with ASYNCHRONOUS SYSTEMS, in which timing is established by START and STOP PULSES associated with each unit of DATA (e.g., each CHARACTER).

synchronous idle An international TRANSMISSION CONTROL CODE transmitted to establish or maintain SYNCHRONIZATION with a RECEIVING TERMINAL.

synchronous mode Relating to communication using SYNCHRONOUS DATA TRANSMISSION.

synchronous operation A method of DATA TRANSMISSION in which CHARACTERS are transferred as a contiguous sequence of bits and there are no gaps or START and STOP BITS between each character. The receiver establishes SYNCHRONIZATION with the first bit of any character sequence and maintains synchronization with a clocking mechanism, which maintains a constant frequency with the periodic time of the incoming BIT STREAM. Contrast with ASYNCHRONOUS OPERATION.

Synchronous Optical Network (SONET) An emerging CCITT/ANSI standard for DATA COMMUNICATIONS that defines TRANSMISSION speeds of 51.84 Mbps to 2.5 Gbps via FIBER OPTIC CABLE. SONET CHANNEL rates are supported in multiples of 1.544-Mbps. A 2.5-Gbps SONET installation is in place for the 1992 Olympic games in Spain.

system boundary The physical limits of a particular system, excluding the USERS at the TRANSMITTING and RECEIVING STATIONS but including the TERMINALS and the intervening TRANSMISSION CHANNEL.

system control signal unit (SCU) A SIGNAL transmitted on a signaling CHANNEL but having the purpose of changing the operation of the SIGNALING SYSTEM, e.g., to switch the signaling TRAFFIC to a designated LINK.

systems network architecture (SNA) A PROTOCOL and implementation for a DATA NETWORK developed by

IBM in the 1970s to provide end-to-end management of ACCESS PATHS. SNA represents one of the first ways to allow TERMINALS in a TREE NETWORK to share a LINE to separate APPLICATIONS in the same HOST PROCESSOR. Later features provided COMPUTER NETWORKING, aiming to allow any terminal to gain an access path to any host processor in the network by the interlinking of tree networks.

SYU See SYNCHRONIZATION SIGNAL UNIT.

T

T carrier A DIGITAL TRANSMISSION LINE that operates at 1.544 Mbps and faster. It uses TIME DIVISION MULTIPLEXING and PULSE CODE MODULATION to provide a 64-kbps voice CHANNEL.

10 Base-T An IEEE standard that specifies running ETHERNET over TWISTED WIRE PARTS.

T interface A four-wire INTERFACE that accesses the T reference point in an ISDN NETWORK—that is, the juncture of the SUBSCRIBER's and the CARRIER's part of the network.

T1 The term T1 refers both to the transmission lines along which DIGITAL SIGNALS travel at a rate of 1.544 Mbps and to the COMMON CARRIER's service that provides 1.544-Mbps transmission. In the United States, a T1 signal has a DS-1 format and equals the capacity of 24 voice CHANNELS. In Europe, however, the data rate for DS-1 is 2.048 Mbps.

T1-C A COMMON CARRIER's facility that can transmit a SIGNAL having the DS-1C format at 3.152 Mbps, which is equal to the capacity of 48 voice CHANNELS.

T2 A COMMON CARRIER's facility that can transmit digital CARRIER SIGNALS having the DS-2 format at 6.312 Mbps, which is equal to the capacity of 96 voice CHANNELS.

T3 A COMMON CARRIER's facility that can transmit digital CARRIER SIGNALS having the DS-3 format at 44 Mbps, which is equal to the capacity of 672 voice CHANNELS.

T4 A COMMON CARRIER's facility that can transmit a digital CARRIER SIGNAL having the DS-4 format at 273 Mbps, which equals the capacity of 4,032 voice CHANNELS.

TA See TERMINAL ADAPTER.

tandem exchange See TANDEM OFFICE.

tandem office A particular method for linking a number of LOCAL EXCHANGES in a TELEPHONE NETWORK so that TRAFFIC may be carried between these local exchanges without having to be ROUTED via TRUNK CIRCUITS and PRIMARY TRUNK EXCHANGES. This practice is often adopted in city areas in which there is high TRAFFIC VOLUME and high SUBSCRIBER density. Also known as TANDEM EXCHANGE.

target probability of service The targets set by the designers of a system to provide service to the USERS. For example, in a CIRCUIT SWITCHED SYSTEM, the target probability of CALL BLOCKING may be set as 0.01.

target user population The group of people or organizations for whom a particular service is designed and promoted.

tariff The charge made to USERS by a supplier of communications services for use of a communications NETWORK. This normally entails the users being registered and given a CUSTOMER REFERENCE NUMBER for BILLING purposes. The identification and recovery of charges is often a significant cost in the development and operation of a service. See also USAGE CHARGE, STANDING CHARGE and CONNECTION CHARGE.

TC See TRANSMISSION CONTROL CODE.

TCM See TRELLIS-CODED MODULATION.

TCP/IP See TRANSMISSION CONTROL PROTOCOL/INTERNET PROTOCOL.

TD See TIME DIVISION.

TDM See TIME DIVISION MULTIPLEXING.

TDM multiplexer A MULTIPLEXER that uses the principles of TIME DIVISION MULTIPLEXING to combine a number of CHANNELS on to the same physical TRANSMISSION PATH.

Technical and Office Protocols (TOP) A communications structure, TOP defines specific options from industry standards; it addresses the networking requirements of engineering, manufacturing and general office applications but focuses mostly on office applications. The development of TOP was sponsored by the Boeing Company. See also MANUFACTURING AUTOMATION PROTOCOL.

telco An abbreviation for telephone CENTRAL OFFICE. See also CENTRAL OFFICE.

telecommunications Communication between two people using equipment to overcome the effects caused by distance and/or physical barriers between them. The communication need not be two way, and the equipment need not necessarily be electronic.

telecommunications authority See COMMON CARRIER.

telecommuting The process of doing work on a COMPUTER at a location that is distant from the site (usually an employer's office) requiring the work. The completed task is sent via DATA COMMUNICATIONS NETWORKS so the USER need not travel to the office in person.

teleconferencing The process of allowing widely dispersed groups of people to have a meeting via electronic systems. Interactive audio communications are provided. Contrast with VIDEOCONFERENCING.

telegraph codes Telegraph codes grew from the need to transmit plain language TEXT and numerals. The codes were designed to represent the letters of the alphabet and numerals. Thus, the early CODES contained just 36 CHARACTERS or codes.

These characters are represented as groups of electrical pulses during transmission, and MESSAGES can be prepared and stored as holes punched in PAPER TAPE. Each row of holes in the paper tape represents a single character, the PULSE CODES being represented by the presence or absence of holes in each row.

In order to incorporate punctuation marks and other special codes, the CHARACTER SET was expanded beyond the basic 36 characters. The international standard set (known as INTERNATIONAL ALPHABET NO. 2) contains 58 different characters.

It is a 5-BIT CODE (each character is represented by a combination of 5 pulses). Strictly speaking, such a code only provides 25 or 32 unique characters, but SHIFT CHARACTERS are used to extend the capacity of the code; i.e., a FIGURES SHIFT code indicates that all following characters are to be treated as figures or other SECONDARY CHARACTERS, while the LETTERS SHIFT signifies that following codes are letters.

In telegraph communications, each character is framed by a START PULSE and a STOP PULSE. Thus, 7 bits are actually transmitted to the LINE for each character.

With the development of computer-based systems, telegraph codes have expanded to meet further requirements. See also DATA COMMUNICATION CODES and INTERNATIONAL ALPHABET NO. 5.

telegraph exchange 1. Refers to the widely used international service, which is based on the transmission and reception of printed MESSAGES over a TELEGRAPH NETWORK using TELETYPEWRITERS as subscriber TERMINALS. Also known as TELEX, a contraction of *tele*graph *ex*change.

2. May also be used specifically to refer to an EXCHANGE (or NODE) that performs the SWITCHING operations in such a NETWORK.

telegraph network A NETWORK designed for the transmission of telegraph TRAFFIC and comprising telegraph TERMINALS (e.g., TELETYPEWRITERS), TRANSMISSION LINKS and automatic EXCHANGES.

telegraph service A service provided by a TELECOMMUNICATIONS authority for carrying one or more kinds of telegraph TRAFFIC. Such services may use different techniques, including ALPHABETIC TELEGRAPHY, DOCUMENT FACSIMILE TELEGRAPHY, PHOTOGRAPHIC FACSIMILE TELEGRAPHY. These services may also be known to the public by specific names that characterize the nature of collection and delivery, such as TELEX, telegram and radio telegram services.

telegraph system A system in which USERS have TERMINALS, known as TELETYPEWRITERS (often the trade name TELEPRINTER is used), to transmit and receive MESSAGES. Teletypewriters are fitted with KEYBOARDS and a PRINTER MECHANISM, and sometimes they can create and read PUNCHED PAPER TAPE.

The MESSAGE SIGNAL output from a teletypewriter is a DIGITAL SIGNAL, which is transmitted along a LINE to operate another teletypewriter remotely. The speed of transmission is usually in the range of from 45 to 200 BAUDS.

A range of ALPHANUMERIC characters can be transmitted and, on standard equipment, each CHARACTER is transmitted as 5 pulses to represent the character plus a START and STOP PULSE.

Teletypewriters operate over NETWORKS controlled by a TELEGRAPH EXCHANGE; often the term TELEX is used to refer to systems of this type. More strictly known as ALPHABETIC TELEGRAPHY.

telegraphy A means of two-way communication for the transmission of MESSAGES between two locations, including: (a) the transmission of ALPHANUMERIC information using TELETYPEWRITERS, which is a form of ALPHABETIC TELEGRAPHY; (b) the transmission of ELECTRICAL SIGNALS representing the images scanned from documents, which is known as DOCUMENT FACSIMILE TELEGRAPHY; (c) the faithful reproduction of continuous tonal densities from documents to a quality allowing good photographic images to be transferred which is known as PHOTOGRAPH FACSIMILE TELEGRAPHY.

telegraphy, alphabetic See ALPHABETIC TELEGRAPHY.

telemetry The measurement of events at a distance (sometimes great distance as in aerospace projects) in which TRANSDUCERS are used to measure physical activities and to convert these to DIGITAL SIGNALS that reflect the measurement of phenomena. The digital signals are transmitted to a DATA COLLECTION center for processing. Sometimes the results of such processing are immediately used to generate signals that are transmitted back to the distant location to control the process being monitored.

telephone 1. Refers to the PUBLIC SWITCHED TELEPHONE NETWORK (PSTN), which is a system for transmitting VOICE SIGNALS in the AUDIO FREQUENCY range over a NETWORK servicing a very large USER population.

2. Also refers to the telephone TERMINAL or telephone HANDSET used as the primary INTERFACE between human users and the system.

telephone channel A TRANSMISSION PATH designed for the transmission of SIGNALS representing human speech and having a BANDWIDTH of about 3 kHz. See TELEPHONE CENTRAL OFFICE.

telephone exchange See CENTRAL OFFICE, EXCHANGE.

telephone system A system for two-way communication in which a USER is able to speak via a telephone TERMINAL (SUBSCRIBER'S INSTRUMENT) to another USER, by dialing the ROUTING required through an EXCHANGE. The exchange connects the caller to the required user by selecting appropriate TRANSMISSION LINKS.

telephony The technology associated with the transmission of MESSAGE SIGNALS in the AUDIO FREQUENCY WAVEBAND between USERS at distant locations, including the techniques associated with the transmission of VOICE SIGNALS by DIGITAL TRANSMISSION methods.

teleport A group of SATELLITE dishes located outside major cities. Voice and data TRAFFIC from large corporations are fed to the teleport via private FIBER OPTIC LINES. See also BYPASS.

teleprinter A registered trade name, but now used by many people to refer to the TELETYPEWRITER.

teleprocessing A term used to define the APPLICATION of DATA COMMUNICATIONS techniques to DATA PROCESSING to create ON-LINE or REAL-TIME PROCESSING SYSTEMS. Generally speaking, a teleprocessing application operates in an environment in which multiple USERS are able to share a common DATABASE and the HARDWARE resources and SOFTWARE facilities provided in a MAINFRAME or MINICOMPUTER system without any user being aware of the activity of other users. The term has also been used to define a system in which programs are downloaded from a mainframe to a TERMINAL to be executed by a MICROPROCESSOR in the terminal under local control of a user.

teleprocessing monitor (TPM) A SOFTWARE system specially designed to ease the development of ON-LINE or REAL-TIME computer APPLICATIONS. Generally speaking, the TPM is the INTERFACE between USER APPLICATIONS and the general-purpose OPERATING SYSTEM of a MAINFRAME or MINICOMPUTER.

The TPM is designed to create an environment in which many of the problems peculiar to on-line computer applications can be easily resolved. These problems include: (a) multiple users sharing the same APPLICATION PROGRAMS; (b) screen formats and editing and validation procedures being easily set up and altered without detailed changes of APPLICATION CODE; (c) the ability to amend easily the conventions associated with TERMINALS, thus leading to flexibility in the number and type of terminals used; (d) LOCKOUT FACILITIES to insure the integrity of DATA, where several users may be amending FILES or reserving objects in the same DATABASE; (e) the establishment of RECOVERY PROCEDURES that preserve the integrity of the database or minimize the work and time involved in recreating a working system after a system failure.

Teletel The name given by the PTT in France to its PUBLIC VIDEOTEX SYSTEM. See also VIDEOTEX SYSTEM.

teletext An electronic system allowing the USER to receive TEXT (for example, the captions on a closed-captioned television program) and GRAPHICS via a specially adapted TELEVISION RECEIVER to respond to SIGNALS broadcast in the blank intervals of a TELEVISION TRANSMISSION SIGNAL. Compare with VIDEOTEX SYSTEM.

teletext decoder A micro-electronic device fitted to a TELEVISION RECEIVER to enable it to detect and display SIGNALS representing TEXT and GRAPHICS that are transmitted in the blank intervals of a TELEVISION TRANSMISSION SIGNAL.

teletypewriter A device used to transmit and receive INFORMATION over a TELEGRAPH NETWORK and consisting of a printer and a KEYBOARD, with a transmitter and receiver to INTERFACE with a LINE and a TELEGRAPH EXCHANGE. The keyboard is similar to a typewriter but has special function keys to control its specific use in a TELEGRAPH SYSTEM. A teletypewriter is able to print a full range of alphabetic, numeric and punctuation CHARACTERS plus special symbols. When the keys are depressed, a series of direct current electrical pulses are generated to represent the selected characters. These SIGNALS are used to activate the printer unit and to transmit to the line and can be thought of as DIGITAL SIGNALS, where each pulse represents a BINARY DIGIT.

The printer can also be activated by signals received remotely from the keyboard of another SUBSCRIBER. Thus, a teletypewriter can be used to conduct a DIALOGUE with a distant subscriber.

The speed of operation is usually fixed at 50 bits per second, which is less than 7 characters per second since each character consists of a START PULSE, five pulses to represent the character itself and a STOP PULSE of longer than standard duration. Some teletypewriters have been made to operate at higher speeds, up to 300 bits per second.

Standard international codes are in use today and have been promoted by the INTERNATIONAL TELECOMMUNICATION UNION (ITU) to achieve compatibility between the different countries of the world.

television channel A path of communication for RADIO SIGNALS carrying television transmission and appropriate AUDIO SIGNALS. The channel may occupy a particular BANDWIDTH, either as a radio broadcast in the atmosphere or as a cable broadcast. See also TELEVISION TRANSMISSION SIGNAL.

television circuit A one-way CIRCUIT for the transmission of the video component of a television program. The sound component is usually delivered on one or more separate SOUND-PROGRAM CIRCUITS.

television receiver A TERMINAL designed to receive pictures and SOUND transmitted as a RADIO SIGNAL. The receiver incorporates a radio frequency FILTER and AMPLIFIER, a DEMODULATOR, VIDEO AMPLIFIER, AUDIO AMPLIFIER, CATHODE RAY TUBE and LOUDSPEAKER.

Normally, the SIGNAL is received as a radio frequency BROADCAST coming from a TELEVISION TRANSMITTER, but signals can be received along COAXIAL CABLES.

The filter and the amplifier are TUNED CIRCUITS used to select the appropriate TRANSMISSION CHANNEL required by the USER.

The demodulator selects the MESSAGE SIGNAL and separates it from the RF CARRIER WAVE. This signal, along with appropriate SYNCHRONIZING PULSES, is fed to the video and audio amplifiers, where the message signal is amplified to drive the cathode ray tube and the loudspeaker system.

TV receivers within a country are built to common standards, but there are 3 major color systems in use today: NTSC—USA, Canada, Japan; SECAM—France, Soviet Union; PAL—United Kingdom and West Germany. Variations of these basic systems have been implemented in other countries.

television transmission signal A RADIO SIGNAL (usually transmitted in the VHF and UHF spectrum) that includes video and audio information transported on separate CARRIER WAVES and combined for the purpose of transmission. The SIGNAL would normally be BROADCAST in the atmosphere or loaded into a TV CABLE SYSTEM for transmission to TV RECEIVERS.

The precise characteristics of a transmitted signal may vary from one country to another, but usually television broadcasts occur in BANDS, e.g., 470–610 MHz. In the 525-line system used in the United States, the bands are divided into 6-MHz channels. In the British 625-line system, these bands are divided into 8-MHz sections called TELEVISION CHANNELS and a broadcast occupies one such channel. There is a GUARD BAND at the upper end of each channel, and the SOUND CARRIER is transmitted close to this band. The sound carrier is separated by 6 MHz from the VISION CARRIER. The SOUND BANDWIDTH is from 20 Hz to 15 kHz, and the VIDEO BANDWIDTH is 5.5 MHz. The VIDEO SIGNAL and AUDIO SIGNAL are MODULATED on to separate carrier waves which are combined and normally broadcast from the same ANTENNA. Usually AMPLITUDE MODULATION (AM) is used for the video component, and the audio component may be AM or FM.

In order to economize in bandwidth and transmission power, the LOWER SIDEBAND and the UPPER SIDEBAND are not both transmitted. Instead, most of the lower sideband and the vision carrier are suppressed. A portion of the lower sideband (known as the VESTIGIAL SIDEBAND) is transmitted, along with the complete upper sideband. VESTIGIAL SIDEBAND MODULATION is chosen to simplify the circuitry required in TV receivers.

television transmitter A device that can accept VIDEO SIGNALS, AUDIO SIGNALS plus SYNCHRONIZATION PULSES and modulate these on to a CARRIER WAVE for transmission as a television RADIO SIGNAL by an ANTENNA. See also TELEVISION TRANSMISSION SIGNAL.

telex The name often given to a service based on the use of TELETYPEWRITERS to send and receive INFORMATION over a SWITCHED NETWORK. The word itself is an abbreviation of TELEGRAPH EXCHANGE. This system is used extensively throughout the world and there are many national and international telex exchanges. See also TELEGRAPH SYSTEM.

telex traffic MESSAGE SIGNALS derived from TELETYPEWRITERS and transmitted in accordance with the international conventions of ALPHABETIC TELEGRAPHY, e.g., using INTERNATIONAL ALPHABET NO. 2.

terminal A device used in a TELECOMMUNICATIONS system for sending or receiving MESSAGE SIGNALS. A MICROPHONE is an example of a TRANSMITTING TERMINAL, and television is an example of a RECEIVING TERMINAL. Some terminals (e.g., the TELEPHONE) can be used for sending or receiving message signals. A TELETYPEWRITER is an example of a terminal that, given appropriate TRANSMISSION CHANNELS, can carry out simultaneous two-way transmission.

There are a great many terminal types to be considered, from the simple telephone terminal to the large general-purpose COMPUTER.

terminal adapter (TA) A device that enables non-ISDN TERMINAL equipment, such as a COMPUTER that has an X.25 INTERFACE, to plug into an ISDN interface.

terminal emulation One way to enable MICROCOMPUTERS to communicate with a variety of HOST PROCESSORS is by running terminal emulation software programs. They let the PC imitate a TERMINAL that would be able to INTERFACE with a given host PROCESSOR. Thus, an IBM PC can communicate with a VAX computer from Digital Equipment Corp., for example, because the PC emulates Digital's VT100 terminal.

terminating traffic This term defines the use made of a particular TERMINAL by INCOMING CALLS and contrasts with OUTGOING CALLS referred to as ORIGINATING TRAFFIC. See also TRAFFIC, INSTANTANEOUS TRAFFIC and TRAFFIC VOLUME.

tertiary trunk exchange The third level of EXCHANGE in an EXCHANGE HIERARCHY and controlling major ROUTES in the TRUNK NETWORK. See also EXCHANGE HIERARCHY.

text In TELECOMMUNICATIONS, this term is used to refer to the parts of a SIGNAL that carry USER information, rather than any CONTROL INFORMATION that is embedded in the MESSAGE SIGNAL to provide LINK CONTROL or ROUTING instructions.

theoretical final route A term used in TELEPHONY to define the ROUTE followed by a CALL through the CIRCUIT GROUPS of the BACKBONE of the NETWORK.

thin Ethernet A type of COAXIAL CABLE preferred for short distances in ETHERNET NETWORKS.

3-bit error An error occurring in a DATA TRANSMISSION sequence in which three consecutive BITS are incorrectly received. See also TRANSMISSION ERRORS.

throughput In DATA COMMUNICATIONS, a measure of the information transmitted during a given time period. Contrast with DATA RATE.

time division multiplexing (TDM) A form of MULTIPLEXING in which a number of separate DIGITAL SIGNALS are sampled to produce a set of interleaved pulses that are transmitted along a single CHANNEL. The individual digital signals are combined to a signal of much higher BIT RATE for transmission. The train of pulses is analyzed at the other end of the channel by logic CIRCUITS that recreate the original MESSAGE SIGNALS. The technique of multiplexing may differ for particular systems, but usually the digital signals making up the CHARACTERS or pulses of each message are grouped as units of short duration (bits/bytes), which are transmitted along with FRAMING BITS providing terminal identification and reference information for the transmission and receiving equipment.

This technique is so called because the elements of different message signals occupy the same TRANSMISSION CHANNEL but for different moments in time. Thus, the process of SWITCHING such circuits requires both a physical connection of channels (SPACE SWITCHING) and a SYNCHRONIZATION of TIME SLOTS (TIME SWITCHING).

This technique can be contrasted with FREQUENCY DIVISION MULTIPLEXING (FDM).

time division system A communication system that utilizes the techniques and principles associated with TIME DIVISION MULTIPLEXING (TDM).

time interval A brief interval in time during which a SIGNAL ELEMENT (i.e., a BIT or pulse) may occur and be recognized. In a SYNCHRONOUS SYSTEM, each CHARACTER may be composed of 8 bits; thus, 8 time intervals are required to transmit a single character. In an ASYNCHRONOUS SYSTEM, a START BIT (one time interval) and a STOP BIT (two time intervals) are needed, in addition to the INFORMATION BITS. Thus, there are 11 time intervals per character.

time shared digital crosspoint An element in a DIGITAL EXCHANGE that enables connections to be made to connect INCOMING CALLS with OUTGOING LINES but that services a system based on TIME DIVISION MULTIPLEXING (TDM) techniques. Thus, a SWITCHING operation entails a physical connection of CHANNELS (SPACE SWITCHING) and the SYNCHRONIZATION of TIME SLOTS (TIME SWITCHING). See also ELECTRONIC DIGITAL CROSSPOINT.

time shifting An operation that takes place in TIME DIVISION MULTIPLEXING systems to adjust the TIME SLOT of an incoming CHANNEL to the required time slots for an outgoing channel. If the time slots are already synchronized, no shifting is needed; otherwise the usual technique is to delay the incoming channel until the next time slot for the outgoing channel occurs. This is achieved by placing incoming BITS into a BUFFER and releasing the bits through an electronic switch to an outgoing buffer at the appropriate time slot.

Usually, DIGITAL EXCHANGES are constructed to combine TIME SWITCHING and SPACE SWITCHING, the latter being achieved by shared ELECTRONIC CROSSPOINTS, which are activated for a few microseconds at the appropriate time for each time slot.

time slot A common concept in all DIGITAL SYSTEMS, a brief period of time in which a particular device is able to obtain access to another to deliver or accept DIGITAL SIGNALS. For example, in TIME DIVISION MULTIPLEXING, each physical COMMUNICATION CHANNEL is TIME SHARED by many signals, each having access to the channel for a prescribed interval of a few microseconds on a cyclic basis.

time switch A device that controls the utilization of a resource by competing processes by allocating a TIME SLOT of a few milliseconds or microseconds to each process.

time switched systems A switching system used to create NETWORKS for DIGITAL TRAFFIC (which may be derived from VOICE OR DATA SOURCES) and in which the techniques of TIME DIVISION MULTIPLEXING (TDM) are used.

time switching An operation that takes place in TIME DIVISION MULTIPLEXED systems to switch SIGNALS from one TIME SLOT to another. See also TIME SHIFTING, and contrast with SPACE SWITCHING.

timesharing Relating to any COMPUTER or communications system in which a device, such as a COMPUTER processor or a TRANSMISSION CHANNEL, is used to control or support a number of separate processes. The priority is given to each process in turn for a few milliseconds, but the overall impression to a human observer is that all processes are operated simultaneously.

timesharing link A COMMUNICATIONS CHANNEL in which several SUBSCRIBERS share the same physical LINE by occupying the line momentarily in bursts of activity occupying a particular TIME SLOT. Each USER is unaware of the others sharing the same resource. The techniques used are known as TIME DIVISION MULTIPLEXING (TDM).

timing jitter See JITTER.

token See TOKEN RING.

token passing See TOKEN RING.

token ring The term refers to a NETWORK TOPOLOGY and a way to access a LOCAL AREA NETWORK. In a LAN, the token (also called a SUPERVISORY FRAME) is a unique set of BITS that travels from STATION to station. Its presence indicates the station can transmit DATA. In LANs that have the ring TOPOLOGY, the token ring access method specifies that a station receives all messages on the ring plus the token. The messages and token are then passed along to the next station in a logical, though not necessarily physical, circle. The token passing access method and ring topology are specified in the IEEE 802.5 physical layer standard. IBM's implementation of token ring runs at speeds up to 4 Mbps or 16 Mbps. Compare with ETHERNET.

toll center An EXCHANGE in a TELEPHONE NETWORK that provides the connections from a group of LOCAL EXCHANGES to the TRUNK NETWORK of the overall TELEPHONE SYSTEM. A SUBSCRIBER thus gains access to the national network via the local exchange and the associated toll center and pays TOLL CHARGES for OUTGOING CALLS.

Also known as PRIMARY TRUNK EXCHANGE, PRIMARY CENTER and, in the United Kingdom, as GROUP SWITCHING CENTER. See also EXCHANGE HIERARCHY.

toll charge An additional charge levied to a SUBSCRIBER when he/she originates a CALL to an ADDRESS outside the LOCAL AREA in which local call charges are applied.

toll circuit A term used to describe specifically the CIRCUIT between a LOCAL EXCHANGE and a TRUNK EXCHANGE in a TELEPHONE SYSTEM. In Britain, the term JUNCTION CIRCUIT is often used to describe this type of circuit, but more generally the term TRUNK is used. It is, however, the CIRCUIT that provides the threshold from the local exchange to the full TRUNK NETWORK.

toll network See TRUNK NETWORK.

toll office An element in the COMMON CARRIER'S NETWORK that provides for the switching of CALLS that are not local calls but that require connection with distant SUBSCRIBERS via TRUNK CIRCUITS and other TOLL OFFICES. The toll office is classified as a class 4 OFFICE, where the information for time- and distance-based toll charges is collected. Sometimes called trunk exchange. See also EXCHANGE HIERARCHY, TRUNK EXCHANGE.

TOP See TECHNICAL AND OFFICE PROTOCOLS.

topology The way STATIONS are configured on a NETWORK, either logically or physically, or both. See also BUS, RING, STAR and TREE.

torn tape center A center in which a number of telegraph CIRCUITS terminate and in which MESSAGES are switched by human operators who remove PAPER TAPES from receiving devices and transmit them over other circuits. Such centers have largely been replaced by automatic switching centers.

TPM See TELEPROCESSING MONITOR.

traffic This term is used to define the utilization or capacity of a TELECOMMUNICATIONS system and is described in terms of the number of CALLS. For example, the number of calls in progress at any one time is referred to as INSTANTANEOUS TRAFFIC. The average value of instantaneous traffic over a given period of time is the AVERAGE TRAFFIC.

Traffic is measured in units called ERLANGS, e.g., an instantaneous traffic of 57 calls would be described as 57 erlangs. See also INSTANTANEOUS TRAFFIC, BUSY HOUR TRAFFIC, ORIGINATING TRAFFIC, TERMINATING TRAFFIC, AVERAGE TRAFFIC, CARRIED TRAFFIC and OFFERED TRAFFIC.

traffic analysis Information resulting from a formal observation of the performance of a TELECOMMUNICATIONS system and intended to assist the system operator to plan improvements in the performance of the system and the service experienced by USERS.

traffic overload A situation of poor service which arises when the TRAFFIC offered to a part of a communication system significantly exceeds the capacity planned in the chosen design.

traffic pressure A measure of the demand for connections in a switched network, usually expressed as the number of BIDS made to secure a connection over a given GROUP of CIRCUITS in a defined period, e.g., bids per circuit per hour.

traffic recorder An item of equipment used to measure the utilization of a particular part of a CIRCUIT SWITCHED SYSTEM.

traffic statistics INFORMATION that has been collected and summarized to represent the pattern of usage of a communications system. Such information is used to plan for the efficient utilization of the NETWORK and to achieve a desired level of user service. See also TRAFFIC and TRAFFIC THEORY.

traffic theory A theory to assist in the planning and development of a communications system in which the planner tries to optimize the equipment and facilities needed to support the requirements of USERS. A system that has too large a capacity for a given population of users is wasteful of resources, but a system that does not have sufficient capacity will become congested and give a poor service.

Traffic theory usually requires planning engineers to consider the average behavior of users of the system and relies upon the fact that, in a large enough population, the random behavior of individuals tends to present a consistent pattern.

Traffic theory includes consideration of the following:

number of CALLS in a period (n)
the holding time of each call (h)
the duration of the period (T)
the rate at which new calls arise (a)

In practice, systems are usually planned to provide capacity to suit the PEAK LOAD generated by the users.

Some equations used in traffic theory are given as follows:

The average traffic E for period T is: $\frac{nh}{T}$
or $E = ah$

The average rate for new calls (a) is given by: n/T. See also TRAFFIC VOLUME, MEAN HOLDING TIME.

traffic unit A unit employed in the measurement of the use made by the USERS of a TELECOMMUNICATIONS system. Usually the TRAFFIC generated by users is measured in terms of the number of concurrent CALLS (see also TRAFFIC THEORY). However, for the purpose of BILLING users of the system, a system operator may also designate a unit of time as the basis of accounting, e.g., a LOCAL CALL may be charged in increments of charge per minute.

traffic volume The amount of TRAFFIC over a given period of time in a TELECOMMUNICATIONS system. If in T seconds n CALLS are made and if the duration of the calls are h_1, h_2, $h_3 \ldots h_n$ seconds, then the utilization of the system is:

$$\sum_{i=1}^{i=n} h_i$$

The AVERAGE TRAFFIC (E) is the amount of traffic in a given period of time and is expressed as:

$$E = \frac{\sum_{i=1}^{i=n} h_i}{T} \text{ ERLANGS}$$

See also MEAN HOLDING TIME.

transaction A specific APPLICATION process in a DATA NETWORK in which there is interaction between TRANSMITTING and RECEIVING STATIONS to perform a specific task, e.g., to record receipt of a payment and to credit a SUBSCRIBER'S account. See also SESSION and DATAGRAM.

transaction log A record of all the activities or TRANSACTIONS performed by a COMPUTER-controlled system. This record may be used to compile statistical information to help in optimizing the operation of the system and also to recover from failures which might otherwise cause MESSAGE SIGNALS to be lost.

transceiver A device that can transmit and receive INFORMATION.

transceiver cable A cable used to connect a transmitting/receiving device to a physical CHANNEL. The cable must have a compatible PHYSICAL and ELECTRICAL INTERFACE to the TRANSMISSION CHANNEL.

transducer The element in a TELECOMMUNICATIONS system that converts SIGNALS into a form required by USERS. For example, a LOUDSPEAKER converts AUDIO FREQUENCY electrical signals into SOUND WAVES. A MICROPHONE is an example of a transducer which converts sound energy into ELECTRICAL SIGNALS. See also ACOUSTIC COUPLER.

transient copy A MESSAGE produced in a communication system but not in a physical form, e.g., a message displayed on a VISUAL DISPLAY. Also known as SOFT COPY, and contrast with HARD COPY or PERMANENT COPY.

transit exchange Any EXCHANGE in a NETWORK that acts for a particular CALL as an intermediate switching center, i.e., not the FIRST EXCHANGE in a ROUTING and not the LAST EXCHANGE.

transit network A NETWORK superimposed upon another for a special purpose.

translator A CONTROL device used during the setup of a CALL to translate the ADDRESS and determine the ROUTING required.

transmission break A particularly significant form of error condition during which LINE signals are lost entirely during transmission of MESSAGE traffic. Breaks of this nature are not uncommon in systems using older types of SWITCHING EQUIPMENT where maintenance can be a problem. See also TRANSMISSION ERRORS.

transmission channel The path between two TERMINALS for communication and including relevant LINKS and EXCHANGE equipment used to handle the CALL. See also DATA CHANNEL and DATA CIRCUIT.

transmission control An element in a NODE of a PACKET SWITCHING SYSTEM that is responsible for interfacing USERS to the NETWORK. It assists in the management of establishment and termination of a SESSION for an end user.

transmission control code Throughout the evolution of DATA TRANSMISSION it has been common practice to send MESSAGE SIGNALS framed by CONTROL CODES that provide instruction to TERMINALS as to the format and structure of message TEXTS and to provide DEVICE CONTROL information. The use of these CODES has varied with advances in communications technology. Standards have been developed internationally, and unique BIT PATTERNS to represent such codes are included in common DATA COMMUNICATIONS CODES such as ASCII and EBCDIC. See also ACK, NAK, ENQ, SOM, STX, EOM, ETX, ETB, EOT, SYN and DLE.

Transmission Control Protocol/Internet Protocol (TCP/IP) Developed by the U.S. Department of Defense and used on ARPANET, TCP/IP is a set of PROTOCOLS that link dissimilar COMPUTERS across NETWORKS. It works on the third and fourth layers of the OSI model.

transmission errors Errors arising in a MESSAGE SIGNAL and caused by DISTORTION or disturbance on the TRANSMISSION CHANNEL. All TELECOMMUNICATIONS systems are prone to errors, and it is necessary to design systems that automatically identify and recover from errors (see also ERROR CHECKING). The quality of a CIRCUIT is usually expressed in terms of its BIT ERROR RATE, and this is a statement of the maximum average number of ERROR BITS to CORRECT BITS which can be expected when transmitting DIGITAL SIGNALS over the circuit.

Very often transmission errors are manifest as the simple reversal of a single pulse; e.g., a 1-bit is received instead of a 0-bit. This is known as a SINGLE-BIT ERROR. If a series of consecutive pulses are in error, the condition is described as a 2-BIT ERROR or a 3-BIT ERROR and so on. When errors occur very close together (i.e., separated by relatively few correct bits), they are known as BURST ERRORS or an ERROR BURST. See also ERROR CORRECTION and CYCLIC REDUNDANCY CHECK.

transmission header A part of the HEADER INFORMATION attached to a PACKET and providing INFORMATION to allow the ACCESS PATH CONTROL system to determine the correct ROUTE.

transmission line A means to connect two TERMINALS so that MESSAGES can be conveyed between them. Often terminals are connected by a two-way transmission line providing a CHANNEL to transmit in either direction. Transmission lines vary in physical characteristics, depending upon the type of MESSAGE traffic and the distances over which the TRAFFIC is to be conveyed.

transmission links Refers to the different physical elements that may make up the TRANSMISSION CHANNELS from source to destination in a TELECOMMUNICATIONS system; for example, LOCAL LINES, LOCAL EXCHANGE, TRUNK LINES, TRUNK EXCHANGE, SATELLITE CHANNEL. Generally speaking, these elements are not apparent to the USER, who operates a terminal to generate and receive a MESSAGE SIGNAL.

transmission loss An impairment of a MESSAGE SIGNAL due to the characteristics of the TRANSMISSION MEDIUM, which causes a reduction in signal strength as a proportion of the energy is absorbed in the TRANSMISSION CHANNEL.

transmission medium The medium used for the transmission of MESSAGE SIGNALS in a TELECOMMUNICATIONS system, e.g., TWISTED WIRE PAIRS. A transmission medium is classified as a BOUNDED MEDIUM or an UNBOUNDED MEDIUM. Examples of a bounded medium include twisted wire pairs, COAXIAL TUBES, WAVEGUIDES and OPTICAL FIBERS. Radio is an example of an unbounded medium.

The characteristics of a transmission medium define the quality of the TRANSMISSION CHANNEL, which can be described in terms of its BANDWIDTH and susceptibility to impairment of the message signals (e.g., impairment by ATTENUATION).

transmission path A COMMUNICATION CHANNEL established for a particular CALL and pertaining to the specific resources utilized to effect the call, including physical CIRCUITS and LOGICAL CHANNELS, where applicable.

transmission systems The term "transmission system" refers to the physical media used to transmit MESSAGE SIGNALS between locations. The simplest TRANSMISSION LINK consists of a pair of wires connecting two TERMINALS. This form of transmission link is used to connect LOCAL LINES to an EXCHANGE, but it would be an expensive way of connecting several terminals over a ROUTE of more than approximately 5 kilometers. It is cheaper to use a method of transmission that permits the MULTIPLEXING of a number of separate CHANNELS onto the same TRANSMISSION MEDIUM.

The equipment needed to multiplex and demultiplex the individual MESSAGES onto a TRANSMISSION CHANNEL of high capacity is expensive, but it provides great savings in the construction and maintenance of individual lines and of the ducts and cableways required to support these lines. See also MULTIPLEXING.

The performance of a transmission system is determined by the various physical elements in the overall system, including MULTIPLEXERS and DEMULTIPLEXERS, TRANSMISSION MEDIUM (e.g., coaxial tubes) and the quality and physical spacing of REPEATERS along the transmission link.

Transmission systems for handling ANALOG VOICE SIGNALS normally use FREQUENCY DIVISION MULTIPLEXING (FDM) and, for DIGITAL SIGNALS, TIME DIVISION MULTIPLEXING (TDM). It should be noted, however, that PULSE CODE MODULATION (PCM) techniques are increasingly used to convert analog to digital signals in part of the transmission system. Of course, a transmission system need not utilize only terrestrial media, such as cables, but could contain radio SATELLITE links or line-of-sight MICROWAVE radio links.

transmission test set A device used by engineers to assist in FAULT DIAGNOSIS in DATA COMMUNICATIONS SYSTEMS. Usually the test set is a portable item that can be connected to a LINE by an engineer or, in some cases, by nonskilled personnel. The test set can generate a number of SIGNALS that are of a predetermined form, according to the speed and nature of the CIRCUIT to be tested. These signals are transmitted to the line and can be looped back to the test set so that the received pattern of signals can be compared with the internally generated pattern. A count of BIT ERRORS is recorded and displayed on the test set to show the quality and performance of that particular circuit.

transmitter clock In SYNCHRONOUS TRANSMISSION, a device that generates the TIME INTERVALS to control the precise timing of BITS passing from a TERMINAL to a LINE. See also RECEIVER CLOCK.

transmitting aerial A device used in RADIO TRANSMISSION to radiate energy into the atmosphere as ELECTROMAGNETIC WAVES; it is also known as an ANTENNA. The RADIO SIGNALS conveyed by this means are detected by a RECEIVING AERIAL. Both transmitting and receiving aerials may be directional or nondirectional, i.e., designed to transmit and receive in one particular direction or in any direction. Aerials are sensitive to particular FREQUENCY BANDS, and this is determined largely by the physical dimensions of the aerial.

transmitting earth station A system designed to transmit RADIO SIGNALS to a COMMUNICATIONS SATELLITE in Earth orbit in order that the signals may be reflected to another point on the earth's surface and be received by a RECEIVING EARTH STATION.

transmitting station 1. Any TERMINAL, or a CONCENTRATOR, controlling a group of terminals that, at a particular instant in time, is transmitting SIGNALS to a communication NETWORK.

2. A RADIO TRANSMITTER designed to propagate RADIO WAVES.

transmitting terminal Any TERMINAL attached to a communications system and operating at a particular instant in time to transmit SIGNALS to the system.

transmit-to-receive crosstalk A form of CROSSTALK that arises on a FOUR-WIRE CIRCUIT in which a SIGNAL transmitted in one direction is inducted onto the opposite CHANNEL. The crosstalk arising should be less than 1 to 40,000 relative to the transmitted signal, and at this level it is insignificant for VOICE and DATA TRAFFIC.

Transpac Name given to a PACKET SWITCHING NETWORK developed and installed as a public system in France.

transparency A concept in COMPUTERS and communications in which two devices or logical units may communicate with each other without being aware of intervening equipment and SOFTWARE. This intervening equipment is said to maintain a transparent INTERFACE, i.e., it can be replaced by any more powerful or less powerful set of equipment, provided the new equipment maintains the same LOGICAL and ELECTRICAL INTERFACE.

transponder Usually part of a COMMUNICATIONS SATELLITE, a transponder receives a SIGNAL and retransmits it after amplifying it. The retransmission occurs on a different frequency than the original transmission.

transport layer In modern NETWORK ARCHITECTURES used for DATA COMMUNICATIONS, the system is represented as layers of logic responsible for different functions needed in operation over the NETWORK. The end-to-end layer provides control between end USERS, including ADDRESSING and FLOW CONTROL. Sometimes known as end-to-end layer, it is level 4 of the OSI reference model. See also OPEN SYSTEMS INTERCONNECTION.

transposition This relates to the pattern of interconnection between groups of interconnecting LINKS in an EXCHANGE; the level of interconnection may allow every group of CROSSPOINTS to be connected to every other group, giving FULL AVAILABILITY transposition. The purpose of GROUPING through successive stages of SWITCHING is to have a low probability of CALL BLOCKING while reducing the number of physical crosspoints required. See also CONCENTRATOR, DISTRIBUTOR, EXPANDOR and GROUPING.

tree See TREE NETWORK.

Trellis-coded Modulation (TCM) A way to change certain characteristics of the electronic signal to achieve FORWARD ERROR CORRECTION. TCM is used in some high-speed modems. See also V.32 and V.32*bis* in V SERIES.

tree network A NETWORK in which there is a hierarchy of NODES providing CONTROL and communication and which can be represented on paper as the inverse of a family tree. The apex of the network, or top of the tree, represents the primary control for the network, but certain levels of control may be delegated down to intermediate branches. See also NETWORK TOPOLOGIES.

triad An arrangement of three phosphor dots to represent a PICTURE ELEMENT on a screen of a COLOR TELEVISION RECEIVER. Each triad includes a red, green and blue phosphor dot from which the colors of a televised scene can be composed.

trunk See TRUNK CIRCUIT.

trunk circuit This is the TRANSMISSION PATH between TRUNK EXCHANGES within the MAIN (or TRUNK) NETWORK of a communication system. Such paths normally have to carry high TRAFFIC VOLUMES over long distances, and some form of MULTIPLEXING takes place. See also TRANSMISSION SYSTEMS and EXCHANGE HIERARCHY.

Often referred to as a TRUNK LINK, TRUNK ROUTE or simply a TRUNK.

trunk exchange An EXCHANGE that provides for the SWITCHING of CALLS that are not local calls but that require connection with distant SUBSCRIBERS via TRUNK CIRCUITS and other TRUNK EXCHANGES. Trunk circuits, but not subscribers' lines, are connected to the trunk exchange. See also TOLL OFFICE, EXCHANGE HIERARCHY.

trunk line Any LINE forming part of the TRUNK NETWORK (i.e., one which is used to connect TRUNK EXCHANGES and thus designed to carry MULTIPLEXED TRAFFIC). Usually consists of a physical medium of relatively BROAD BANDWIDTH and thus may carry hundreds or thousands of LOGICAL CHANNELS.

trunk link See TRUNK CIRCUIT.

trunk network That part of a public TELEPHONE SYSTEM (or other communications systems) that consists of the major TRANSMISSION PATHS and EXCHANGES that provide for the interlinking of SUBSCRIBERS in the total NETWORK. It is usually defined to exclude the LOCAL NETWORK, which incorporates the LOCAL EXCHANGES and local SUBSCRIBER LINES. Also known as the TOLL NETWORK or MAIN NETWORK. See also EXCHANGE HIERARCHY.

trunk route See TRUNK CIRCUIT.

tuned circuit A CIRCUIT designed to respond to a particular frequency to which it has been tuned by varying characteristics of a component forming part of the circuit; e.g., a circuit for selecting SIGNALS related to RADIO TRANSMISSION.

tuner An element in a RADIO or TELEVISION RECEIVER that enables the USER to select a particular broadcast CHANNEL.

turnaround time The time taken to reverse the direction of DATA FLOW. An expression used when referring to a HALF-DUPLEX channel in which the directional flow of data can be reversed.

TV cable system A system in which SIGNALS to be detected and displayed by a TELEVISION RECEIVER are propagated along a COAXIAL CABLE. These techniques are applied to geographic areas of poor radio reception and to provide programs of special or local interest that can be propagated over a cable without interfering with other RADIO TRANSMISSIONS. Cable TV systems are also used in industrial APPLICATIONS to provide remote inspection of processes or conditions.

TV receiver See TELEVISION RECEIVER.

23 B+D See PRIMARY RATE INTERFACE.

twisted wire pairs The simplest and most common TRANSMISSION MEDIUM used in TELEPHONY, in which the TRANSMISSION channel consists of a single wire with an earth return. They are used for links between individual telephone TERMINALS and LOCAL EXCHANGES. The cable pairs are twisted to reduce the effect of CROSSTALK with other pairs, which may be carried in the same cable or duct. Twisted pairs have limited application for BROADBAND MULTIPLEXED CHANNELS using ANALOG SIGNALS, because at higher frequencies ATTENUATION and crosstalk are severe. By using REPEATERS to regenerate the MESSAGE SIGNALS at frequent intervals, twisted wire pairs have been used with frequencies up to 500 kHz.

2 B+D See BASIC RATE INTERFACE.

two condition code Any CODE used to represent BINARY INFORMATION consisting of the values 0 and 1; to be contrasted with a code in which MULTI-STATE SIGNALING is used to represent more than just two values (for example, to represent 00, 01, 10 and 11). See also TWO-STATE SIGNALING.

2-bit error An error occurring in a DATA TRANSMISSION sequence in which two consecutive BITS are incorrectly received. See also TRANSMISSION ERRORS.

two-state signaling A method of transmitting INFORMATION in which only two voltage values are used serially to represent the BINARY NUMBERS 0 and 1. Each UNIT SIGNAL ELEMENT has a predefined duration, and the frequency of transmission occurs as an alternation between one voltage value and the other. If more than two voltage levels are used at the same frequency, the DATA SIGNALING RATE is higher, e.g., using 4 voltage levels, the binary numbers 01, 00, 10 and 11 can be represented.

two-way call A CALL in which USERS at each end of the CIRCUIT can act to send or receive MESSAGES simultaneously. For example, in a TELEPHONE call, the SUBSCRIBERS are linked by a two-way TRANSMISSION CHANNEL over which they both can speak and listen.

two-wire channel A TRANSMISSION LINK consisting of just a single pair of wires, which is most commonly used for LOCAL LINES connecting telephone SUBSCRIBERS to a LOCAL EXCHANGE. It may also be used as a TRUNK LINK over short distances up to 2 kilometers. A two-wire channel is normally converted to a FOUR-WIRE CHANNEL to facilitate AMPLIFICATION and to permit MULTIPLEXING.

U

U interface A reference point indicating the separation of NETWORK TERMINATION TYPE 1 devices (which link the CPE with the service provider's ISDN and handle OSI LAYER 1 activities) from the line-termination equipment.

UHF A range of electromagnetic frequencies used in BROADCASTING. See ULTRA HIGH FREQUENCY.

UIT See UNION INTERNATIONALE DES TELECOMMUNICATIONS.

ultra high frequency RADIO WAVES in the range from 300 MHz to 3 GHz which can be propagated as SPACE WAVES over distances up to 200 kilometers. Used primarily for television BROADCASTS and, because of the limited range of propagation, relatively free from interference by distant transmissions in the same BAND.

unbalanced double-current interchange circuit An INTERFACE circuit between a DATA TERMINAL (DTE) and a MODEM having certain electrical characteristics as defined in the CCITT recommendation V.10; concerned with DATA TRANSMISSION over telephone CIRCUITS. See also V SERIES.

unbounded medium A TRANSMISSION MEDIUM in which the SIGNAL is radiated in all directions rather than directed along a physical medium such as a cable or an OPTICAL FIBER link. The latter are examples of a BOUNDED MEDIUM; a radio BROADCAST transmitted through the atmosphere is an example of an unbounded medium.

uniform quantization A QUANTIZATION method in which the intervals of quantization are equal.

unintelligible crosstalk CROSSTALK that results in intrusive but unintelligible SPEECH SIGNALS being transferred from one CIRCUIT to another adjacent circuit.

uninterruptible power supply (UPS) A device that conditions the power supply between a commercial source and a PBX or COMPUTER equipment to ensure continuous power and the avoidance of power surges that might harm the equipment. The UPS, which draws its power from batteries that are charged by the commercial source, generates a reliable AC SIGNAL.

Union Internationale des Telecommunications (UIT) This organization was originally founded in 1865 as the International Telegraph Union (ITU) and later it became the INTERNATIONAL TELECOMMUNICATION UNION. In 1947 it became a special agency of the United Nations. Its main objectives are:

1. The promotion of international cooperation for efficient use of TELECOMMUNICATIONS services.
2. Creation of widest possible public access to communication facilities.
3. Harmonization of activities between national interests in this field.

The membership of the UIT at present numbers some 154 countries, and its headquarters are in Geneva, Switzerland. See also COMITE CONSULTATIF INTERNATIONAL TELEGRAPHIQUE ET TELEPHONIQUE (CCITT).

unit separator A special CODE under the general classification known as INFORMATION SEPARATORS and used in a DATA COMMUNICATIONS CODE to denote the boundary between FIELDS in BINARY CODED form.

unit signal element Refers to the TIME INTERVAL allocated to a basic unit of INFORMATION in a SIGNAL used to represent binary information, i.e., to represent BINARY DIGITS 0 and 1. The structure of the SIGNAL ELEMENT will depend on the method of transmission—it may be a single pulse of defined duration or, as in the case of FREQUENCY SHIFT KEYING and in VARIABLE AMPLITUDE MODULATION, may be a number of contiguous cycles at a particular frequency or AMPLITUDE, and used to represent a signal value.

Unix An OPERATING SYSTEM developed by Bell Laboratories, Unix can handle several tasks and multiple USERS at once. There are several implementations of Unix, and they are not necessarily compatible.

unobtainable tone A SIGNAL heard by the USER of a TELEPHONE when the number called is out of service.

unshielded twisted pair (UTP) Two insulated wires that are twisted around each other to partially counteract the effects of electromagnetic radiation but are not enclosed in a cable sheath. They are commonly used in TELEPHONE NETWORKS and often called a twisted pair. Compare with SHIELDED TWISTED PAIR.

uplink A COMMUNICATIONS SATELLITE CIRCUIT is divided into the uplink and DOWNLINK segments. The portion extending from the EARTH STATION or TERMINAL to the SATELLITE is the uplink. See also DOWNLINK.

upper sideband The process known as MODULATION (imprinting a MESSAGE SIGNAL onto a CARRIER WAVE) generates a series of harmonic frequencies known as the SPECTRUM ENVELOPE. For each CARRIER frequency, the principal outputs generated are two SIDEBAND signals, equally displaced in frequency. One, the LOWER SIDEBAND, is below the frequency of the carrier; the other is above and is known as the UPPER SIDEBAND. See also MODULATION.

UPS See UNINTERRUPTIBLE POWER SUPPLY.

U S West See REGIONAL BELL HOLDING COMPANY.

US See UNIT SEPARATOR.

usage charge A charge made to a USER of a communications service as part of the TARIFF for use of the service. The usage charge is based upon the actual utilization made by the SUBSCRIBER and may include the number of CALLS, duration, volume, distance and time segment in which the calls are made. Contrast with STANDING CHARGE, and see also VOLUME SENSITIVE TARIFF.

user A person sending or receiving MESSAGE SIGNALS in a TELECOMMUNICATIONS system. A user utilizes a TERMINAL or a PERSONAL COMPUTER to provide inputs or obtain outputs.

user application In a COMPUTER system, this expression refers to the programs and procedures that define the particular job being performed for a group of USERS, as distinct from other general-purpose programs that may support the user application, such as the OPERATING SYSTEM or TELEPROCESSING MONITOR.

user characteristics It is extremely important in designing TELECOMMUNICATIONS systems to evaluate and allow for the requirements of USERS.

For example, a TELEPHONE NETWORK must provide a level of reception satisfactory to users wishing to carry out a two-way CONVERSATION. Telephone administrations carry out tests of user perception to identify a level of reception that is satisfactory, without incurring unnecessary cost or complexity in the system.

user data That part of a MESSAGE (or PACKET) that contains INFORMATION for the end user's APPLICATION, rather than CONTROL or HEADER INFORMATION used to regulate transmission.

user data packet A unit of INFORMATION forming part of a MESSAGE transmitted from one USER to another in a PACKET SWITCHING NETWORK.

user data signaling rate The rate at which a TERMINAL can receive INFORMATION, usually expressed in BITS per second. This may not be exactly the same rate as information received by any MODEM associated with the TERMINAL since, in some forms of DATA TRANSMISSION, ENVELOPES of CONTROL INFORMATION pass between distant modems but only higher-level user information within the envelopes is passed to and from the terminals.

user dialing state A STATE that exists when a SUBSCRIBER is calling another TERMINAL and has started (but not completed) the dialing process.

user node A point in a NETWORK at which a user TERMINAL is stationed and used to distinguish from a NODE at which CONTROL functions, such as SWITCHING or DATABASE retrieval/updating operations, take place.

UTP See UNSHIELDED TWISTED PAIR.

V

V series A series of recommendations by the CCITT that govern DATA TRANSMISSION over telephone CIRCUITS. At the time of writing, the main recommendations are identified from V.1 to V.57. They are summarized below (compare also with X SERIES):

V.1—provides equivalence between BINARY NOTATION and the significance of a TWO-CONDITION code

V.2—specifies power levels for data transmission over a telephone circuit

V.3—defines the DATA COMMUNICATIONS CODE known as INTERNATIONAL ALPHABET NO. 5

V.4—defines the structure of SIGNALS to represent the International Alphabet No. 5 for data transmission over public TELEPHONE NETWORKS

V.5—the standardization of MODULATION RATES for SYNCHRONOUS DATA TRANSMISSION and the associated DATA SIGNALING RATES on PUBLIC SWITCHED TELEPHONE CIRCUITS

V.6—the standardization of modulation rates and data signaling rates for SYNCHRONOUS OPERATION on LEASED CIRCUITS

V.10—a recommendation for the electrical requirements for UNBALANCED DOUBLE-CURRENT INTERCHANGE CIRCUITS for use with integrated circuits in DATA TRANSMISSION

V.11—a recommendation for the electrical requirements for BALANCED DOUBLE-CURRENT INTERCHANGE CIRCUITS for use with integrated circuits in DATA COMMUNICATIONS

V.13—the definition of a simulator for an ANSWER-BACK UNIT

V.15—requirements for the use of ACOUSTIC COUPLERS

V.16—recommendations for special MODEMS to transmit ANALOG SIGNALS associated with the medical field

V.17—recommendations for facsimile transmission at 14.4 kbps in half-duplex mode

V.19—requirements for modems for PARALLEL DATA TRANSMISSION using signal frequencies relevant to telephone networks

V.20—a universal standard for modems for parallel data transmission over the SWITCHED TELEPHONE NETWORK

V.21—a standard for a 200-BAUD modem for use over the switched telephone network

V.22—a standard for a modem operating at 1,200 bps in FULL DUPLEX on a 2-WIRE CIRCUIT over the switched telephone network

V.23—a standard for a modem operating at 600/1,200 bps over the switched telephone network

V.24—a most important recommendation, since it is a standard adopted internationally by most COMPUTER manufacturers at the HARDWARE level. It does not, however, govern the SOFTWARE INTERFACE that defines the method for controlling information flow across the V.24 INTERFACE. This recommendation does provide an important hardware interface covering functions controlled, standard pin positions for connections and electrical characteristics.

Over 40 separate CONTROL CIRCUITS are defined and most DATA TERMINAL EQUIPMENT (DTE) as supplied by computer and communications companies will comply with a subset of this specification. The V.24 recommendation allows for: local connections of terminals to a computer over a cable length of 50 feet; operation with modems over switched circuits; and operation with modems over LEASED LINES. The recommendation consists of detailed definitions for INTERCHANGE SIGNALS between the data terminal (DTE) and the modem (DCE).

V.25—a recommendation for AUTOMATIC CALLING of AUTOMATIC ANSWERING equipment on the PUBLIC SWITCHED TELEPHONE NETWORK

V.26—a standard for a modem operating at 2,400 bps on a FOUR-WIRE CIRCUIT for POINT-TO-POINT connection

V.26*bis*—a standard for a modem operating at 2,400/1,200 bps over the switched telephone network

V.27—a standard for a modem operating at 4,800 bps over a leased circuit

V.27*bis*—a standard for a modem operating at 2,400/4,800 bps for use on leased circuits with ADAPTIVE EQUALIZERS

V.27*ter*—a standard for a modem operating at 2,400/4,800 bps for use in the public switched telephone network

V.28—a recommendation for the electrical characteristics for unbalanced double-current interchange circuits
V.29—a standard for a modem operating at 9,600 bps over a leased circuit
V.31—a recommendation for the electrical characteristics for SINGLE CURRENT INTERCHANGE CIRCUITS controlled by closure of physical contacts
V.32—specifies the use of Trellis-coded modulation and ECHO CANCELLATION to overcome noise on DIAL-UP CONNECTIONS. Implementing V.32 helps MODEMS achieve SYNCHRONOUS, FULL-DUPLEX transmission over two-wire SWITCHED CIRCUITS at 9.6 kbps.
V.32*bis*—specifies full-duplex transmission at 14.4 kbps over dial-up connections. It uses Trellis coding and ECHO CANCELLATION.
V.35—a recommendation for data transmission at 48 kbps per second over circuits in the GROUP from 60 to 108 kHz
V.36—a standard for modems used in SYNCHRONOUS TRANSMISSION over circuits in the group from 60 to 108 kHz
V.40—the specification of error indications using electromechanical equipment
V.41—the specification of a CODE INDEPENDENT error control system
V.42—ratified by the CCITT in 1988, V.42 handles error correction for ASYNCHRONOUS MODEMS, enabling asynchronous-to-synchronous conversion. It incorporates LAP-M (Link Access Procedure for Modems).
V.42*bis*—ratified by the CCITT in 1989, V.42*bis* specifies DATA COMPRESSION techniques for MODEMS that use the LAP-M ERROR CONTROL procedure used in V.42 modems.
V.50—a definition of recommended limits for quality of circuits in data transmission
V.51—relates to the method of organizing maintenance for telephone circuits used in data transmission
V.52—a specification of the characteristics of equipment used for measuring DISTORTION and ERROR RATES in data transmission over telephone circuits
V.53—specification of limits for the maintenance of telephone circuits used in data transmission
V.54—the definition of devices used for conducting LOOP TESTS on modems
V.55—specification of equipment for measuring IMPULSIVE NOISE on telephone circuits
V.56—a series of comparative tests for modems
V.57—the definition of a data test set for measuring the performance of systems at high data signaling rates

value-added common carrier A company that sells the services of a VALUE-ADDED NETWORK.

value-added network (VAN) A type of public NETWORK that leases basic TRANSMISSION facilities from a COMMON CARRIER, adds features that enhance the service and provides the improved communications capability to end USERS. PROTOCOL CONVERSION, AUTOMATIC ALTERNATE ROUTING, NETWORK management and ERROR CORRECTION are examples of the value added.

VAN See VALUE-ADDED NETWORK.

variable amplitude modulation A form of AMPLITUDE MODULATION in which binary information (i.e., 0 and 1 BITS) are each represented by predetermined levels of AMPLITUDE. Several contiguous frequency cycles at a particular level represent 1 and at another level represent 0. See also MODULATION and UNIT SIGNAL ELEMENT.

variation of insertion loss The INSERTION LOSS experienced in a CIRCUIT is not usually constant but varies with time. In specifying the QUALITY OF A CIRCUIT, it is usual to state the possible variation of insertion loss. For example, an 800 Hz SIGNAL may produce an insertion loss of +10 DECIBELS (dB), but it may vary between +7 dB and +13 dB.

vertical resolution A definition of the number of discrete PICTURE ELEMENTS that can be resolved along a vertical line drawn upon a display screen, e.g., in the British 625-line television system, 402 picture elements; in the U.S. 525-line system, 340 picture elements. See also RESOLUTION.

vertical tabulation A function represented as a special FORMAT EFFECTOR in a DATA COMMUNICATION CODE, serving as an instruction to move a PRINT MECHANISM or the CURSOR of a VISUAL DISPLAY UNIT to the next predetermined position down the page of a document.

very high frequency (VHF) RADIO WAVES, in the range from 30 MHz to 300 MHz that can be propagated as SPACE WAVES over distances up to 200 kilometers. Used primarily for high-quality radio BROADCASTS using FREQUENCY MODULATION techniques, where a relatively wide radio frequency BANDWIDTH can be used for a much narrower AUDIO FREQUENCY signal. This practice offers a high SIGNAL-TO-NOISE RATIO and, because of the limited range of VHF signals, there is relatively little interference from distant STATIONS using the same part of the FREQUENCY BAND.

The VHF spectrum is also used for television broadcasts.

very large scale integration (VLSI) The application of MICRO-ELECTRONIC TECHNOLOGY to the integration of tens of thousands of components onto a single SILICON CHIP of small physical size. Such devices can be designed, manufactured and tested by automated methods.

very small aperture terminal (VSAT) An EARTH STATION with a small ANTENNA, typically no larger than six meters in diameter.

vestigial sideband A portion of a SIDEBAND that remains after AMPLITUDE MODULATION of a CARRIER WAVE using VESTIGIAL SIDEBAND MODULATION (VSB) techniques.

vestigial sideband modulation (VSB) A form of MODULATION used in television systems to remove almost the whole of one of the SIDEBANDS plus the CARRIER WAVE, e.g., the complete UPPER SIDEBAND will be transmitted but only part of the LOWER SIDEBAND. This technique is adopted to economize in the power and BANDWIDTH required in transmission of the television signal while maintaining a waveform that can be handled without unnecessary complexity and cost in each TV RECEIVER.

VFT See VOICE FREQUENCY TELEGRAPH.

VHF A range of electromagnetic frequencies used in BROADCASTING. See also VERY HIGH FREQUENCY.

video amplifier A device used to increase the magnitude of a VIDEO SIGNAL received from a television camera prior to combining the SIGNAL with SYNC PULSES and prior to modulating the signal for RADIO TRANSMISSION. Also used to denote an AMPLIFIER in a TELEVISION RECEIVER used to increase the power of a detected video signal before it is delivered to the CATHODE RAY TUBE (CRT) for display.

video bandwidth This refers to the BANDWIDTH required to carry a television picture and depends mainly upon the amount of detail (i.e., HORIZONTAL and VERTICAL RESOLUTIONS) in the particular television system. This detail is given by the number of horizontal lines that form the RASTER and the number of PICTURE ELEMENTS along each horizontal line. In practice, some LINE SCANS take place during FIELD FLYBACK, when the SCANNING BEAM is blanked so the number of lines is multiplied by an appropriate factor less than unity (e.g., 0.92), in performing a calculation to derive the number of picture elements. The 525-line system used in the United States requires an actual video bandwidth of 4.2 MHz. In Britain, where a 625-line system is used, the actual bandwidth required in 5.5 MHz. In France, where a 625-line system is also used, a 6 MHz bandwidth is needed, because the French system produces a horizontal resolution that is greater than the vertical resolution.

video signal When a television picture is created by means of a camera focused on a scene, the image of the scene is formed on a light-sensitive surface inside the television camera. This establishes an electrical charge pattern that is related to the light coming from objects in the scene. This pattern is scanned by an ELECTRON BEAM inside the camera to create a video signal.

The scanning operation is achieved by MAGNETIC DEFLECTION COILS to produce horizontal and vertical movements of the beam. The pattern traced by the beam is a zig-zag movement across and down the screen, known as a RASTER. When the beam has been passed from left to right across the screen, it traverses rapidly back to the other side. This return motion is known as FLYBACK.

The horizontal movement of the raster is known as a LINE SCAN and the vertical movement as a FIELD SCAN.

The flyback movement after each line scan movement is known as LINE FLYBACK. The return of the raster from the bottom to the top of the screen is known as FIELD FLYBACK.

The more lines occurring in the raster, the higher the definition of the image produced, i.e., a greater degree of detail can be captured from the original scene. The standards adopted vary from one country to another, but in Western Europe 625 lines are used in a television picture and in North America 525 lines. The CCIR recommendation is for 625 lines.

The reproduction of a television picture in a TV RECEIVER reverses the process described above. See also TELEVISION TRANSMISSION SIGNAL.

video traffic The video component of a television transmission; normally carried on a television circuit that provides a unidirectional path of suitable BANDWIDTH.

videoconference A multimedia interactive electronic meeting between geographically separated groups; a videoconference may include full-motion video, voice and graphics.

videotex adaptor A device that INTERFACES a standard TELEVISION RECEIVER to a telephone LINE so that it can be used to display INFORMATION from a VIDEOTEX system. Usually external to the television, it consists of a MODEM, FRAME STORE, DECODER and a lead to connect to the VHF or RGB socket of the television.

videotex decoder A micro-electronic device fitted to a TELEVISION RECEIVER to enable it to receive, display and send TEXT and GRAPHICS to a TELEPHONE line. See also VIDEOTEX SYSTEM.

videotex standards Standards required to create compatibility between different national VIDEOTEX SYSTEMS and, for example, to allow for interaction between VIDEOTEX TERMINALS and DATABASES in different countries. The standards cover: (a) STANDARD CODE SETS (CHARACTER SETS), (b) EXTENSION CODES, (c) COMPOSITION CODING, (d) GRAPHICS DISPLAY STANDARDS, (e) DYNAMICALLY REDEFINABLE CHARACTER SETS.

The standard code sets include code set CØ which provides definition of CURSOR CONTROL or FORMAT EFFECTORS, and TRANSMISSION CONTROL characters. This is known as the basic control set or primary control set.

The CØ set (also known as primary CHARACTER SET) includes the basic set of ALPHANUMERIC CHARACTERS.

The number of Latin-based character sets requiring diacritical marks is high and to create devices capable of responding efficiently to all characters requires a technique known as composition coding. In this system, the character code and the diacritical mark are transmitted separately and then combined in the TERMINAL for display. The recommendation prepared by CCITT for composition coding requires a few extra characters to represent all Latin character sets. It does, however, lead to extra logic and slightly more PAGE STORE in each terminal.

Display standards cover two major techniques: (a) ALPHAMOSAIC CODING, (b) ALPHAGEOMETRIC CODING. The first (a) allows GRAPHICS of LOW RESOLUTION to be displayed where pictures are formed of GRAPHICS CHARACTERS made up by dividing each character space into a matrix of 2×3 elements. The pictures thus created are made up of combinations of up to 63 special graphics characters. This system enables graphics to be produced using cheap terminals.

The alphageometric coding system enables graphics of much HIGHER RESOLUTION to be composed, including line drawings composed of arcs, points and polygons. The early geometric systems produce a resolution of 320×240 PICTURE ELEMENTS (PIXELS). To utilize such a system efficiently in a PUBLIC VIDEOTEX service requires a CODE COMPRESSION technique to transmit PICTURE DESCRIPTION INSTRUCTIONS (PDIS), which are transmitted to the LINE and interpreted in the terminal. Without such a technique, every pixel would have to be individually addressed down the line, which would provide unacceptable transmission delays in a TELEPHONE NETWORK.

A further refinement for alphamosaic systems is represented by the concepts inherent in DYNAMICALLY REDEFINABLE CHARACTER SETS (DRCS).

videotex system The generic name given to an information system that allows for the collection and retrieval of INFORMATION through TERMINALS that are specially adapted TELEVISION RECEIVERS and are able to interact with a DATABASE stored in a central COMPUTER, using the PUBLIC SWITCHED TELEPHONE NETWORK as the basic communication medium.

The concept of the service is that suppliers of information (known as INFORMATION PROVIDERS [IPs]) are able to offer information for sale to members of the business or domestic community; IPs may also provide information at no charge, e.g., to advertise products and services.

Such systems can also be used to collect information from users, e.g., goods and services can be requested by a user who enters information through a KEYBOARD. This process of DATA COLLECTION is associated with preset pages of information (known as RESPONSE FRAMES) designed by the IPs as order forms to be completed by users.

The major components in a videotex system are (a) DIGITAL COMPUTER to store the database, (b) TELEPHONE SYSTEM to provide the NETWORK, (c) 1,200/75 baud MODEM to connect terminals to the network, (d) simple user terminals to access and display pages and (e) EDITING TERMINALS to allow information providers to create pages.

For further definitions associated with this concept, see VIDEOTEX TERMINAL, VIDEOTEX STANDARDS, ALPHAGEOMETRIC CODING, ALPHAMOSAIC CODING, CHARACTER GENERATOR, COMPOSITION CODING, DYNAMICALLY REDEFINABLE CHARACTER SETS, PARALLEL ATTRIBUTE CODING and SERIAL ATTRIBUTE CODING.

Videotex systems should be compared with TELETEXT broadcast systems, which use RADIO WAVES instead of the telephone network.

videotex terminal A terminal designed to receive and display SIGNALS from a VIDEOTEX SYSTEM and to enable USERS to retrieve or input INFORMATION to such a system. The concept of a videotex is based upon the use of a domestic TELEVISION RECEIVER as a TERMINAL, able to communicate with a DATABASE over the PUBLIC SWITCHED TELEPHONE NETWORK. This requires the TV receiver to be modified to include a special VIDEOTEX DECODER and a MODEM. This modification may be made inside the receiver during its manufacture or by an external VIDEOTEX ADAPTOR, which plugs into the UHF or RGB input sockets of a standard TV. The additional components required to convert a standard TV receiver include the following: (a) MODEM, (b) LINE ISOLATOR, (c) MEMORY UNIT, (d) PROCESSING LOGIC, (e) KEYBOARD or KEYPAD and (f) AUTOMATIC DIALER (an optional feature to enable users to select the telephone number of the particular videotex service required); otherwise, the telephone dial is used in the normal way.

In most countries there is commonality between the functional components of a VIDEOTEX DECODER and a TELETEXT DECODER that responds to RADIO SIGNALS rather than to signals from the TELEPHONE SYSTEM.

The accepted display standard for videotex terminals consists basically of 24 rows of CHARACTERS per PAGE or FRAME and 40 characters per row. It is referred to as a 40-COLUMN DISPLAY, which compares with the 65 column or 80-COLUMN DISPLAY more commonly found with COMPUTER terminals.

The videotex terminal will usually display up to 7 colors, with TEXT and GRAPHICS, and a range of basic characters described under videotex standard CODE SETS. There are many variations in videotex terminals. See also ALPHAMOSAIC GRAPHICS, ALPHAGEOMETRIC GRAPHICS, VIDEOTEX STANDARDS.

videotex traffic MESSAGE SIGNALS representing CHARACTERS of INFORMATION transmitted over the PUBLIC TELEPHONE NETWORK, or a PACKET SWITCHING NETWORK, between VIDEOTEX TERMINALS and a central VIDEOTEX SYSTEM. The line protocol is based upon the ASCII DATA COMMUNICATION CODE for TEXT.

viewdata A generic term used in English-speaking countries to refer to a public information service that incorporates the use of modified TELEVISION RECEIVERS to gain access to INFORMATION stored in a COMPUTER and transmitted to USERS over the PUBLIC SWITCHED TELEPHONE NETWORK. See also VIDEOTEX SYSTEM.

viewdata adaptor See VIDEOTEX ADAPTOR.

viewdata terminal See VIDEOTEX TERMINAL.

virtual circuit In a PACKET SWITCHING NETWORK, MESSAGES share LINKS between various NODES, usually using some form of TIME DIVISION MULTIPLEXING (TDM). Consequently, there is no ACCESS PATH associated with each CALL to provide an end-to-end connection for the duration of the call. Instead, messages are transmitted as a number of small PACKETS of BINARY INFORMATION, which contain ROUTING and ADDRESS INFORMATION. These packets pass through the network, sharing certain paths with packets from other messages, and packets are reassembled (or DE-PACKETIZED) on arrival at their RECEIVING STATION.

The path through such a NETWORK for any particular message is referred to as a virtual circuit, and it can provide a FULL DUPLEX link between the HIGH LEVEL CONTROL FUNCTIONS at the TRANSMITTING and RECEIVING TERMINALS. See also PERMANENT VIRTUAL CIRCUIT.

virus Widely accepted term referring to an error in a SOFTWARE program—introduced mistakenly, mischievously or with criminal intent—that causes COMPUTERS and NETWORKS to malfunction in a variety of ways. The virus can enter an OPERATING SYSTEM via the source code of third-party software. It can cause portions of software to replicate infinitely and thus use up PROCESSING power and the MEMORY UNIT on the computer.

visibility function This relates to the average visual response of humans to ELECTROMAGNETIC WAVES, which varies with frequency or WAVELENGTH. The human eye can respond to wavelengths between those corresponding to violet (400 nanometers [nm]) and deep red (760 nm). However, it cannot perceive ultraviolet or INFRARED LIGHT, which have wavelengths beyond this spectrum. Also, the response varies within the VISIBLE COLOR SPECTRUM, and the average human eye is far more responsive to light in the yellow spectrum around 580 nm. ($1 \text{ nm} = 10^{-9}$ meters.)

This visibility function has to be considered in all forms of VISUAL DISPLAY and in the concepts of television. A source of red light at 680 nm would require 100 times more luminous power to invoke the same response in a human as a source of yellow/green light at 550 nm.

The visibility function is also known as the PHOTOPIC RESPONSE and is part of the science of PHOTOMETRY.

visible color spectrum The spectrum of ELECTROMAGNETIC WAVES that gives rise to colors as perceived by humans.

Humans cannot perceive colors beyond this spectrum, e.g., ultraviolet light around 380 nanometers (nm) and INFRARED LIGHT around 780 nm.

The visible color spectrum corresponds to electromagnetic waves in the FREQUENCY SPECTRUM from 420 to 790 THz (1 THz = 10^{12} Hz). See also Appendix 5.

visible light spectrum The range of ELECTROMAGNETIC WAVES that are visible to humans, including the frequencies between violet and deep red. This spectrum contains all the frequencies that can be combined to produce the various colors perceived by humans. See also VISIBLE COLOR SPECTRUM.

vision Pertaining to the VIDEO SIGNALS that originate from television cameras, in which light reflected from an object is detected and represented as an ELECTRICAL SIGNAL.

vision carrier In television broadcasting, a CARRIER WAVE that is modulated using a form of AMPLITUDE MODULATION to carry the VIDEO SIGNAL. A separate carrier is used for the SOUND SIGNAL. See also VESTIGIAL SIDEBAND MODULATION and TELEVISION TRANSMISSION SIGNAL.

visual acuity This is a measure of the amount of detail that can be detected visually by humans. A formal definition says that it is the reciprocal of the angle *a* subtended at the eye by two small images that can be separately identified. The average viewer can just resolve 425 lines on the surface of a TV screen at normal viewing distance. In fact, the RASTER used to generate such a display will need 607 lines. See also KELL FACTOR.

visual display An input/output TERMINAL based upon the technology of the CATHODE RAY TUBE and used to display DATA, TEXT and GRAPHICS INFORMATION.

visual message signal A component of a TELEVISION TRANSMISSION SIGNAL that consists of a VIDEO SIGNAL plus SYNCHRONIZATION PULSES used to maintain SYNCHRONIZATION between a TV camera and a TV RECEIVER. It does not include the AUDIO SIGNAL associated with the visual message to form the complete television transmission signal. Also known as COMPOSITE VIDEO SIGNAL. See also VIDEO SIGNAL.

VLSI See VERY LARGE SCALE INTEGRATION. See also MICRO-ELECTRONIC TECHNOLOGY.

voice Relating to the representation of human speech as ELECTRICAL SIGNALS, as in VOICE CHANNEL, VOICE FREQUENCY or VOICE TRAFFIC.

voice analog signal An ELECTRICAL SIGNAL that is a direct representation of an AUDIO SIGNAL corresponding to human speech. See also ANALOG ELECTRICAL SIGNAL.

voice channel A communications CIRCUIT designed to carry VOICE SIGNALS and therefore designed to accept an ELECTRICAL ANALOG of an AUDIO FREQUENCY SIGNAL corresponding to human speech. But note that, today, speech can be converted to DIGITAL SIGNALS by using PULSE CODE MODULATION techniques.

voice circuit A CIRCUIT used to carry SIGNALS representing human speech and normally having a BANDWIDTH of from 300 to 3,400 Hz.

voice digitization Pertaining to the techniques used to convert SPEECH SIGNALS into DIGITAL SIGNALS by means of PULSE CODE MODULATION. Digitization can take place in the telephone HANDSET or at the point of entry to a DIGITAL EXCHANGE.

voice frequency Relating to the range of SIGNALS used to convey a representation of human speech in a TELEPHONE SYSTEM, and usually in the BANDWIDTH from 300 to 3,400 Hz.

voice frequency telegraph A TELEGRAPH SYSTEM in which SIGNALS are transmitted at AUDIO FREQUENCIES at all intermediate stages in the NETWORK.

voice packet switching Refers to the use of PACKET SWITCHING NETWORKS to carry speech information. Although such networks were originally (and are primarily) used for DATA, it is possible to use them for speech transmission.

The ELECTRICAL ANALOG SIGNALS representing speech must first be digitized, using PULSE CODE MODULATION techniques, then PACKETIZED in the entry NODE of the PACKET NETWORK. It has been shown that a network designed to present a nominal end-to-end PACKET DELAY of around 200 milliseconds will allow two people to enjoy a normal telephone CONVERSATION.

voice signal 1. A sound energy signal corresponding to human speech.

2. An ELECTRICAL ANALOG SIGNAL representing human speech and used to convey speech information as ELECTROMAGNETIC WAVES. Such a signal is usually within the FREQUENCY BAND from 0.3 to 3.4 kHz.

voice telephony The concepts and principles associated with the transmission of speech in a TELEPHONE NETWORK.

voice traffic TRAFFIC corresponding to human speech and requiring a CHANNEL capable of handling an ANALOG SIGNAL in the range from 0.3 to 3.4 kHz.

voiceband frequency A frequency occurring in the relatively narrow band used for carrying SIGNALS representing human speech; usually in the range from 300 to 3,400 Hz.

volume sensitive tariff A method of charging for the use of a CIRCUIT or PUBLIC DATA NETWORK in which the charges are related to the volume of TRAFFIC a particular SUBSCRIBER delivers to the system rather than the distance. The unit of delivery is predetermined by the service operator and varies from service to service, but in DATA TRANSMISSION systems, a DATA SEGMENT of 64 CHARACTERS may be defined as a minimum unit. Discounts or penalties may apply to USERS at certain TRAFFIC VOLUMES within specified durations. See also TARIFF and USAGE CHARGE.

VSAT See VERY SMALL APERTURE TERMINAL.

VSB See VESTIGIAL SIDEBAND.

VT See VERTICAL TABULATION.

W

WAN See WIDE AREA NETWORK.

WATS See WIDE AREA TELECOMMUNICATIONS SERVICE.

waveguides A TRANSMISSION MEDIUM in which RADIO WAVES are propagated along hollow conducting tubes. The cross-sectional dimensions of the tube need to be equal to, or greater than, the WAVELENGTH of the radio waves. This means that waveguides are suitable for use with MICROWAVES, e.g., in the range of 2 GHz to 11 GHz. See also OPTICAL WAVEGUIDES.

wavelength All ELECTROMAGNETIC WAVES travel through SPACE at approximately the same speed—300,000,000 meters per second. The wavelength of an electromagnetic signal is obtained by dividing this number by the signal frequency in cycles per second (Hertz).

Thus, the wavelength for a signal of 1,000,000 cycles per second (1 MHz) is 300 meters. The higher the frequency, the shorter the wavelength. See also ELECTROMAGNETIC WAVES and BANDWIDTH.

white noise A form of interference that manifests itself as a hiss on telephone or radio channels and is caused by the natural movement of electrons in CIRCUITS, which varies with temperature. Also known as GAUSSION NOISE and RANDOM NOISE.

who are you A CHARACTER CODE that occurs in a DATA COMMUNICATIONS CODE such as the INTERNATIONAL ALPHABET NO. 2 and that has the purpose of invoking an automatic response from a TERMINAL causing it to reply with a CALL sign.

wide area network (WAN) A DATA COMMUNICATIONS NETWORK that spans long distances, typically from city to city and across countries as opposed to a METROPOLITAN AREA NETWORK, which covers the area of one city. A WAN generally uses POINT-TO-POINT LINES at DATA RATES of 1.544 Mbps or slower, although emerging SONET-complaint equipment will yield much faster rates. Compare with LOCAL AREA NETWORK. A COMMON CARRIER usually owns the communications network on which the WAN is built, and the HOST PROCESSORS on the WAN may be owned by multiple organizations.

wide area telecommunications service (WATS) A billing arrangement whereby the TELEPHONE company offers SUBSCRIBERS reduced rates, such as 800 service. The cost may be based on hourly usage per CIRCUIT or on a number of other parameters.

wideband circuit A CIRCUIT of BROAD BANDWIDTH, e.g., allowing DATA TRANSMISSION at speeds of 48, 64 or 72 kbps.

window In COMPUTER GRAPHICS, a given portion of the virtual space on the display screen. The windows feature in an APPLICATION program lets the USER view several tasks, or parts of the same task, simultaneously.

wiring center In DATA COMMUNICATIONS NETWORKS having a RING TOPOLOGY, each STATION may be physically connected to a wiring center, which is a room that contains relay devices that enable a failed station to be bypassed. It is used for concentrating and connecting the wires of data and voice NETWORKS. Devices are patched into the network, or deleted, at the wiring center. Also called a wiring closet.

In TELEPHONE networks, a wiring center is the building that houses local switching systems, which are connected to the CENTRAL OFFICE equipment.

wiring closet See WIRING CENTER.

word A unit of DATA used in COMPUTER systems and operated upon by the computer as an entity. A word may consist of a defined number of CHARACTERS and BITS, e.g., 4 characters of 8 bits, making 32 bits per word. See also BYTE.

word processor A system for the preparation and distribution of MESSAGES and documents, based upon the principles of the conventional typewriter but enhanced to provide more advanced facilities that are realized by COMPUTER techniques, e.g., editing features, automatic tabulating features, storage and filing capabilities and automatic generation of type fonts, formats and numbers of copies.

word processor networks A system in which WORD PROCESSORS are interconnected by communications facilities to provide for the distribution of INFORMATION recorded as documents within a word-processing environment. Such systems presage the evolution of integrated office systems based upon the concepts of ELECTRONIC MAIL—the so-called office of the future.

worm A type of COMPUTER storage in which the USER can "write once, read many times." Also, a SOFTWARE programming error that can cause a computer or NETWORK to malfunction. See also VIRUS.

X

X series (X.1–X.500) The CCITT has produced a number of recommendations to PTTS and other communication authorities establishing communications INTERFACES for users' DATA TERMINAL EQUIPMENT (DTE) and for NETWORK INTERFACE UNITS or MODEMS known as DATA CIRCUIT TERMINATING EQUIPMENT (DCE). The X series recommendations thus govern the attachment of TERMINALS to a PUBLIC DATA NETWORK (PDN) and constitute a family of standards for INTERFACING terminals to networks. In principle, they recognize the growth of BIT-STREAM oriented systems dealing in so-called high level PROTOCOLS and represent a major step in evolution from the long-standing V SERIES INTERFACES, which dealt with the attachment of digital devices to ANALOG facilities, represented by existing TELEPHONE NETWORKS.

Some of the more commonly used standards are listed below; a little more detail is provided under the headings X.21 and X.25:

X.1—defines classes of service for international PDN USERS
X.2—defines international user facilities in a PDN
X.3—defines PACKET ASSEMBLY and DISASSEMBLY
X.4—defines the structure of SIGNALS to represent the INTERNATIONAL ALPHABET NO. 5 for DATA TRANSMISSION over PDN
X.20—defines the interface for START-STOP TRANSMISSION services between DTE and DCE, including an extension (X.20*bis*) for V.21 compatible interfaces for such services on a PDN
X.20*bis*—PUBLIC DATA NETWORKS of DTE use X.20*bis* when the equipment is designed to INTERFACE with ASYNCHRONOUS V-SERIES MODEMS
X.21—defines the interface between DTE and DCE for SYNCHRONOUS OPERATION on PDNs, including an extension (X.21 *bis*) for terminals designed to interface to V SERIES modems for synchronous operation. (But see more detailed definition under X.21.)
X.21*bis*—PUBLIC DATA NETWORKS of DTE use X.21*bis* where the equipment is designed to interface with SYNCHRONOUS V-SERIES MODEMS
X.24—definitions relating to INTERCHANGE CIRCUITS between DTE and DCE on PDNs
X.25—defines the interface between DTE and DCE operating in packet switching mode in a PDN. (But see more detailed definition under X.25).
X.28—defines interface requirements for a nonintelligent start-stop mode terminal accessing the packet assembly and disassembly facility in a PDN
X.29—procedures for the exchange of CONTROL INFORMATION and USER DATA between a PAD and DTE capable of packet assembly and disassembly functions
X.32—specifies the INTERFACE between DTE and DCE via a public PACKET SWITCHED DATA NETWORK, for example, to allow users X.25 access via DIAL-UP MODEMS
X.75—specifies some of the parameters for connecting X.25 PACKET SWITCHED DATA NETWORKS, for example, CALL CONTROL PROCEDURES
X.121—a numbering plan for international PUBLIC DATA NETWORKS
X.400—specifies the standards for exchange of MESSAGES between ELECTRONIC MAIL SYSTEMS operated by different companies. It uses a STORE-AND-FORWARD MESSAGING SYSTEM.

X.500—specifies the standards for a directory service that can provide a database of names and addresses used in X.400 systems

There are a number of other X series recommendations and, for accurate up-to-date details, reference should be made to CCITT publications. The objective of the recommendations is to cover: (a) methods of terminal attachment, (b) LINK CONTROL procedures and (c) DATA TRANSFER, embracing: LEASED CIRCUITS, SWITCHED CIRCUITS, and PACKET SWITCHING.

Xmodem A FILE transfer PROTOCOL in the public domain that specifies an eight-bit format and ERROR CORRECTION. There are many variations on the original protocol distinguished mainly by the type of error correction that is used: for example, CRC. See also ERROR CHECKING, REDUNDANCY CHECKING.

X9.17 An ANSI standard PROTOCOL, X9.17 "Financial Institution Key Management (Wholesale)" specifies a way to ensure secure key management for ENCRYPTED DATA MESSAGES.

X-off/X-on A CONTROL mechanism used in some DATA COMMUNICATIONS equipment that allows a TERMINAL to engage or to disengage a communications line.

X.21 A member of the family of X SERIES INTERFACES, designed to replace the earlier V.24 and V.25 interface recommendations of the CCITT. It deals with the connection of TERMINALS to MODEMS, including AUTOMATIC CALLING operations for SWITCHED CIRCUITS on synchronous PUBLIC DATA NETWORKS (PDNS). The benefits of X.21 over the equivalent V SERIES include: (a) the number of INTERCHANGE CIRCUITS and pin connections is greatly reduced, because many terminal-to-network CONTROL signals are represented as CODE STRINGS rather than as discrete circuits; (b) the electrical characteristics defined for X.21 incorporate a PHYSICAL INTERFACE capable of supporting LARGE SCALE INTEGRATION (LSI) micro components, which can operate at very high BIT RATES and over greater distances than the V series recommendation; (c) enhanced functions are available, including the ability to transfer more detailed call status information, relating to the CALLED TERMINAL and the network.

The X.21 recommendation maintains TRANSPARENCY during the DATA TRANSFER stage and provides a distinct separation of SIGNALING and data transfer.

X.25 This recommendation of the CCITT is intended as a PROTOCOL for PACKET SWITCHING NETWORKS and for supporting the attachment of INTELLIGENT TERMINALS as well as COMMUNICATION CONTROLLERS and HOST PROCESSORS. There are also some supporting recommendations (X.3, X.28 and X.29) that relate to the support of START-STOP terminals, as well as intelligent terminals.

The major emphasis with a PACKET NETWORK is that the USER DATA must be formatted into relatively small units, known as PACKETS. All packets delivered by user terminals to the network under the X.25 INTERFACE must have HEADER INFORMATION to control the progress of the packet in the network. For terminals of the non-intelligent type, designed according to X.3, X.28 and X.29 recommendations, the network creates the additional information and provides the function to create the correct packet formats.

An important aspect of X.25 is that a user interacts indirectly with any remote terminal. The user interaction is, in fact, with the NODE through which it gains access to the network, i.e., it operates under a NODE-TO-NETWORK PROTOCOL rather than an END-TO-END PROTOCOL.

The X.25 recommendation has a complex HIGH LEVEL CONTROL FUNCTION, which is structured in three levels: (a) physical and electrical—provides for the activation, maintenance and deactivation of LINKS between the terminal (DTE) and the local DATA CIRCUIT TERMINATING EQUIPMENT or NETWORK INTERFACE UNIT; (b) LINK ACCESS PROCEDURE—provides

FRAMING, SYNCHRONIZATION and ERROR DETECTION and CORRECTION between the terminal and the adjacent network node through which network access is obtained; (c) packet format and control—provides for the establishment, DATA TRANSFER and clearing of VIRTUAL CIRCUITS between the terminal and the network via the adjacent network node.

The preferred link access procedure (LAP-B) provides a HIGH LEVEL DATA LINK CONTROL, which is a subset of the ISO HDLC protocol.

The recommendation of the packet format includes call request, CALL ACCEPTED and CALL CONNECTED PACKETS that control the establishment and activation of virtual circuits plus the definition of data packets that contain user information. The user data packet contains the following CONTROL and identification DATA: header format identifier, logical channel group number, LOGICAL CHANNEL NUMBER, packet receive sequence number, flag to indicate if more data is to follow, packet send sequence number and USER DATA (from 128 to 1,024 OCTETS).

The concept of logical channel number relates to the CHANNEL occupied by the CALL between the terminal and the network. The CHANNEL IDENTIFICATION is assigned when the virtual circuit is set up. It should be noted in this respect that under X.25 up to 4,095 separate LOGICAL CHANNELS can be connected to a single input/output PORT on a COMPUTER.

It will also be noted that the user's data packet does not contain the CALLED and CALLING ADDRESSES; these are conveyed to the network as part of the CALL REQUEST PACKET originally used to set up the virtual call.

Y

Ymodem A FILE transfer PROTOCOL based on the XMODEM protocol. It uses a 1,024-byte PACKET size.

Z

zero loss A condition that arises when the GAIN in power in a CIRCUIT due to AMPLIFICATION is just sufficient to overcome the inevitable loss in power attributed to the LINE and associated operating equipment.

Zmodem An eight-BIT FILE TRANSFER PROTOCOL that uses a 128-byte data block and CRC or CHECKSUM ERROR CHECKING. A variation on XMODEM.

APPENDIXES

Appendix 1: International Alphabet No. 5

This is a 7-bit code in which combinations of BITS provide unique patterns to represent CHARACTERS, numerals, special symbols and functions. Bits 1 to 4 form a basic group giving binary values from 0 to 15; for example:

0 = 0000
7 = 0111
11 = 1011
15 = 1111

Bits 5 to 7 provide for 8 separate cases:

0 = 000	Transmission control functions
1 = 001	
2 = 010	Symbols
3 = 011	Numerals 0 to 9 plus symbols
4 = 100	Mainly upper-case letters A to O
5 = 101	Mainly upper-case letters P to Z
6 = 110	Mainly lower-case letters a to o
7 = 111	Mainly lower-case letters p to z

In DATA TRANSMISSION, a PARITY BIT is added to the CODE, making 8 bits in all.

The code does allow for national variations to cover the requirement for alphabet extensions or for diacritical signs. These positions have been left blank in the table overleaf (for example, 4/0 and 5/14).

Column Row	0	1	2	3	4	5	6	7
0	NUL	DLE	SP	0		P		p
1	SOH	DC1	!	1	A	Q	a	q
2	STX	DC2	″	2	B	R	b	r
3	ETX	DC3	£ or #	3	C	S	c	s
4	EOT	DC4	$	4	D	T	d	t
5	ENQ	TC8	%	5	E	U	e	u
6	ACK	SYN	&	6	F	V	f	v
7	BEL	ETB	′	7	G	W	g	w
8	BS	CAN	(	8	H	X	h	x
9	HT	EM	)	9	I	Y	i	y
10	LF	SUB	*	:	J	Z	j	z
11	VT	ESC	+	;	K		k	
12	FF	FS	,	<	L		l	
13	CR	GS	-	=	M		m	
14	SO	RS	.	>	N		n	-
15	SI	US	/	?	O	-	o	DEL

Appendix 2: Notation Used for Abbreviation of Frequency Ranges

Hz	hertz	cycles per second
kHz	kilohertz	thousand cycles per second
MHz	megahertz	million cycles per second
GHz	gigahertz	thousand million cycles per second
THz	terahertz	million million cycles per second

Examples

50 kHz = 50,000 cps or 50×10^3 Hz
30 MHz = 30,000,000 cps or 30×10^6 Hz
300 GHz = 300,000,000,000 cps or 300×10^9 Hz
790 THz = 790,000,000,000,000 cps or 790×10^{12} Hz

Appendix 3: Wavelength

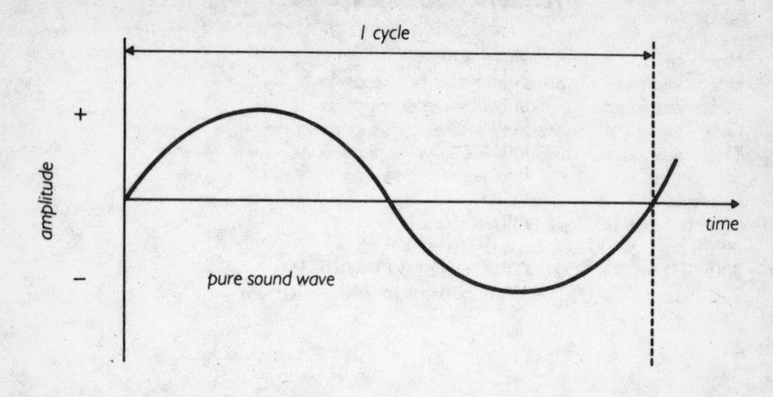

The velocity of SOUND in air is 340 meters/second. For a sound at a pitch or frequency of 1,000 cycles per second (1 kHz), the wavelength is 340/1000 or 0.34 meters.

The velocity of ELECTROMAGNETIC WAVES in space is 300,000,000 meters per second. Thus, for a RADIO WAVE of 30 MHz, the wavelength is $3 \times 10^8 \div 3 \times 10^7 = 10$ meters.

$$\text{Wavelength } (\lambda) = \frac{\text{velocity}}{\text{frequency}}$$

Appendix 4: The Electromagnetic Spectrum

	APPROXIMATE WAVELENGTH (NM)
gamma-rays	10^{-3}
X-rays	10^{-1}
ultraviolet rays	10
visible light	10^{3}
infrared	10^{4}
heat	10^{6}
radar	10^{7}
radio	10^{11}

nm = nanometer(s)
1 nm = 10^{-9} meters

Appendix 5: Visible Light Spectrum

The light spectrum visible to humans occurs between ultraviolet and infrared frequency ranges and includes the following:

	wavelength (nm)
violet	420
blue	460
blue-green	490
green	530
yellow-green	550
yellow	590
orange	620
red	660
deep red	740

Note: In each case, a range of frequencies apply, and the table gives an approximate point in the range. (One nanometer [nm] equals 10^{-9} meters.)

Appendix 6: Bandwidth and Information

The basic relationship between bandwidth and information is given in the following illustration:

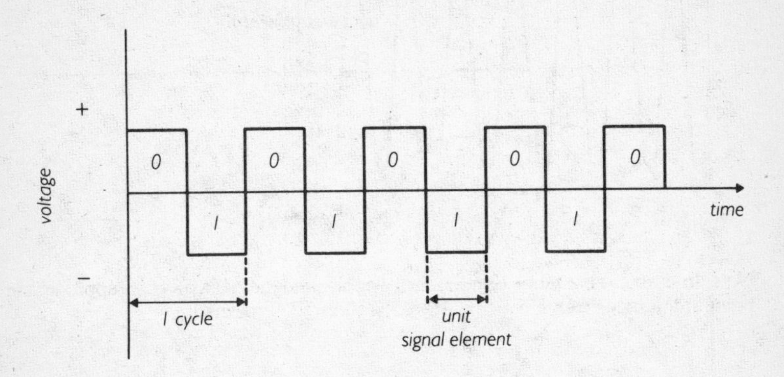

Assume maximum cycle frequency = 50 Hz
Then DATA SIGNALING RATE = 100 BITS per second (0 or 1)
and minimum frequency = 0 Hz (i.e., all 0's or all 1's).
One hundred bits (or one hundred unit SIGNAL ELEMENTS) per second can be achieved. This is referred to as 100 BAUDS.

In this example, only 2 voltage levels are used but, by using 4 voltage levels, the BINARY DIGITS 11, 00, 01 and 10 can be represented, thus increasing the data signaling rate to 200 bits per second at the same maximum frequency.

Appendix 7: Basis of Amplitude Modulation

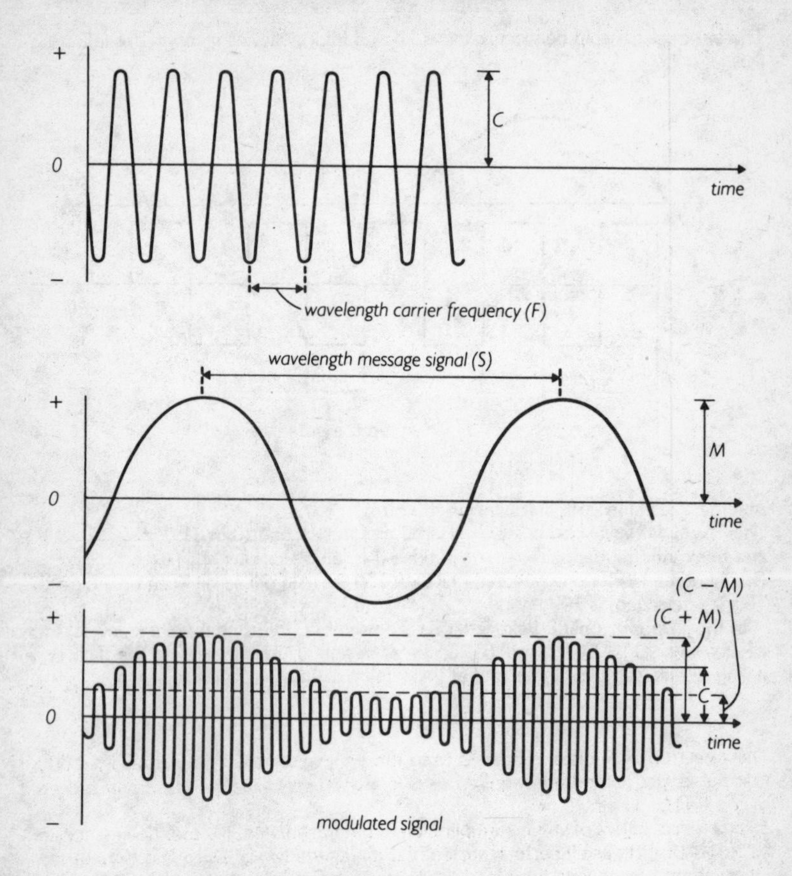

The original carrier frequency F is modulated by a MESSAGE SIGNAL S to create an ENVELOPE containing F and S. The envelope can provide:

the carrier frequency F
the message signal S.

The principles apply to FREQUENCY MODULATION, in which the message signal, instead of altering the AMPLITUDE of the CARRIER SIGNAL, causes the carrier to vary its frequency in sympathy with the frequency of the message signal.

Appendix 8: Basis of Pulse Amplitude Modulation

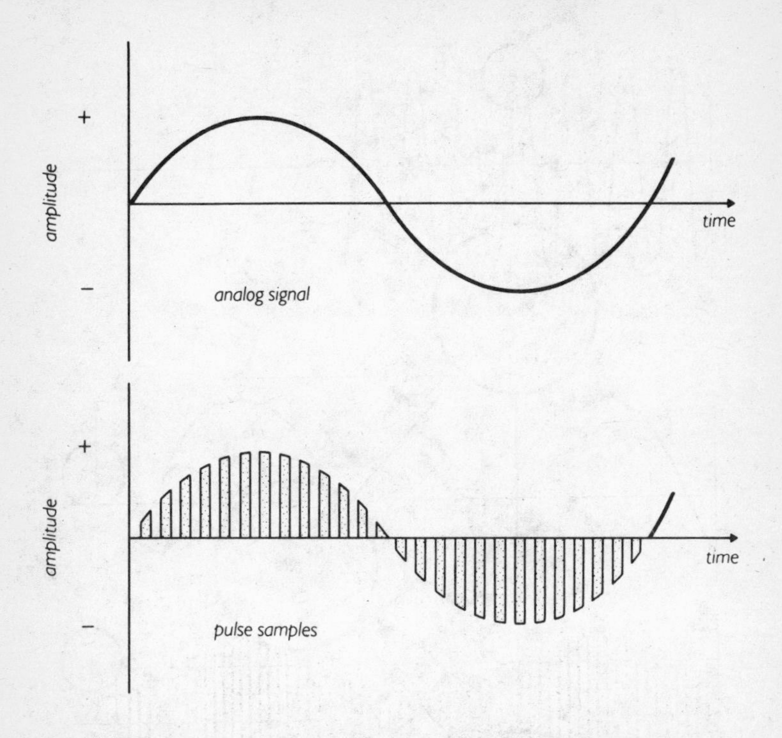

The AMPLITUDE of pulses is derived from the original SIGNAL. Approximately 8,000 PAM pulses per second are required to give a good reproduction of human speech over a 4 kHz CIRCUIT.

In practice, pulses of varying amplitude are not transmitted; instead, BINARY CODED INFORMATION is transmitted to represent the amplitude levels. Decoding logic at the receiving end reconverts the binary code to the amplitude signals and enables the original ANALOG SIGNAL to be reconstructed.

Appendix 9: Packet Switching Network

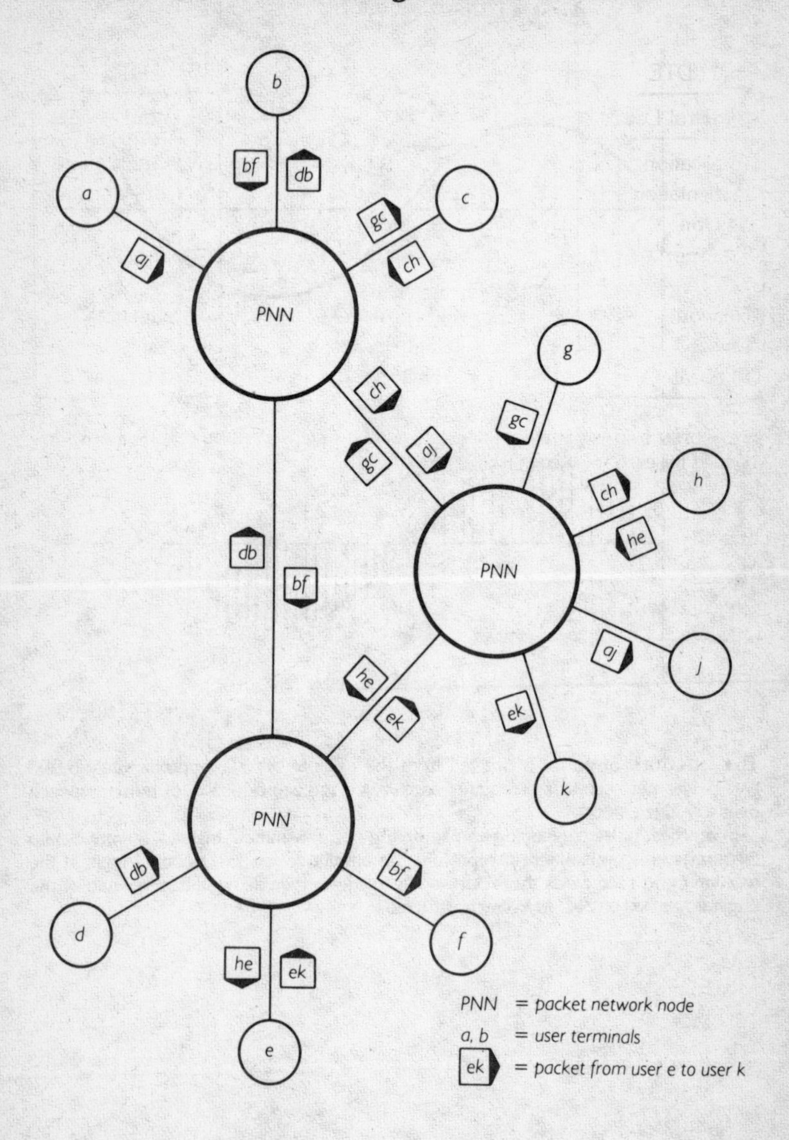

Appendix 10: OSI Model Showing Layered Protocols for X.25 Transmission

DTE Control Levels				DTE Control Levels
Application	7	←→ peer to peer protocols between DTEs	7	Application
Presentation	6		6	Presentation
Session	5		5	Session
Transport	4		4	Transport
Network	3	X.25 protocol within Packet Network	3	Network
Link	2		2	Link
Physical	1		1	Physical

In the OPEN SYSTEMS INTERCONNECTION model, seven CONTROL LEVELS are recommended for each USER connected to a NETWORK.

Appendix 11: Network Topologies

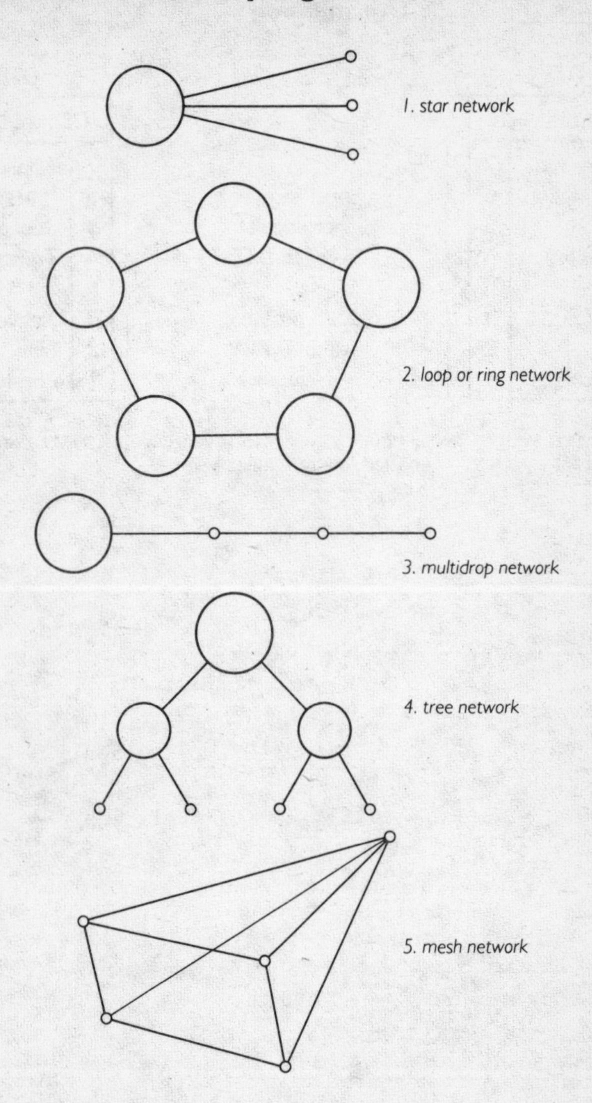